Mechanisms of Tolerance and Dependence

Editor:

Charles Wm. Sharp. Ph.D.

Division of Preclinical Research
National Institute on Drug Abuse

NIDA Research Monograph 54

1984

DEPARTMENT OF HEALTH AND HUMAN SERVICES
Public Health Service
Alcohol, Drug Abuse, and Mental Health Administration

National Institute on Drug Abuse
5600 Fishers Lane
Rockville, Maryland 20857

NIDA Research Monographs are prepared by the research divisions of the National Institute on Drug Abuse and published by its Office of Science. The primary objective of the series is to provide critical reviews of research problem areas and techniques, the content of state-of-the-art conferences, integrative research reviews and significant original research. Its dual publication emphasis is rapid and targeted dissemination to the scientific and professional community.

Editorial Advisory Board

NIDA Research Monograph Series

Parklawn Building, 5600 Fishers Lane, Rockville, Maryland 20857

Mechanisms of Tolerance and Dependence

ACKNOWLEDGMENT

This monograph is based upon papers presented at a technical review which was held on November 11 and 12, 1983, in Boston, Massachusetts. The meeting was sponsored by the Division of Preclinical Research, National Institute on Drug Abuse.

Library of Congress catalog card number 84-601105

DHHS publication number (ADM)84-1330
Printed 1984

NIDA Research Monographs are indexed in the Index Medicus. They are selectively included in the coverage of American Statistics Index, BioSciences Information Service, Chemical Abstracts, Current Contents, Psychological Abstracts, and Psychopharmacology Abstracts.

For sale by the Superintendent of Documents, U.S. Government Printing Office
Washington, D.C. 20402

Contents

v

Preface

When the topic of mechanisms of tolerance/dependence was considered by the National Institute on Drug Abuse for a major review, it seemed at first to lack sufficient substance. Although there is voluminous material on pharmacological dose response and on signs and symptoms associated with the actions of opiates and other drugs, only limited progress has been made on defining the basic mechanisms involved.

For several reasons, progress has been slow in this area. As Eric Simon stated at the symposium, progress has been encumbered by several factors, some of which will eventually assist in defining basic biochemical systems and subsequently the area of tolerance and dependence. These include the discovery that there are several types of opiate receptors, the discovery of at least three types of endogenous pro-opioid peptides, the difficulties in measuring dynamic biological turnover of these peptides and/or related systems; the lack of an understanding of post-receptor events (especially in vivo); and finally, the difficulty in establishing any regulation of opiate receptors.

Yet progress has been made, and it is essential that we continue to define the mechanisms of tolerance and/or dependence. This knowledge is important in determining the underlying biological factors that lead some individuals to abuse drugs. When we have more precise knowledge of these processes we will be able to cope more effectively with the ever increasing drug problem.

It took the quiet enthusiasm of Professor H.O.J. Collier during a visit to NIDA in late 1982 to instigate this review. His confidence in his colleagues and especially in his own work was contagious. Once the seed had been planted with Institute Director Dr. William Pollin and the rest of the NIDA staff, we undertook the task of organizing this review of important recent findings defining the mechanisms of tolerance and dependence.

We were buoyed by the interest and enthusiasm of those we spoke with regarding a discussion of this topic--one that has been of major concern to NIDA for a long time. Ever since the discovery of endogenous opioids in 1975, the Institute has encouraged investigators not only to identify the site of action of those substances, but more importantly, to utilize these substances and their systems to study the mechanisms through which tolerance and/or dependence are mediated.

Unfortunately, shortly before the meeting, Professor Collier died. Thus, not only did the group miss his knowledgeable contributions, we missed and will continue to miss his probing and articulate discussions. In lieu of the original thoughts Professor Collier would have contributed at the meeting, it is worth reflecting on his most recent thoughts on the topic, which were published recently following another symposium.[1] We have drawn from this illuminating manuscript pertinent and provocative excerpts which may serve as guidelines for those interested in narcotic tolerance and dependence.

Let us first consider what he thought to be important criteria for defining tolerance and dependence:

> To analyse cellular mechanisms of tolerance and dependence, it is necessary to reproduce models of these states in isolated or partly isolated preparations. It is therefore important to have strict criteria of tolerance and dependence with which to recognize them in such models. Tolerance is generally agreed to be a lessened response to a drug after its continued application, and which may be observed in several ways:
> 1. Decreased response to the same dose of drug.
> 2. Increased dose of drug to yield the same response.
> 3. Lessened response to drug during continued exposure.
> Dependence is, however, more difficult to define and three criteria have largely been used:
> 1. "Spontaneous behavioural disturbance produced by removal of drug and suppressed by its replacement.
> 2. Increased potency of the drug's specific antagonist.
> 3. Behavioural disturbance on precipitated withdrawal of drug with its specific antagonist.
> 4. Heightened response to external stimulation after withdrawal of inhibitory drug.....(p.109)

> Another criterion, sometimes also used to measure the intensity of dependence, is a heightened potency of the drug's specific antagonist....A third criterion is also sometimes used--that of increased excitability of the preparation to external stimulation after withdrawal of an inhibitory drug such as opiate....(p.109-110)

> Whatever criteria of dependence we use, valid ones, in my opinion, rely on withdrawing a drug from a preparation exposed to it....We cannot measure tolerance, however, without applying the drug. We therefore cannot measure both tolerance and dependence in the same preparation at the same time. This principle of uncertainty makes it difficult to determine the relationship between opioid tolerance and dependence, as may be illustrated by experiments on the isolated ileum of the guinea-pig....(p.110)

> Naturally, the uncertainty principle does not stop us measuring tolerance and dependence in parallel

preparations at the same time, or in the same preparation at different times. To validate such measurements, large numbers of replicates are needed for which isolated preparations are suitable....(p.111)

Based upon the above considerations, Professor Collier chose the guinea-pig ileum as a model for exploring these areas of research. Before he utilized the guinea pig ileum for these investigations, he considered several important questions:

First, how closely does opioid dependence in the preparation resemble that in experimental animals or man in vivo? Second, can dependence on drugs other than opioids be induced in the guinea pig ileum and, if so, how are the different dependencies related? Third, what neurone or combination of neurones of the myenteric plexus participates in these dependencies? Fourth, what are the cellular and molecular mechanisms of dependence in the neurones involved? (p.116-117)

Furthermore, he considered the breadth of the problem:

That dependence occurs within the opiate-sensitive neurone does not mean that factors outside this cell may not also contribute to the effect. Among these factors, which may be termed circumcellular, I include: supersensitivity of a neurone or muscle cell downstream of the opiate-sensitive neurone; and changes in the production by adjoining cells of endogenous opioid transmitter or of an enzyme destroying it. (p.115)

Thus, embarking on his inquest, he recently provided important observations and conclusions to assist in the development of his thoughts and hypothesis. These include:

...The same neurone can be made dependent on three distinct types of agonist. When the neurone is dependent on one of these agonists a withdrawal contracture cannot be precipitated with specific antagonists of either of the other two types of drug....Any one of the three different types of agonist, however, readily suppresses the withdrawal contracture of ileum made dependent on either of the other two agonists. We have therefore termed convergent those dependencies that begin through activation of different recognition sites in the cholinergic motor neurone and end in the common process of liberating acetycholine at the termi:al on withdrawal.

Since we have not yet observed any difference in character between the three convergent dependencies in this neurone, other than in the inducing drugs and their specific antagonists, we provisionally assume that they have a common mechanism, which must lie downstream of the different recognition sites. (p.118)

He further postulated:

> That dependence occurs in the cholinergic neurone at a
> point below the recognition site still leaves a number of
> possible mechanisms for opioid dependence. The
> likelihood that several of these operate is diminished by
> the finding that withdrawal elicits a sharp increase in
> impulse production recorded at the cell body...Hence the
> most likely possibilities are that dependence occurs in
> the post-recognition site part of the receptor apparatus
> or in an associated second messenger system that
> translates the message of site activation into the
> language of cellular response. (p.120)

In regard to why progress in this area developed slowly, Collier
stated:

> Until recently, there has been relatively little
> opportunity to test these hypotheses in normal neurones,
> but the discovery of convergent dependencies on
> normorphine, clonidine and adenosine in the final
> cholinergic motor neurone...now offers an opportunity to
> do so. The general concept that dependence in normal
> neurones arises in response to continued inhibition of
> adenylate cyclase is supported by the fact that all of
> the three agonists that induce dependence in the
> myenteric plexus...have been shown to inhibit adenylate
> cyclase in other biological preparations, as a result of
> binding with their distinct and specific recognition
> sites. Unfortunately, it has so far proved impossible to
> test directly whether normorphine, clonidine and
> adenosine each inhibits adenylate cyclase in the
> cholinergic motor neurone of the myenteric plexus.
> (pp.121-122)

Yet he remained optimistic that we were poised at the edge of a
major scientific breakthrough. He ended his paper with the
following statements those of us in the field should well remember.

> 1. The relationship between opiate tolerance and
> dependence is not well understood...

> 2. The withdrawal syndrome of opiate dependence may
> represent a physiological mechanism for rapid arousal
> from inhibition induced by endogenous opioid.

> 3. The main site of opiate dependence is the opiate-
> sensitive neurone...

> 4. The isolated ileum of the guinea-pig so far provides
> the only model in which opiate dependence
> and associated tolerance can be consistently induced and
> measured in normal neurones in vitro....

5. The characteristics of opiate dependence displayed by the ileal model closely resemble those of dependence in whole animals...

6. Distinct but convergent dependences on normorphine, clonidine and adenosine can be separately induced in the guinea-pig ileum in vitro.

7. ...The final cholinergic motoneurone of the myenteric plexus participates in all three of these dependences.

8. With the cholinergic motor neurone these dependences probaby arise at a point below the separate recognition sites and above the site of acetylcholine release at the terminal.

9. A second transmitter, substance P, also participates in dependences in the myenteric plexus. (p.123)

10. There is direct experimental evidence that opiate dependence and associated tolerance in cultures of neuroblastoma x glioma hybrid cells arises through an hypertrophy of cellular adenylate cyclase.

FOOTNOTE

1. The quotations herein are taken from: Collier, H.O.J. Cellular aspects of opioid tolerance and dependence. In: Hughes, J.; Collier, H.O.J.; Rance, M.J.; and Tyers, M.B., eds. Opioids, Past, Present and Future. London and Philadelphia: Taylor & Francis 1984. pp. 109-125. Copyright 1984, Taylor & Francis Ltd.

In Memoriam: H. O. J. Collier

On 29 August 1983, Harry Collier passed away, the victim of a failed heart that for the past several years was sustained by a pacemaker. To those who knew him as a friend as well as a colleague, his death is a severe personal loss. This news was particularly poignant in our household because on the very day he died we received a letter from Harry confirming that he would visit us right after the technical review on mechanisms of tolerance and dependence on November 11-12, 1983. Unfortunately, the visit was not to be. Instead, with a heavy heart and tearful eye, I have prepared a eulogy for the man to whom the meeting and this monograph are dedicated.

For this purpose, I have borrowed heavily from the obituary which appeared in the Times of London on 2 September 1983. It was written by Harry's son, Joseph Collier, and his former son-in-law, Andrew Herxheimer, both of whom are pharmacologists.

Henry Oswald Jackson Collier was born on March 14, 1912, and educated at the Royal Grammar School, Worcester, from where he went to Trinity Hall, Cambridge. Here he graduated B.A. with First Class Honors in the Natural Sciences Tripos (an honors examination) in 1933 and went on to do research in the Department of Zoology, being awarded his Ph.D. in 1938.

From 1937 to 1941 he was an assistant lecturer and demonstrator in Comparative Physiology at the University of Manchester, and in 1941 he joined Imperial Chemical (Pharmaceuticals) Ltd. as a parasitologist. From here he was loaned to do research in chemotherapy at Liverpool School of Tropical Medicine.

In 1945 he went to Allen and Hanbury's Ltd. at Ware to set up a new pharmacology department for the firm. This he built up and ran until 1958 when he left to join Parke-Davis at Hounslow as Director of Pharmacological Research. Here he remained until 1969.

During this period, the natural materials known as prostaglandins were discovered and recognized to be a novel kind of locally produced and locally effective hormone, "the coinage of the body's defenses," as Harry later described them.

In 1968, indeed, he even suggested that anti-inflammatory drugs such as aspirin might function by interfering with the production of naturally occurring hormones such as prostaglandins. Shortly thereafter Harry became Director of the Stokes Court Laboratory of Miles Laboratories, Ltd., and it was at this critical juncture of his career that he did not have access to a laboratory wherein he could test his hypothesis experimentally.

The demonstration that this is indeed what happens came 3 years later, in Dr. J. R. Vane's Nobel Prize-winning study at the Royal College of Surgeons.

In the latter part of his life his interests turned more specifically to questions of the mechanism of tolerance and dependence, and he published a number of papers on these and kindred topics, many of which evoked considerable interest. This work brought him international recognition as a leading authority in the field.

In 1969 he and Hans Kosterlitz organized a satellite meeting on opiates at the International Union on Pharmacology Congress in Basel. This session, which attracted about 25 participants, was the forerunner of the International Narcotic Research Conference which has now a membership of over 500 scientists.

After his retirement from Miles in 1982, Harry Collier returned to academic work as an Honorary Professor of London University at Chelsea College, where he set up and directed a research unit to study the mechanisms of drug dependence. There he showed that adenosine, a substance which occurs naturally in the brain, can interfere with the development of opiate dependence and its later manifestations. This may well prove to be an important step towards finding some means of preventing opiate dependence.

A highly literate man, Harry's interests outside his professional concerns ranged widely over the cultural field, and he was particularly fond of poetry and the theater.

2

His favorite poet was William Shakespeare, and it was altogether fitting that the funeral service for Harry Collier closed with a reading of the song from Cymbeline, the first six lines of which are:

> Fear no more the heat o'th' sun
>   Nor the furious winter's rages;
> Thou thy worldly task has done,
>   Home art gone, and ta'en thy wages.
> Golden lads and girls all must,
>   As chimney-sweepers, come to dust.

Sydney Archer, Ph.D.
School of Science
Rensselaer Polytechnic Institute
Troy, New York 12181

Mechanisms of Tolerance and Dependence: An Overview

Leo G. Abood

Despite extensive knowledge of the mechanisms involved in the acute action of drugs of abuse, relatively little is known of their chronic effects and the mechanisms responsible for drug dependence and tolerance associated with the compulsive use of drugs. The phenomena of tolerance and dependence occur with a variety of psychotropic drugs and are not unique to the opiates and other drugs of abuse. Throughout the symposium, it was repeatedly emphasized that the problem of physical dependence is highly complex, involving a series of adaptive changes beginning with the diverse and widely scattered opioid receptors and extending to complex arrays of autonomic and sensorimotor neural networks; adaptive changes which are influenced by genetic, species, and environmental factors.

The main emphasis of the symposium was opiate dependence and tolerance, examining the biochemical, pharmacologic, and electrophysiologic mechanisms in the central nervous and neuroendocrine systems as well as various peripheral systems known to possess opioid peptides and receptor subtypes. The most characteristic phenomenon associated with opiate dependence is the abstinence syndrome following drug withdrawal or administration of an opiate antagonist such as naloxone. The phenomenon, which is manifested biochemically as well as physiologically, involves virtually every system containing opioid receptors, and it provides an index for assessing physical dependence in a variety of animal species, organ systems, and cell cultures.

Martin stressed the fact that drug tolerance and dependence involves a variety of adaptive mechanisms—both autonomic and sensorimotor—and the necessity for model systems to be relevant to the problem of tolerance and dependence in man as well as animals. Adler presented an overview of neuropharmacologic procedures to assess drug tolerance and dependence, including measurements of EEG, body temperature, brain lesions, and behavioral paradigms. He pointed out that pharmacokinetic factors, such as the dose schedule, route of administration, and lipid solubility, influence the drug's effectiveness in producing tolerance and dependence. Dewey called attention to a recent report by Ternes demonstrating tolerance and dependence with hydromorphone in rhesus but not cynamologus monkeys and emphasized the differences in tolerance and dependence liability among animal species as well as of various classes of opiates. Pharmacokinetic factors must be considered both in accounting for the differential effectiveness of classes of opiate agonists and antagonists in producing tolerance and dependence within a given species and when accounting for dependence liability of a given drug among different species. He stated that $\Delta 9$-THC (intravenously) is as potent as morphine in producing analgesia in rodents and that only tolerance and no withdrawal effects (loss of body weight) are seen with the drug.

Herz considered tolerance and dependence to opiates to be a function of the multiplicity of receptors. By taking advantage of the fact that tolerance development to prolonged opioid exposure in a given receptor subtype is selective for that subtype, one can demonstrate the presence of μ, κ, and δ-receptors in the mouse vas deferens and μ and κ - receptors in guinea pig ileum. It appears that κ -receptor ligands induce sedation, are not self-administered, and do not suppress withdrawal. His observation that the rewarding and analgesic properties of diprenorphine (a multiple receptor-ligand) are mediated separately by a δ (possibly) and μ receptor, respectively, poses a challenge to the prevalent notion that both effects are mediated by the μ receptors. Herz described experiments with the opiate-dependent ileum which indicated that tolerance and dependence were not interdependent. With the use of the mouse vas deferens made tolerant to opiates, it was not possible to demonstrate cross-tolerance among any of the various receptor subtypes. Conceivably, tolerance involves a modification of the receptor, while dependence is related to adaptive changes at either the effector or regulatory (adenylate cyclase) link. During the discussion period, it was noted that physical dependence reflects a drug-seeking behavior aimed at attenuating the aversive withdrawal effects of opiates.

Shuster addressed the problem of the genetic factors influencing responsiveness to opiates and other drugs of abuse, employing inbred and congenic lines of mouse. The naloxone-induced jumping after chronically administered morphine was observed in C_{57} but not A/J mice; and, although little correlation was observed between ^{3}H-naloxone binding to brain membranes and analgetic responsiveness to opiates, those strains having the lowest receptor density were the least responsive. The observed relationship between receptor density and analgetic responsiveness appeared to involve the μ but not δ or κ receptors. Such pharmacogenetic studies reveal the significance of genetic factors in determining individual vulnerability to physical dependence on drugs of abuse.

One of the most useful and interesting preparations for studying opiate dependence in vitro is the isolated myenteric plexus of the guinea pig after chronic opiate administration. Dependency in the ileum is manifested by a naloxone-precipitated contracture which can be overcome by morphine. Tucker described the recent studies of the late Collier demonstrating the existence of three separate but convergent systems impinging on the final cholinergic motorneurons responsible for ileal contraction. The ileum exhibits a dependency on normorphine, clonidine (α_2-norepinephrine agonist), and adenosine (an activator of adenylate cyclase); furthermore, cyclohexyladenosine, an adenosine receptor antagonist, is a potent inhibitor of the withdrawal response of the ileum.

A number of speakers focused on the possible role of adenylate cyclase, which is presumed to be one of the regulatory links between the receptor and the effector components of the opioid system. Evidence for the involvement of adenylate cyclase in the opioid system stems mainly from the work of Klee and collaborators demonstrating that opioids inhibit adenylate cyclase in a neuroblastoma-glioma cell line (NG 108-15). There also exist receptors which stimulate adenylate cyclase, such as Cl-adenosine and prostaglandin E_1, the response of the latter being inhibited by opiates. Klee expanded on his recent report that the suppressive action of opiates on adenylate cyclase resulted from stimulation of GTPase, which regulates the cyclase by controlling the levels of the essential cofactor GTP. Some discussion was devoted to pertussin toxin, which, by promoting ribosylation of the Ni subunit, abolishes the hormone inactivation of adenylate cyclase in a variety of inhibitory systems. The toxin also decreases opiate receptor binding as well as inhibition of the cyclase in the NG cell line. From studies showing that the toxin had no effect on the acute action of normorphine on ileum, while inhibiting the withdrawal response of the ileum, in vivo and in vitro, Tucker proposed that the toxin was activating an inhibitory regulator of adenylate cyclase and that physical dependence may involve such a regulator.

A possible mechanism for drug tolerance and dependence would involve an alteration in either the density or affinity of its receptor. The well-known phenomenon of supersensitivity to dopamine (DA) agonists following chronic exposure to the neuroleptic DA antagonists is attributable to an increase in the number of DA receptors. Attempts by many investigators to modify the density or affinity of opioid receptors by chronic administration of opiate agonists or antagonists have led to variable results. Zukin reported that chronic treatment of rats with naltrexone resulted in a two-fold increase in the brain density of opiate receptors (^{3}H-etorphine binding), returning to normal levels after 6 days without drug. Autoradiographic studies after chronic naltrexone revealed that the density of μ and δ, but not κ and σ receptor, in specific brain areas increased. Clouet viewed tolerance as any change resulting from the occupancy of the receptor by an opiate and reviewed changes in the neostriatum associated with acute and chronic exposure to opiates. These included an increase in DA-stimulated adenylate cyclase (acute and chronic), increase in DA turnover (especially with δ agonists), a biphasic response in the Ca/calmodulin-dependent protein kinase (acute morphine), and a suppression of the increased kinase activity after chronic morphine. Protein phosphorylation, by regulating neuro-transmitter turnover, adenylate cyclase, and ionic channels, may be another mechanism associated with tolerance-dependence.

Loh described the use in his laboratory of the NG 108-15 cell line to examine the phenomena of opiate desensitization and withdrawal.

Chronic exposure to etorphine produces a down-regulation of opiate receptors and a naloxone-reversible inhibition of PGE_1-stimulated adenylate cyclase. He postulates that the down-regulation is due to internalization of the receptor; while the rebound effect, which is suppressed by Cl-adenosine and NaF, may involve a restoration of the uncoupled inhibitory regulatory-coupling units of the cyclase complex. A similar mechanism for opiate desensitization was proposed by Wuster, who provided additional evidence for the dissociation of tolerance and naloxone-induced withdrawal in the mouse vas deferens and guinea pig ileum as well as the NG cell line. The opiate desensitization resulting from pertussis toxin involves a suppression of the inhibitory coupling unit (Ni) of the cyclase complex; and insofar as opioid receptors are also decreased by the toxin, he proposed that Ni is needed to maintain the receptors.

Based on studies with a variety of opioid peptides including β-endorphin and dynorphin (κ agonist), Lee proposed that a balance of endogenous opioid peptides was involved in analgesia, β-endorphin serving as the major effector and the others as modulatory. Dynorphin alone was not analgetic, and whereas it potentiated opiate-induced analgesia in naive mice, it prevented withdrawal in mice, monkeys, and man and suppressed opiate binding in vivo.

Cicero discussed the mechanisms involved in opioid tolerance and dependence in the rat hypothalamic-pituitary-luteinizing hormone (LH) axis. The release of LHRH from the hypothalamus is modulated by opioid receptors of unknown subtype; after acute or chronic morphine treatment followed by naloxone, there is a dramatic increase (order of magnitude) in serum LH levels. When morphine is given 31 days following castration, there occurs an increase (instead of a suppression) of LH along with a tolerance to opiate analgesia. The study is illustrative of the multifarious nature of the opioid system and its vulnerability to physical dependence.

Mains briefly reviewed the current knowledge of the precursors, biosynthesis, and processing of neuropeptides, particularly those that are pro-ACTH/endorphin-derived. With the use of mouse pituitary tumor cells, he studied the process of α-amidation, which results in the formation of TRH, vasopressin, substance P, and many other neuropeptides from the corresponding peptides with a terminus COOH.

With the use of the hibernating ground squirrel, Beckman was able to demonstrate an absence of naloxone-induced withdrawal (vocalization and shakes) following chronic exposure to morphine. Since DA turnover decreased, while DA levels increased 10-fold in the hibernating animal, he inferred that DA supersensitivity, which may be a withdrawal mechanism, could not develop. Autoradiographic studies revealed a decrease of opiate receptors in regional brain areas. Henriksen presented a review of the neurophysiological literature concerned with opioid tolerance and dependence, highlighting the use of slices of rat hippocampus and locus coeruleus. When dynorphin is iontophoretically applied to the CA3 pyramidal neurons of the hippocampal slice,

7

excitation occurs without acute desensitization; however, the application of a synthetic κ agonist, U50-488H, produces inhibition. Herz reported an increase in field potentials of hippocampal slices with exposure to met-enkephalin, but not with morphine.

Crain described the use of organotypic cultures of mouse spinal cord and sensory ganglia in studying acute and chronic effects by electrophysiologic analyses. Sensory-evoked synaptic responses from dorsal, but not ventral, root ganglia are depressed in a naloxone-dependent manner by morphine; and after exposure to morphine for 2 days, the depressant effect of opiates vanishes, but is restored by naloxone. Proceeding on the assumption that drug tolerance should be reflected in altered activity of regional brain areas, Elde measured cytochrome oxidase histochemically in chronically morphinized mice. The most apparent change was a decrease in the mammillary bodies. With the use of the ^{14}C-deoxyglucose method, others have reported a decreased metabolism in frontal motor cortex and striatum and increases in other brain areas. Because of the depressant effects of opiates in respiration, it is difficult to determine whether the observed metabolic changes are direct or indirect. With the demonstration of the existence of opiate receptors in lymphocytes and other blood cells, interest has centered on the possible functional role of the receptors in white cells. Plotnikoff reviewed his and other findings showing that met-enkephalin was an immunostimulant, which in mice increased the size of the thymus, decreased the size of the spleen, increased lymphocytic blastogenesis induced by mitogens, and enhanced the natural killer cell activity on cancer cells.

The final session of the symposium was devoted to drugs of abuse other than the opiates. Groves reported that since the stereotypic behavioral effects of amphetamine are enhanced by long-term administration while others are attenuated, multiple mechanisms must be involved in the drug's action. Apart from such mechanisms as increased release of catecholamines and supersensitivity of postsynaptic and subsensitivity of pre-synaptic DA receptors, there are widespread adaptive changes in many brain areas affecting the integrative activity of brain in coping with its disrupted environment. Karler found that increased sensitivity to the cannabinoids develops concomitantly with tolerance, a phenomenon that was first noted with cocaine. Furthermore, the cannabinoids enhance the sensitization to convulsant drugs and electroconvulsive shock, an effect which may endure for months. Although some of the behavioral effects of cocaine may involve activation of the catecholaminergic systems, many of the effects cannot be accounted for by such mechanisms. In the search for alternate mechanisms, Gale reported that chronic administration of cocaine or cocaine + droperidol (a DA antagonist) resulted in a significant increase in striatal glutamate decarboxylase, a concomitant increase in GABA, and a decrease in ^{3}H-GABA binding. The findings are indicative of increased GABA turnover following chronic exposure to cocaine; however, the neurotransmitter system directly involved in cocaine's action is still uncertain.

8

Okamoto reported that the dispositional (pharmacokinetic) tolerance to barbiturates had a rapid onset and was of long duration, while the functional (CNS depression) tolerance developed slowly and progressed with treatment. By examining a variety of barbiturates, various dose schedules, and pharmacokinetics, she demonstrated that tolerance and dependence were dependent on the blood level of the barbiturate needed to maintain CNS depression.

Abood described the behavioral and biochemical studies in rats given nicotine chronically. No changes were observed in the density or affinity of $(-)-^3H$-nicotine binding sites to brain membranes or in the metabolism of nicotine by isolated hepatocytes. Although tolerance develops to the central effects of nicotine, the effect is transitory.

In addition to providing a number of conceptual and methodological approaches towards understanding drug tolerance and dependence, the symposium has attempted to better characterize the terms for specific drugs of abuse. The mechanisms for drug tolerance, which are comparable for most drugs and better understood than those for dependence, generally involve adaptive biochemical mechanisms affecting the rate of drug metabolism and elimination, the sensitivity of receptors, and responsiveness of secondary messenger systems. On the other hand, the phenomenon of dependence, which is more characteristic of drugs of abuse, is highly complex and involves a variety of biochemical and neurophysiological mechanisms. A number of experimental models, ranging from neuronal tissue cultures to the whole animals, are available for exploring the mechanisms of withdrawal of opiates and, to a lesser extent, barbiturates and amphetamines. Such models, which provide the basis for examining the underlying mechanisms for dependence and withdrawal, have yet to be developed for the cannabinoids, cocaine, nicotine, and other abused drugs. The further development and refinement of such experimental models will continue to be significant factors in elucidating such mechanisms.

There arises the question concerning the nature of the physiological substrate that is mimicked and, presumably, replaced by the dependent drug and the possible dependence of the organism on the endogenous substrate. With respect to the opiates, we have some knowledge of the endogenous substrates (β-endorphin, dynorphin, and enkephalins) and their receptors (μ, κ, and δ, respectively); and one might concur with Collier that the organism is "physically dependent" on the endogenous opioids. A similar argument holds for amphetamine which interacts with catecholaminergic systems. The nature of the endogenous substrates for barbiturates and other drugs of abuse is not known; however, many of the drugs do appear to involve specific receptors. One of the important problems for future research is to characterize the endogenous substrate for the receptors and demonstrate its ability to mimic drug-induced dependence and withdrawal.

By encompassing a wide spectrum of abused drugs and a number of disciplinary approaches, the symposium, in its attempt to deal with mechanisms of drug dependence, has highlighted some important issues concerning the nature of the problem. If a drug's action is receptor-mediated, and the receptor exists in multiple forms, can a unitary molecular mechanism be involved? Are there common mechanisms among different drugs of abuse? Is the development of dependence associated with more than one subtype (e.g., the μ-form) of the opiate receptor? If it is assumed that dependence is a complex process involving a number of neural circuits, is it necessary for an adaptive molecular mechanism to occur at the level of the receptor or the second intermediary messenger?

Much of our information concerning the involvement of receptor-linked mechanisms in drug tolerance and dependence derives from studies on neuroblastoma-glioma cultures, where the second messenger appears to be a prostoglandin-stimulated adenylate cyclase linked to a δ-receptor. How applicable is this model to the central nervous system which contains μ and κ receptors as well? With the possible exception of the nigrostriatum, attempts to demonstrate the involvement of adenylate cyclase in opiate action in brain have been unsuccessful. Relatively little progress has been made in demonstrating a primary action of opiates on ionic conductances and neurotransmitter function and turnover. Answers to these and other questions relating to the complex problem of drug dependence must continue to come from a multi-disciplinary approach, so well exemplified by this symposium.

Finally, there remains the problem of the criteria for determining whether a drug of abuse is addictive. Some might argue that any drug or substance which is abused, i.e., used compulsively, is addictive; in which case the term would be applicable to innumerable drugs, substances, and compulsive behavioral patterns. Since the degree or intensity of abuse varies greatly among drugs and substances, this definition requires a categorization in terms of their degree of addictive liability. The term "habitual," which is more generally used to describe compulsive tendencies, would be synonymous with "addictive." It may, however, be useful to reserve the term "addictive" for abused agents and tendencies exhibiting a "high degree" of compulsiveness. The problem would then be to define the psychophysical parameters associated with compulsive behavior and to decide arbitrarily when an agent is to be labeled "addictive."

At the present state of our knowledge, the most characteristic psychophysical parameters associated with compulsive use of drugs are those resulting from either their abrupt withdrawal or administration of an appropriate antagonist. In the case of the opiates, barbiturates, amphetamines, and alcohol, the withdrawal signs are well-defined and severe; whereas, with the cannabinoids and nicotine, they are not easily definable by physiological measures and tend to be far less severe. If the term "addictive" is reserved for those drugs promoting severe, definable withdrawal signs—often life-threatening in humans—the class of addictive drugs would be small; but, if the term is to be more generally applicable to abused drugs, it will be necessary to develop, in both animal and human models, the psychophysical, pharmacologic, and biochemical criteria for assessing their relative degree of compulsive liability.

AUTHOR

Leo G. Abood, Ph.D.
Center for Brain Research
Box 605
University of Rochester Medical Center
601 Elmwood Avenue
Rochester, New York 14642

Phenomenology and Theoretical Basis of Tolerance and Dependence

William R. Martin

I am pleased to dedicate this chapter on tolerance and dependence to an acquaintance of many years, Harry O. J. Collier. Our paths first crossed in the early 1960s when we both were in the process of developing our ideas concerning tolerance and dependence. Over the years, Dr. Collier became concerned with the phenomenology of tolerance and dependence and its basis.

Those of us who work on drug abuse problems tend to view the drugs as toxins, tolerance as a protective mechanism, and physical dependence as an aversive consequence of recruitment of these protective mechanisms. Yet another view is that dependence-producing drugs are pleasure-giving and that physical dependence is the price that is paid for their use; the view that if one dances one should be expected to pay the piper. For several reasons included herein, this chapter will deal with the underlying concepts of tolerance and dependence. Both are fundamental biologic properties of most animals and probably to some degree of all biological tissues. They are intimately concerned with motivation, instincts, adaptive behavior, survival, homeostasis, needs, drives, arousal and finally with desires--concepts which have subtle but broad-reaching distinctions and implications. Tolerance and dependence will be approached here from a theoretical point of view as it relates to these apparently diverse concepts.

Concepts of tolerance and dependence still plague us both conceptually and phenomenologically. Preoccupation with the phenomenology of tolerance and dependence and their molecular basis has created problems that are new and important in their own right but causes one to disregard important dimensions which relate these phenomena to psychopathology and to public health. In the end all of these phenomena have to be viewed from the standpoint of evolution and survival and are unique in that therapeutic chemostimuli (drugs interacting with receptors) are being developed systematically.

It is important to remember that dependencies are needs. This concept is frequently forgotten as we identify and use experimental models which are presumed to be models of dependence. It will serve a purpose to distinguish between two aspects of the concept of needs. A general definition of need is a life requirement for an environmental circumstance which is conducive to survival or well-being. A more specific definition refers to the mechanisms whereby congenial and hostile environments are recognized. It is in this restricted meaning that needs will be used in the following discussion.

Figure 1 illustrates the simplest and presumedly most primitive control mechanisms in organisms which have acquired the ability to sense and to make integrated adaptive movements. In this model the sensory system is the need system. We will assume for example that the animal senses a nutrient need (environment) through a chemoreceptive mechanism and moves toward it. Thus the organism is dependent on a nutrient chemical (need) and has a motor mechanism for acquiring it (drive). An important control mechanism which must have evolved early was negative feedback regulation (tolerance to chemostimulation). This was necessary for motor control so that the organism could (1) slow, stop, and make directional corrections as it approached a food-rich environment and (2) stop feeding when satiation occurred. Thus it is reasonable to conceive that tolerance to chemostimulation evolved early in evolution as an adaptive mechanism.

A second major principle evolved when organisms became more complex, had to integrate the activity of different functional systems, eventually to regulate internal environments, and finally to develop new abstract needs such as aggression, power, and developmental dependencies related to complex ecological and social influences. These new needs as well as old ones became manifest by the activity of neuronal nets which were stimulated by disequilibriums and hostile environments. This neuronal activity produced discomforting feelings such as pain, fear, anxiety, suffering, depression, and hypophoria. Thus the activity of these neuronal nets is the sine qua non of internal needs and associated affective states. Figure 2 is a scheme indicating this internalization of need mechanisms which maintain homeostasis and enhance survival. With this internalization, new systems of controls evolved which involve reciprocal inhibition, a type of negative feedback regulation. Here, too, negative feedback is necessary for central need reduction and provides the mechanism whereby an organism can integrate movements and recognize satiety. It is important to recognize that all drugs of abuse diminish a variety of needs (table 1), a relationship first emphasized by Himmelsbach (1943) and Wikler (1952). An extensive body of research indicating that these drugs also alter brain neurohumoral processes has a number of implications, among which is the proposition that chemostimulation continues to play an important role in need states.

13

FIGURE 1

BASIC IMPORTANCE OF TOLERANCE TO EXTERNAL
CHEMORECEPTIVE-NEED-DRIVE PROCESSES

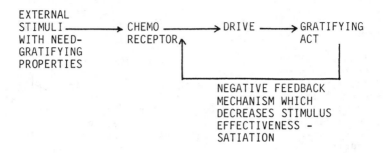

FIGURE 2

PROPOSED PROCESSES RELATING NEEDS (DEPENDENCIES), AFFECT
AND NEGATIVE FEEDBACK MECHANISMS (TOLERANCE)

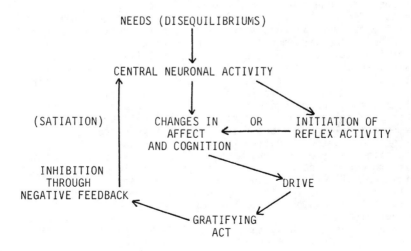

14

TABLE 1

Drugs of Abuse Which Reduce Needs and Drives and Alter Homeostats, and the Putative Neurotransmitters and Neuromodulators Involved

Opiates $\left\{\begin{array}{l}\text{Endorphins} \\ \text{Enkephalins} \\ \text{and Dynorphins}\end{array}\right\}$

Food
CO_2
Pain
Sex
Temperature Regulation
Vasomotor Function
Hypophoria

Amphetamines $\{DA, NE\}$

Food
Sleep
Pain
Hypophoria

Alcohol $\{GABA\}$

Pain
Hypophoria

Benzodiazepines $\{GABA\}$

Sleep
Anxiety

Tobacco $\{ACh\}$

Sex
Pain
Food
Hypophoria

Sedative-Hypnotics $\{GABA\}$

Sleep
Pain
Hypophoria

Marijuana

Pain
Hypophoria

LSD-Like Hallucinogens $\left\{\begin{array}{l}\text{Tryptamine} \\ \text{Serotonin}\end{array}\right\}$

Pain
Hypophoria

Tolerance and physical dependence in man have been explored most extensively for the opiates. Himmelsbach (1943) conceptualized the processes of tolerance and physical dependence to opiates as an alteration of autonomic homeostasis and the recruitment of contra-adaptive mechanisms. This hypothesis has been very attractive; however, it has been rigorously tested only for the regulatory system in man. There are many complexities in conceptualizing tolerance and dependence and in devising measures of these phenomena (cf. Martin and Sloan 1977). In nonhuman studies there is evidence that this mechanism may be of importance in the regulation of certain endocrine functions and in the temperataure regulation of the dog Table 2 and figure 3

15

TABLE 2

The effects of morphine in nondependent, morphine-dependent (240 mg/day) and morphine-abstinent subjects on the responsivity (slope) and sensitivity (intercept) of the respiratory system to CO_2 (from Martin et al. 1968).

	Slope ± S.E.	Intercept ± S.E.
	Preaddiction	
Control	1.5 + 0.1	51.7 + 2.2
Morphine (30 mg/70 kg)	1.1 + 0.1(0.05)	62.8 + 2.6(0.05)
	Late Dependence	
Predrug	1.9 + 0.2	62.1 + 2.2
Morphine (60 mg/70 kg)	1.7 + 0.2	63.4 + 1.6
	Early Abstinence (20 Hours)	
	3.2 + 0.3(0.05)	52.7 + 1.6
	Protracted Abstinence	
	1.3 + 0.2(0.25)	57.0 + 1.9(0.005)

p values in parentheses when compared to control values.

summarize the effects of morphine and morphine abstinence on the responsivity and sensitivity of the respiratory center to CO_2 (Martin et al. 1968). In the nondependent subject morphine shifted the partial pressure of CO_2-minute-volume stimulus – response curve to the right and depressed its slope. In stabilized dependent subjects the stimulus-response line remained shifted to the right; however, its slope was steeper than that of the stimulus-response line prior to the subject's becoming physically dependent. Very large doses of morphine (60 and 120 mg/70 kg) had no effect on the stimulus-response line, a not unexpected finding since 240 mg/day of morphine probably produced maximum physical dependence by occupying all of the morphine receptors (Martin et al. 1972). When the subjects were abstinent 20 hours (mild to moderate abstinence syndrome had developed), the slope of the stimulus-response line was twice as steep as that of the control stimulus-response line. Thus, even in this relatively simple system, tolerance and dependence have complex dimensions. Morphine continued to depress the respiratory center's sensitivity to CO_2 throughout the period of chronic intoxication; however, chronic intoxication enhanced the responsivity (increased the

16

FIGURE 3

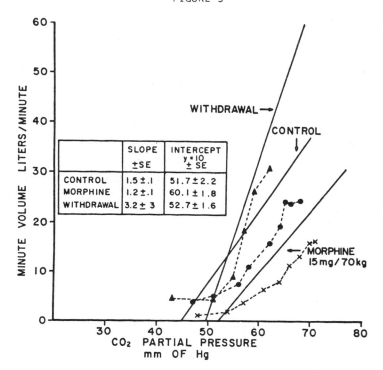

Mean calculated regression lines (solid) for partial pressure
(pCO$_2$)-minute volume (Va) response curves obtained during the
control period, after 15 mg/70 kg of morphine, and during early
withdrawal in subjects dependent on 240 mg/day of morphine. The
means for each parameter were determined from values obtained in 7
subjects. There was great variability in the first and last points
of the response curves. The top of the regression lines represents
the maximum Va obtained. A control (•), a 15 mg/70 kg dose of
morphine (x) and a withdrawal (▲) paCO$_2$-Va response of one
subject (dashed lines) are presented to further illustrate these
changes. (From Martin et al. 1968.)

slope) of the respiratory center to CO$_2$. Despite the persisting
depression, additional morphine was without effect. The respiratory studies provided further evidence about the relationship
between need and affective state. When alveolar ventilation
exceeded 10 ℓ/minute, subjects experienced some discomfort which
increased as the minute-volume increased. In these studies the
intensity of the discomfort was indicated by hand signals. No
discomfort was reported by the subjects after they received single
doses of morphine (15 or 30 mg/70 kg) even when minute-volume
exceeded 10 ℓ/minute. This may mean that subjective discomfort
associated with a need can be diminished without producing an equal
diminution of the drive mechanism.

Tolerance to and dependence on drugs of abuse are even more compli-
cated phenomena when other parameters and drugs are considered.
This point is of sufficient importance to be emphasized, as much of
our effort, at the more basic levels, may be describing phenomena
that are not obviously related to the phenomena of tolerance and
dependence as seen in man with chronic drug administration. Figure
4 illustrates the effects of chronic intoxication to morphine (240
mg/day) on a variety of physiologic parameters. It is believed
that 240 mg/day of morphine saturates nearly all of the u receptors
and produces a maximal degree of physical dependence. Chronic
administration of morphine increases blood pressure, pulse rate,
and body temperature and decreases pupillary diameter and respiratory rate. Single doses of morphine in nondependent subjects
do not markedly alter blood pressure, pulse rate, or body
temperature. It is emphasized that these changes persist
throughout the period of chronic intoxication.

FIGURE 4

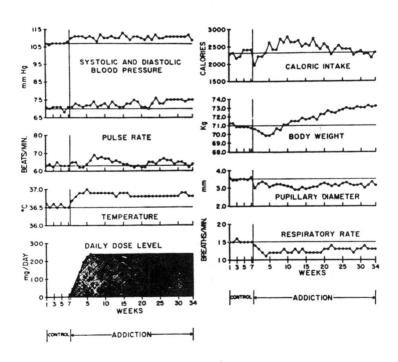

The effects of chronic administration of morphine on clinical
variables. Each point represents the weekly mean a.m. observation
for 7 subjects. The horizontal line represents the mean of control
determinations for 7 subjects. (From Martin and Jasinski 1969.)

18

Figure 5 illustrates changes that occurred in subjects who received methadone in a dose of 100 mg/day chronically. A decrease in pupillary diameter and respiratory rate and an increase in body temperature was seen, changes similar to those produced by chronic morphine. The chronic methadone syndrome differed from the chronic morphine syndrome in that blood pressure and pulse rate were decreased. Thus the chronic effects of closely related opioids differ.

FIGURE 5

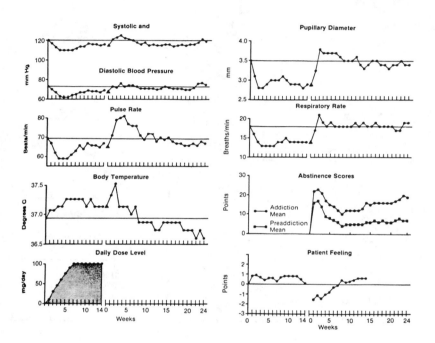

Changes in physiological indices and intensity of abstinence and feeling state during cycle of methadone dependence. Horizontal line in each graph represents mean of control observations made three times daily (6 AM, 12 noon, and 6 PM) for 42 days in 5 patients. Each point represents mean weekly value. Triangles indicate mean of observations obtained during last three weeks of addiction cycle. (From Martin et al. 1973.)

19

Figure 6 shows the various signs of the morphine abstinence syndrome. Blood pressure, pulse rate, body temperatures, and respiratory rate are significantly increased. Although pupils return to control value following withdrawal, they do not markedly dilate. A similar abstinence syndrome was seen in methadone-dependent subjects (figure 5). Thus the abstinence syndrome is not the mirror image of the signs of acute or chronic intoxication with morphine and has unique dimensions of its own. Figure 5 and table 2 illustrate another important feature of the morphine abstinence syndrome. The acute abstinence syndrome persists for about a month and then a new syndrome develops which is characterized by a mild hypotension, bradycardia, hypothermia, miosis, and hyposensitivity of the respiratory center to CO_2. This syndrome persists for several months and was still evident when the studies were terminated. It is important to emphasize that there are both an acute and a protracted abstinence syndrome which are different and indicate

FIGURE 6

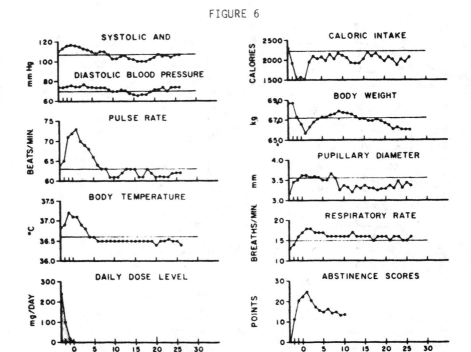

Changes seen during early and protracted abstinence. Each point represents the mean weekly a.m. values for 6 subjects. The first point of each curve represents the mean value for the last 7 weeks of addiction. The horizontal line represents the mean control value for the 6 subjects. One subject was withdrawn from the study near the end of the chronic intoxication phase because of episodes of acute cholecystitis. (From Martin and Jasinski 1969.)

20

that chronic administration of opioids alters neuronal excitability in diverse ways and probably through several mechanisms.

Morphine-like drugs produce feelings of well-being (euphoria or anti-hypophoria) in abstinent addicts. It is not generally recognized or attended to that chronic opiate-intoxicated patients become hypochondriac, develop feelings of tiredness, inefficiency, unpopularity, and become withdrawn (table 3). These symptoms are more marked during early withdrawal and remained exacerbated during protracted abstinence (Martin et al. 1973). This constellation of symptoms has been called hypophoria and their disappearance, euphoria (Martin et al. 1977). All of these negative feelings are decreased in a dose-related way by opiates, amphetamines (Martin et al. 1971), and barbiturates (Martin et al. 1974; Jasinski 1977). Although systematic studies have not been done, anecdotal accounts indicate that they are also probably reduced by nicotine, alcohol, marijuana, and the LSD-like hallucinogens. Thus the effect of chronic opioid administration is not merely the loss of its ability to produce feelings of well- being but the reduction of hypophoria and withdrawal from social interactions. These feelings are exacerbated during both early and protracted abstinence.

It is known that opiates in single doses decrease all types of sleep (Kay et al. 1969). Figure 7 illustrates changes in different types of sleep seen during a cycle of methadone dependence. As can be seen, sleep is increased during both the stabilization phase of dependence and protracted abstinence (Martin et al. 1973). Thus the effect of chronic opioid treatment on sleep is not simply the reduction of the insomniac action in the presence of opioids. It also produces hypersomnia in protracted abstinence.

Whereas a single dose of opioids can reduce a number of needs, chronic administration may both decrease (e.g., CO_2 elimination) and increase (e.g., hypophoria, sleep) needs. Although many need states are enhanced during early abstinence, some may be decreased (e.g., sleep). Perhaps, more importantly, during protracted abstinence some needs are increased (hypophoria and sleep) and others decreased (responsivity to CO_2) (see table 4).

CONCLUSION

Most, if not all, drugs of abuse are intimately involved in needs and need reduction. These needs are dependencies which have inherent tolerance mechanisms necessary for the control of need reduction. With internalization of need states and the evolution of cognitive processes, affect has become a fundamental need mechanism. Chronically administered drugs of abuse interact with and change need states. The characterization of these changes in terms of conventional definitions of tolerance and dependence greatly oversimplifies the impacts of chronic drug administration. Indeed this oversimplification of the concepts of tolerance and dependence and the development of methods for assessing them

21

TABLE 3

Changes in certain ARCI and MMPI scale scores during a cycle of addiction to methadone

	Controlled Addiction (4 and 10 Weeks)		Early Abstinence	Protracted Abstinence
ARCI Scale Score			**Negative Feelings**	
PCAG	48	55	73**	47
Weak	42	51	72**	47
Tired	44	61**	73**	47**
Social Withdrawal	56	56	58**	61
ARCI Scale Score			**Positive Feelings**	
MBG	55	53	38**	48
Efficiency	58	48**	24**	51**
MMPI Scale Scores				
Hs	54	71*	75*	53
Hy	53	66*	71*	58
Sc	62	70**	74*	74*

PCAG=(Pentobarbital, Chlorpromazine, Alcohol Group Scale) - Apathetic Sedation
MBG=(Morphine, Benzedrine Group Scale) - Euphoria - Antihypophoria
Hs=(Hysteria); Hy=(Hypochondriasis); Sc=(Schizophrenia); * $P<0.05$; ** $P<0.01$

FIGURE 7

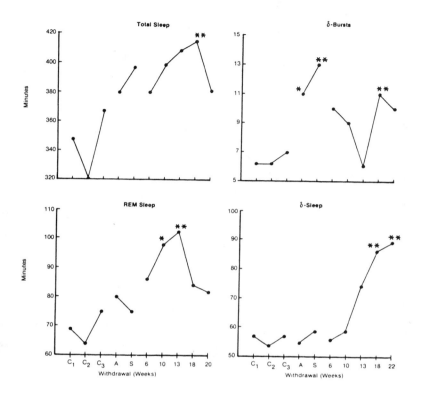

Number of minutes during various phases of the addiction cycle of
total sleep, δ-bursts, REM sleep, and δ-sleep. Each point
represents the mean obtained for 5 patients. Three control
observations were obtained (C1, C2, C3) as well as observations
during the ascending (A) and stabilization (S) phases and during
withdrawal (numbers in weeks). Asterisks indicate values are
significantly different from control values: *P<0.1; **P < 0.05.
(From Martin et al. 1973.)

TABLE 4

Summary of the Effects of a Cycle of Opioid Dependence on Three Needs

	Acute Effects	Stabilization (Tolerance)	Early Abstinence	Protracted Abstinence
Respiration	Decreased sensitivity and responsivity to CO_2	Decreased sensitivity and increased responsivity to CO_2	Increased responsivity and probably sensitivity	Increased and decreased sensitivity
Mood	Decreased hypophoria (euphoria)	Increased hypophoria	Increased hypophoria	Increased hypophoria
Sleep	Decreased all sleep stages	Increased total sleep and δ bursts		Increased δ and total sleep

24

may result in the study of phenomena which may not be related to the clinically relevant changes produced by chronic administrations of opioids and perhaps of other drugs.

Chronically administered opiates clearly produce long-persisting changes in need states and affect, enhancing some and depressing others, and may induce new needs which can only be met with drugs which may have the potential for abuse. The changes which are induced are enormously complex, probably involving multiple mechanisms such as homeostasis at molecular, cellular and tissue levels, supersensitivities, up- and down-regulations of receptors and their endogenous agonists and recruitment of redundant mechanisms. The enormous amount of research which has been done with chronic opiate administration has shown that these drugs produce long-lasting changes. Our own work continues to show that individuals with drug problems have exaggerated needs and associated affective disorders (hypophoria).

Drug-induced tolerance and dependence still have major clinical importance. Many patients with excessive needs and hypophoria attempt to cope with these discomforting subjective states by using drugs which possess antihypophoric properties. Most of these drugs interact with need states and alter them. Some of these alterations may cause long-persisting changes and worsen existing psychopathologic processes. Since one of the alternative strategies for treating drug abusers is chemotherapy, an understanding of the basic mechanisms of phenomena designated as tolerance and dependence is important, as these phenomena may alter brain functions related to needs and affect. Thus the search for new chemotherapeutics for the treatment of drug dependence presents a formidable challenge, for we will be interceding in functional systems which are intimately concerned with basic motivation. Interventions, because of the complexities of need systems, may have unexpected outcomes.

REFERENCES

Himmelsbach, C.K. Morphine with reference to physical dependence. Fed Proc 2:201-203, 1943
Jasinski, D.R. Clinical evaluation of sedative-hypnotic for abuse potential. In: Thompson, T., and Unna, K., eds. Predicting Dependence Liability of Stimulants and Depressant Drugs. Baltimore: University Park Press, 1977. pp. 285-289.
Kay, D.C., Eisenstein, R.B., and Jasinski, D.R. Morphine effects on human REM state, waking state and NREM sleep. Psychopharm 14:404-416, 1969.
Martin, W.R., Gorodetzky, C.W., and Thompson, W.O. Receptor dualism: Some kinetic implications. In: Kosterlitz, H.W., Collier, H.O.J., and Villarreal, J.E., eds. Agonist and Antagonist Actions of Narcotic Analgesic Drugs. Macmillan: New York, 1972. pp. 30-44.
Martin, W.R., Hewett, B.B., Baker, A.J., and Haertzen, C.A. Aspects of the psychopathology and pathophysiology of addiction. Drug Alc Depend 2:185-202, 1977.

25

Martin, W.R., and Jasinski, D.R. Physiological parameters of
morphine dependence in man--tolerance, early abstinence,
protracted abstinence. J Psychiatric Res 7:9-17, 1969.
Martin, W.R., Jasinski, D.R., Haertzen, C.A., Kay, D.C., Jones,
B.E., Hansky, D.A. and Carpenter, R.W. Methadone: A
re-evaluation. Arch Gen Psychiatry 28:286-295, 1973.
Martin, W.R., Jasinski, D.R., Sapira, J.D., Flanary, H.G., Kelly,
O.A., Thompson, A.K., and Logan, C.R. The respiratory effects
of morphine during a cycle of dependence. J Pharmacol Exp Ther
162:182-189, 1968.
Martin, W.R. and Sloan, J.W. Neuropharmacology and neurochemistry
of subjective effects, analgesia, tolerance and dependence
produced by narcotic analgesics. In: Martin, W.R., ed. Drug
Addiction I. Handbook of Experimental Pharmacology, Vol. 45,
Heidelberg: Springer-Verlag, 1977. pp. 43-158,
Martin, W.R., Sloan, J.W., Sapira, J.D., and Jasinski, D.R.
Physiologic, subjective and behavioral effects of amphetamine,
methamphetamine, ephedrine, phenmetrazine and methylphenidate in
man. Clin Pharmacol Ther 12:245-258, 1971.
Martin, W.R., Thompson, W.O., and Fraser, H.F. Comparison of
graded single intramuscular doses of morphine and pentobarbital
in man. Clin Pharmacol Ther 15:623-630, 1974.
Wikler, A. Opiate Addiction. Psychological and
Neurophysiological Aspects in Relation to Clinical Problems.
Springfield: Charles C. Thomas, 1952.

AUTHOR

William R. Martin, M.D.
Department of Pharmacology
University of Kentucky
Lexington, Kentucky 40506

Contributions of Neuropharmacology to Understanding Mechanisms of Tolerance and Dependence

Martin W. Adler and Ellen B. Geller

INTRODUCTION

Neuropharmacological research has played a major role in the formulation of our concepts regarding tolerance and dependence to abused drugs. As our knowledge about these phenomena has increased, certain ideas have been reevaluated and modified. To compile a comprehensive review of all the studies in this field which have contributed to our present state of knowledge about tolerance and dependence for all drugs of abuse is a formidable task and one which will not be attempted here. By way of merely indicating the diversity of research in this area, some of the techniques and endpoints used in studying the neuropharmacology of drugs of abuse appear in table 1. The necessity of having so many approaches available to us has become more apparent as we have gradually moved away from the notion of a single, global mechanism of tolerance and dependence. Only a short time ago, for example, the view that there must be one discrete locus in the brain responsible for opiate dependence was generally accepted. However, as a result of research involving brain lesions (e.g., Linseman 1976; Adler et al. 1978; Calvino et al. 1979) and modification of neurotransmitter systems (review, Takemori 1974), this idea has been largely abandoned. With the recognition of the multiplicity of both chemical and anatomical systems that are involved in tolerance and dependence to drugs of even a single class, the value of examining a variety of drug-induced responses is readily understood. Furthermore, in light of the broad spectrum of drug classes to which tolerance and/or dependence may develop, the need for such an array of techniques and endpoints becomes even more obvious.

TABLE 1. Neuropharmacological studies of drugs of abuse

Techniques	Endpoints
EEG	Body Temperature
Microiontophoresis	Body Weight
Operant Techniques	Antinociceptive
Brain Lesions	Thresholds
Intraventricular Cannulation	Pupil Size
Selective Agonist & Antagonist	Seizure Thresholds
Drugs	Neuronal Firing Patterns
Drugs to Modify Neurotransmitter	Neurotransmitter Levels
Systems	& Turnover
Electrically & Chemically Induced	Locomotor Activity
Seizures	Behavior
In-vivo pA Determinations	Drug Discrimination
Binding Studies	Cross-Tolerance
Isolated Tissue Studies	Cross-Dependence
Drug Infusion Methods	

TOLERANCE

Despite the lack of a clear understanding of the mechanisms
responsible for the phenomenon we call tolerance, we can define
the term in an operational sense. Tolerance can be defined
either as the reduced effect of the same dose of a drug on subsequent administrations, or as a need to increase the dosage in
order to maintain the same level of effect. This simple definition allows for a variety of pharmacokinetic, pharmacodynamic,
and other mechanisms to be implicated in the tolerant state.
Although our definition of tolerance has not changed, many of
our concepts relating to it have. For example, a belief held by
most workers in this field until recently was that "tolerance to
the depressant but not to the excitant effects of narcotics
develops at the spinal cord level, just as elsewhere in the
cerebrospinal axis" (Goodman and Gilman 1955). It is now known
that tolerance can be demonstrated to the classical excitant
effects, namely, pupillary response and gastrointestinal tract
activity. Both the miotic effect of heroin in humans (Tress et
al. 1978) and the mydriatic effect of morphine in mice (Adler et
al. 1980) and rats (Adler et al. 1981) are subject to tolerance
development. Similarly, tolerance has been found to the effects
of morphine on intestinal motility in dogs (Weisbrodt et al.
1980) and rats (Cowan et al. 1977). Although the degree of
tolerance may not be equivalent for all of the actions of an
opioid, at least a partial tolerance is demonstrable for most
effects. One exception may be found in the effect of morphine
on lowering reward threshold. Not only does no tolerance develop on repeated administration, but an increased effect has been
reported (Kornetsky and Bain 1982).

Another commonly accepted idea in the recent past was that
tolerance develops to all of the effects of amphetamine. While
it is true that one sees marked tolerance to some of the actions
of this drug (e.g., anorexic, cardiovascular), reverse

tolerance, or increased responsiveness with repeated administration, occurs with some stereotypies (Rebec and Segal 1980).
Interestingly, no tolerance to its effect against narcolepsy
seems to occur (Weiner 1980). Marijuana, on the other hand, is
an example of a drug to which no tolerance was thought to develop. In fact, it was felt by many that increased sensitivity
occurred with repeated administration. Experiments such as
those by Domino (1971), however, have shown conclusively that
tolerance does develop to at least some of marijuana's effects.

While it was once believed that tolerance development requires
repeated administrations of a drug, in recent years the
occurrence of single-dose tolerance to morphine has been
reported (e.g., Cochin and Kornetsky 1964; Kornetsky and Bain
1968; Huidobro et al. 1976). In some cases, tolerance can be
demonstrated within hours of a single priming dose; in other
instances intervals of days are necessary.

The examples cited above serve to illustrate how a more detailed
look at tolerance has resulted in a recognition of new elements
involved in that phenomenon. Examination of these factors has
yielded important insights into the mechanisms behind tolerance.

Although the terms tolerance and dependence are inextricably
woven into the fabric of our thinking about several classes of
drugs, there is recent in vivo evidence with opiates, for
instance, that the two phenomena, though linked, are not insep-
arable (Cochin and Mushlin 1976; Dafny 1982). Other types of
studies have also indicated the separability of the two phenomena. One must be careful, however, to consider other explanations, such as differences in dose or duration of drug
administration, that may be required for the demonstration of
each. Furthermore, if a drug acts on a particular receptor type
to produce a relatively irreversible or slowly reversible
complex, tolerance may become apparent without concomitant
signs of physical dependence. Only careful evaluation can
determine if the tolerance exists without physical dependence.
There are also examples of drugs showing relatively low degrees
of tolerance but marked physical dependence (barbiturates), and
vice versa (Δ9-THC).

DEPENDENCE

Traditionally, dependence has been defined in terms of the physiological and psychological symptoms that appear when the drug
is withdrawn or antagonized. As our knowledge about dependence
has grown, acceptance of such a simple definition has waned.
Although the term may be used in an operational sense to denote
the entire series of events associated with chronic abuse of a
drug, dependence really comprises two components: the abuse
liability of a drug (potential for abuse) and its dependence
potential (potential for behavioral and/or physical signs of
abstinence). The "abstinence syndrome" can be reversed by readministering the drug or another one with which it is cross-
dependent. Each class of drugs, however, has its own dependence

characteristics, and thus it may be better to describe dependence in terms of a particular class. In fact, newer developments in pharmacology have even produced drugs of the same class
which show different dependence characteristics. Examples of
this situation can be found with the mixed agonist/antagonist
opioids. Although it was originally contended that these
opioids would not produce dependence, unfortunately, this has
turned out not to be the case for most drugs of this type. For
example, our view of pentazocine as a non-dependence-inducing
opioid has undergone radical change, and dependence to pentazocine is now well known (Jaffe and Martin 1980).
Buprenorphine seems to have little, if any, dependence associated with it, as judged by the virtual absence of a withdrawal
syndrome. However, the weak withdrawal syndrome is probably the
result of the stability of the drug-receptor complex and its
slow dissociation, since some abstinence signs can be
demonstrated under certain conditions (Dum et al. 1981).

Amphetamine was at one time considered a nonaddicting substance.
Yet, both physical and psychological signs appear after cessation of drug administration following chronic use (Jaffe 1980).
Even more controversial is the dependence developed to nicotine.
Recent studies have documented both physical and psychological
withdrawal symptoms on cessation of cigarette smoking (Shiffman
1979). Although additional cases and more details could be
cited, the above examples serve to illustrate how our conception
of dependence has evolved. With each advance in our thinking,
we discover more about the mechanisms involved.

PHARMACOLOGICAL PRINCIPLES

One of the problems encountered in the evaluation of research in
this area is that too often the basic principles of pharmacology
are forgotten or ignored. What happens to a drug after administration is a critical determinant of its actions and this,
in turn, can influence interpretation of data on tolerance and
dependence. Obviously, the levels of drug in plasma and brain
can be markedly affected by first-pass effects through the liver
and by drug metabolism. Moreover, route of administration can
dramatically alter both free and bound drug levels, as in the
case of morphine (table 2). Peak plasma levels of free morphine
following a dose of 4 mg/kg were approximately three times
higher after subcutaneous (sc) than after intraperitoneal (ip)
injections, and brain levels were about four times higher. With
the 64 mg/kg dose, however, plasma and brain levels of free
morphine rose to a higher level and fell more rapidly after ip
than after sc administration.

The effect of route of administration on the amounts of pharmacologically active morphine is shown in table 3. These studies are discussed in more detail by Cerletti et al. (1980). An'
additional factor to consider when dealing with centrally acting
drugs is the blood-brain barrier (BBB). What many investigators

30

TABLE 2. Concentration of free morphine in rat plasma and brain after injection of 4 mg/kg or 64 mg/kg morphine sulfate sc or ip

Min Post-	Plasma		Brain	
Injection	ng/ml ± S.E.M.		ng/ml ± S.E.M.	
	sc	ip	sc	ip

4 mg/kg

5	569+24	189+18*	29+3	12+1*
10	642+36	196+22*	50+5	20+2*
15	712+43	242+30*	64+5	21+2*
30	460+26	123+22*	87+3	17+4*
60	260+25	84+11	53+11	19+2*
120	64+9	38+8**	35+1	13+3*
180	33+9	34+14	15+2	6+1*

64 mg/kg

15	4941+ 570	7202+819**	394+66	654+117
30	4823+ 395	10531+2777	562+43	1249+129*
60	10897+1416	12722+4228	1762+170	1980+374
120	6610+1276	5788 +3065	1634+232	990+315
180	2831	1849 + 860	815	469+42

*p < 0.01 vs. sc; **p < 0.05 vs. sc

fail to take into account, though, is that even when the BBB is circumvented by intracerebroventricular (icv) administration, the drug must still leave the ventricular compartment and reach specific areas of the brain in order to be effective. Differences in drug distribution to various brain parts probably contribute to the disparity in qualitative as well as quantitative responses often seen with systemic vs. central administration. For example, differences can be seen on seizure threshold. Table 4 shows that although morphine and etorphine are anticonvulsant after both sc and icv administration, pentazocine and meperidine are proconvulsant by the sc route but anticonvulsant by the icv route. Normeperidine is proconvulsant irrespective of the route of administration. Even sensitivity to naloxone blockade may be altered by the route used (e.g., meperidine). Further details may be found in a paper by Tortella et al. (1984, in press).

Another example may be seen with body temperature (figure 1). Although morphine exhibits the well-known dual response after sc administration, only a dose-related hyperthermia is produced in rats when morphine is administered icv at an ambient temperature of 20°C (Adler et al. 1983; Geller et al. 1983). The examples

TABLE 3. Morphine in rat plasma following injection of 4 or 64 mg/kg morphine sulfate sc or ip. Glucuronide percentage is calculated as (total - free morphine) ÷ (total morphine)

	Min Post-Injection	Total Morphine ng/ml ± S.E.M.		% Morphine as Glucuronide	
		sc	ip	sc	ip
4mg/kg					
	5	695+ 31	283+ 37*	18.1	33.2
	10	726+ 52	400+ 51*	11.6	51.0
	15	796+ 74	748+ 253	10.6	67.6
64mg/kg					
	15	6700+ 894	19580+1190*	26.3	63.2
	60	15590+3649	24520+5186	30.1	48.1

*p < 0.01 vs. sc.

Substance and Alcohol Actions/Misuse, 1:65-70, 1980.
© 1980, Pergamon Press, Ltd. Reprinted by permission.

TABLE 4. Effect of route of administration on seizure threshold changes induced by opioids in rats

Drug	Route of Administration	Change in Flurothyl Seizure Threshold	Antagonized by Naloxone
Morphine	sc	▲	Yes
	icv	▲	Yes
Etorphine	sc	▲	Yes
	icv	▲	Yes
Pentazocine	sc	▼	No
	icv	▲	No
Meperidine	sc	▼	No
	icv	▲	Yes
Normeperidine	sc	▼	No
	icv	▼	No

(Table courtesy of Dr. F.C. Tortella, Walter Reed Army Institute of Research)

cited above serve to demonstrate that comparisons of efficacy and potency between drugs given by different routes are invalid and can lead to erroneous interpretation of data and false conclusions.

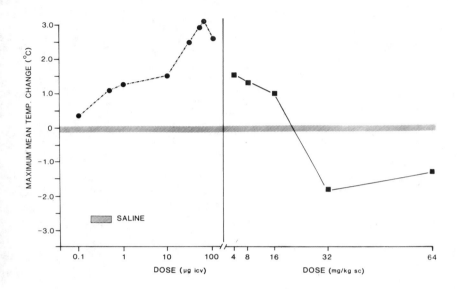

FIGURE 1   Effect of morphine on body temperature: icv vs sc
            administration. Subjects were male Sprague-Dawley
            rats.

Another basic pharmacological principle relates to receptor occupancy. Whether or not a receptor is continuously occupied by a drug may well determine the development of tolerance and dependence and the degree to which they occur. A study by Cochin and Mushlin (1976) showed that tolerance to morphine can be blocked by the concurrent administration of naloxone. Further work from this laboratory has shown that tolerance can be blocked even if naloxone is administered an hour or more after morphine. This is illustrated in figure 2. As can be seen, if a single dose of naloxone (6 mg/kg, sc) is administered to mice at various periods of time after 15 mg/kg morphine

33

sulfate, tolerance to morphine is partially blocked when sensitivity to morphine is tested 3 days later. The shorter the time interval between the first dose of morphine and the administration of naloxone, the more effective the blockade. It appears from this and other work by Cochin and his colleagues that tolerance and cross-tolerance can be attenuated if the drug-receptor complex is broken even after the agonist effect of

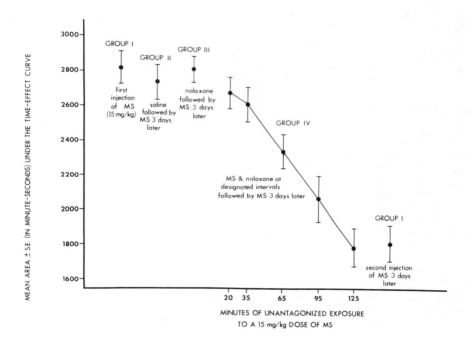

FIGURE 2   Results of hot-plate assay performed in mice 3 days after initial drug treatment. The ordinate shows the mean area derived from multiplying the number of minutes naloxone is given after morphine by the number of seconds on the hot plate. (Figure courtesy of Dr. J. Cochin, Boston University School of Medicine.)

34

morphine has occurred. Work in our laboratory demonstrated that the severity of the morphine abstinence syndrome depends on whether the drug is administered continuously by pellet or intermittently via injection (Cerletti et al. 1976). If the morphine is given so that equivalent levels of drug are measured in plasma over 72 hours, the pelleted animals display a more pronounced withdrawal syndrome even though abstinence signs are qualitatively identical.

SUMMARY

In summary, many of our once generally accepted ideas about tolerance and dependence have been revised as the result of neuropharmacological research. Included among these concepts are the following: (1) Although tolerance and dependence are usually linked, they appear to be separable phenomena in some instances. Further exploration into each should be profitable. (2) Although chronic administration of a drug is usually required to produce tolerance and dependence, even a single dose can result in these effects under certain conditions. That fact may provide us with clues as to the neuroadaptive changes occurring during the development of tolerance and dependence. (3) A fruitful line of research emanates from the findings that tolerance may be pharmacokinetic or neuronal and that time of receptor occupancy appears to be a vital factor in neuronal tolerance. (4) It is now known that tolerance does not develop equally to all actions of a drug and reverse tolerance (increased responsiveness) can occur. Further studies along these lines are needed to correct many false assumptions about this issue and to shed new light on the receptors and transmitter systems involved. (5) We now accept the notion that a drug usually exerts effects on more than one receptor type or subtype. Consequently, the actions of drugs on the various receptors and the responses to receptor blockade promise to yield significant new knowledge about the mechanisms involved in tolerance and dependence to a wide variety of drugs. (6) We have become increasingly aware of species differences and genetic determinants of responses to drugs of abuse, after both acute and chronic dosing. Other papers in this volume will focus on this topic.

Our current state of knowledge about tolerance and dependence suggests a number of questions whose answers will undoubtedly lead to a much better understanding of these phenomena. First, we have learned much about the endogenous opioid peptides and opiate receptors in the last few years. But what is the role of these chemicals in tolerance and dependence? Moreover, are they continuously released and, if so, why doesn't naloxone precipitate an abstinence syndrome when administered to otherwise untreated subjects? As they appear to be released when opioid drugs are administered, what role does this release play in the development of tolerance and dependence to opioids? Second, since we live in a society where polydrug abuse is the rule and not the exception among drug abusers, what are the interactions among the drugs of abuse? Right now we know very little about these interactions per se, let alone the mechanisms that may be involved. Third, is there a commonality of mechanisms for tolerance and dependence among the drugs of abuse? Although such hypotheses have been advanced, little scientific support for these ideas has been forthcoming. Fourth, what are the correlations between binding data and pharmacological effects? This is a crucial question, for both acute and chronic administration of drugs, that must be addressed to a greater degree than it presently is. Lastly, what are the interactions between transmitter systems that have been implicated in tolerance and dependence, both in cases where pharmacological receptors have been identified (e.g., opioids) and in cases where they have not (e.g., cocaine, marijuana)?

A little over 10 years ago, Harry Collier, to whose memory this symposium is dedicated, wrote a paper entitled "A Pharmacological Analysis of Drug-Dependence" (1972). In it he stated that the neuropsychological properties of a drug help to determine its abuse liability. He felt that since drugs produce dependence, other drugs should be able to reverse or ameliorate it. He proposed that "we should now try to develop drugs especially to help combat dependence. To do this effectively and to make progress in the pharmacotherapy of drug abuse, we need to know more about the basic mechanisms whereby dependencies arise and about the interactions of other drugs with these mechanisms." We have made good progress in elucidating the mechanisms involved. Nevertheless, much more basic research must be carried out before we can design specific drugs to affect specific receptors in specific loci and before we can develop drugs to correct any underlying deficiencies that may play a role in drug dependence.

REFERENCES

Adler, C.H., Keren, O., and Korczyn, A.D.   Tolerance to the
    mydriatic effects of morphine in mice. J Neural Transm,
    48:43-47, 1980.
Adler, C.H., Robin, M., and Adler, M.W.   Tolerance to morphine-
    induced mydriasis in the rat pupil. Life Sci, 28:2469-2475,
    1981.
Adler, M.W., Geller, E.B., Beeton, P.B., and Gildenberg, P.L.
    Inability of acute or chronic thalamic, limbic, or cortical
    lesions to alter narcotic dependence and abstinence in rats.   In:
    Van Ree, J.M., and Terenius, L., eds. Characteristics and
    Function of Opioids. Amsterdam: Elsevier/North-Holland, 1978.
    pp. 51-52.
Adler, M.W., Hawk, C., and Geller, E.B. Comparison of intra-
    ventricular morphine and opioid peptides on body temperature of
    rats. In Lomax, P. and Schonbaum, E., eds. Environment, Drugs,
    and Thermoregulation. Basel: Karger, 1983. pp. 90-93.
Calvino, B., Lagowska, J., and Ben-Ari, Y. Morphine withdrawal
    syndrome: Differential participation of structures located

within the amygdaloid complex and striatum of the rat. Brain
Res, 177:19-34, 1979.

Cerletti, C., Keinath, S.H., Reidenberg, M.M., and Adler, M.W.
Chronic morphine administration: Plasma levels and withdrawal
syndrome in rats. Pharmacol Biochem Behav, 4:323-327, 1976.

Cerletti, C., Keinath, S.H., Tallarida, R.J., Reidenberg, M.M.
and Adler, M.W. Morphine concentrations in the rat after intraperitoneal or subcutaneous injection. Subst Alcohol Actions
Misuse, 1:65-70, 1980.

Cochin, J., and Kornetsky, C. Development and loss of tolerance
to morphine in the rat after single and multiple injections.
J. Pharmacol Exp Ther, 145:1-10, 1964.

Cochin, J., and Mushlin, B.E. Effect of agonist-antagonist
interaction on the development of tolerance and dependence. In:
Vesell, E.S., and Braude, M.C., eds. Interactions of Drugs of
Abuse. Ann NY Acad Sci, Vol. 281. New York: NY Academy of
Sciences, 1976. pp.244-251.

Collier, H.O.J. A pharmacological analysis of drug dependence.
In: van Pragg, H.M., ed. Biochemical and Pharmacological Aspects
of Dependence and Reports on Marijuana Research, Haarlem: Bohn,
1972. pp. 23-45.

Cowan, A., Boardman, S., and Robinson, T. Buprenorphine and
intestinal motility: A pharmacological analysis of the biphasic
dose-response curve. Fed Proc, 36:994, 1977.

Dafny, N. The hypothalamus exhibits electrophysiologic evidence
for morphine tolerance and dependence. Exp Neurol, 77:66-77,
1982.

Domino, E.F. Neuropsychopharmacologic studies of marijuana:
Some synthetic and natural THC derivatives in animals and man.
In: Singer, A.J., ed. Marijuana: Chemistry, Pharmacology, and
Patterns of Social Use. Ann NY Acad Sci, Vol 191. New York: NY
Academy of Sciences, 1971. pp. 166-191.

Dum, J., Blasig, J., and Herz, A. Buprenorphine: Demonstration
of physical dependence liability. Eur J Pharmacol, 70:293-300,
1981.

Geller, E.B., Hawk, C., Keinath, S.H., Tallarida, R.J., and
Adler, M.W. Subclasses of opioids based on body temperature
change in rats: Acute subcutaneous administration. J Pharmacol
Exp Ther, 225:391-398, 1983.

Goodman, L.S., and Gilman, A. The Pharmacological Basis of
Therapeutics. 2nd edition. New York: Macmillan, 1955. p. 223.

Huidobro, F., Huidobro-Toro, J.P., and Way, E.L. Studies on
tolerance development to single doses of morphine in mice. J
Pharmacol Exp Ther, 198:318-329, 1976.

Jaffe, J.H. Drug addiction and drug abuse. In: Gilman, A.G.,
Goodman, L.S., and Gilman, A., eds. Goodman and Gilman's The
Pharmacological Basis of Therapeutics. 6th edition. New York:
Macmillan, 1980, pp. 535-584.

Jaffe, J.H., and Martin, W.R. Opioid analgesics and antagonists.
In: Gilman, A.G., Goodman, L.S., and Gilman, A., eds. Goodman and
Gilman's The Pharmacological Basis of Therapeutics. 6th edition.
New York: Macmillan, 1980, pp. 494-534.

Kornetsky, C., and Bain, G. Biobehavioral bases of the reinforcing properties of opiate drugs. In: Verebey, K., ed. Opioids
in Mental Illness. Ann NY Acad Sci, Vol 398. New York: NY

Academy of Sciences, 1982. pp. 241-259.

Kornetsky, C., and Bain, G. Morphine: single-dose tolerance. Science, 162:1011-1012, 1968.

Linseman, M.A. Effects of lesions of the ventromedial hypothalamus on naloxone-induced morphine withdrawal in rats. Psychopharmacologia (Berl.), 45:271-276, 1976.

Rebec, G.V., and Segal, D.S. Apparent tolerance to some aspects of amphetamine stereotypy with long-term treatment. Pharmacol Biochem Behav, 13:793-797, 1980.

Shiffman, S.M. The tobacco withdrawal syndrome. In: Krasnegor, N.A., ed. Cigarette Smoking as a Dependence Process, National Institute on Drug Abuse Research Monograph 23. DHEW Pub. No. (ADM) 79-800. Washington, D.C: Supt. of Docs., U.S. Govt. Print. Off., 1979. pp. 158-184.

Takemori, A.E. Biochemistry of drug dependence. Annu Rev Biochem, 43:15-33, 1974.

Tortella, F.C., Cowan, A., and Adler, M.W. Studies on the excitatory and inhibitory influences of icv opioids on seizure threshold in rats. Neuropharmacology, 1984, in press.

Tress, K.H., El-Sobky, A.A., Aherne, W., and Piall, E. Degree of tolerance and the relationship between plasma morphine concentration and pupil diameter following intravenous heroin in man. Br J Clin Pharmacol, 5:299-303, 1978.

Weiner, N. Norepinephrine, epinephrine, and the sympathomimetic amines. In: Gilman, A.G., Goodman, L.S., and Gilman, A., eds. Goodman and Gilman's the Pharmacological Basis of Therapeutics. 6th edition. New York: Macmillan, 1980. pp. 138-175.

Weisbrodt, N.W., Thor, P.J., Copeland, E.M., and Burks, T.F. Tolerance to the effects of morphine on intestinal motility of unanesthetized dogs. J Pharmacol Exp Ther, 215:515-521, 1980.

ACKNOWLEDGMENTS

Drs. Joseph Cochin and Frank Tortella provided some of the data presented in this paper. Work in the authors' laboratory was supported in part by Grant DA 00376 from the National Institute on Drug Abuse.

AUTHORS

Martin W. Adler, Ph.D.
Ellen B. Geller, M.A.
Department of Pharmacology
Temple University School of Medicine
3420 N. Broad Street
Philadelphia, PA 19140

Various Factors Which Affect the Rate of Development of Tolerance and Physical Dependence to Abused Drugs

William L. Dewey

A recent study by Ternes and his colleagues (1983) showed that tolerance and physical dependence developed to the chronic treatment of hydromorphine in rhesus monkeys but not in cynomolgus monkeys. This report prompted us to reevaluate the factors which are involved in the differences which have been reported for the rates of development of tolerance and physical dependence in various species. It is clear that even in the same animal tolerance develops to different effects of opiates and other drugs at different rates. This observation rules out the possibility of an alteration in drug absorption, metabolism, excretion, etc., as a basis for the tolerance. There are certain effects to which tolerance does not develop. For instance, most reports indicate that although tolerance develops to many of the effects of the opiates, miosis appears to be resistant to tolerance development. Apparently, the drug receptors on the cells of different tissues become less sensitive to the drug at different rates, whereas pupil changes are always sensitive to opiates. These observations support the hypothesis generated from other types of data that many different types of opiate receptors exist. The number might exceed by far the seven or eight types reported to date. There is no question that metabolic tolerance does occur with some drugs. When this is the only factor involved in the development of tolerance, tolerance would be expected to develop to all the effects of the drug at the same rate. It is important to differentiate and quantitate the contribution of metabolic and pharmacodynamic factors in the development of tolerance. The discussion that follows will be devoted to pharmacodynamic tolerance.

Aceto et al. (1977) have shown that the subcutaneous injection of 3 mg/kg of morphine sulfate every 6 hrs for 30 days to rhesus monkeys did not render them dependent as measured by the ability of naloxone or nalorphine to induce

39

vomiting. Vomiting as a withdrawal sign is an indication of
severe dependence of the morphine type in rhesus monkeys. Some
other less severe signs of dependence were observed following the
30 days of treatment. The ED50 for naloxone required to induce
vomiting was higher following 60 days of morphine treatment than
following 90 days of treatment. These data support the
hypothesis that the level of dependence, like that of tolerance,
increases as the time of treatment is extended. These results
were confirmed further by the observation that nalorphine was
able to induce vomiting in rhesus monkeys only following 90 days
of treatment. These results along with those of Ternes et al.
(1983) make another important point concerning the development of
tolerance and dependence to drugs. That is, the end point
measured should be very carefully stipulated and monitored.
Ternes et al. (1983) reported that in the rhesus monkey
dependence and to some extent tolerance and withdrawal developed
following chronic treatment with hydromorphine. This was not
observed following more frequent and longer treatment with
morphine in rhesus monkeys (Aceto et al. 1977).

For a number of years, we have been investigating the effects of
chronic opiate treatment of rats using the ip infusion technique
of Teiger (1974). Animals are infused constantly, 24 hrs a day,
with the test drug. The animals are freely moving, with access
to food and water ad libitum. One of the advantages of this
procedure is that after the end of the morphine infusion,
spontaneous withdrawal symptoms are observed. These symptoms are
characterized by a pronounced loss in body weight of 20% or more
within 24 hrs after the infusion of the opiate. Other signs of
the opiate withdrawal previously described, including
hyperexcitability, irritability, chewing, scratching, wet dog
shakes and diarrhea, are quantitated at various times throughout
the first 96 hrs of withdrawal. We have utilized this technique
to study the importance of a number of variables on the
development of tolerance and physical dependence in the rat. We
first studied the alteration of the duration of morphine infusion
to determine the time required to induce physical dependence in
rats. We compared the infusion schedules, as shown, in the table
below:

TABLE 1

Study	Dose of Morphine Infused (mg/kg/day)
1	200 for one day (on day 1)
2	100 on day 1
	200 on day 2
3	50 on day 1
	100 on day 2
	200 on day 3
4	50 on day 1
	100 on day 2
	200 on day 3, 4, 5 and 6

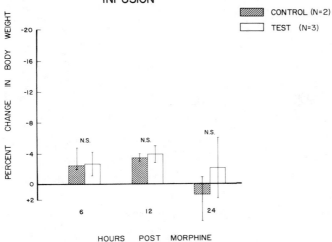

FIGURE 1.   Loss in Body Weight Following Schedule 1

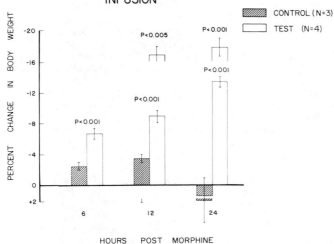

FIGURE 2.   Loss in Body Weight Following Schedule 2

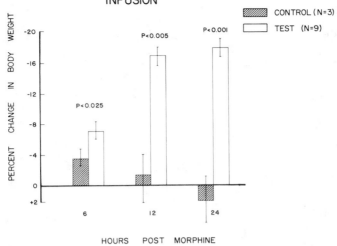

FIGURE 3.   Loss in Body Weight Following the 3-Day Schedule

There was no loss in body weight after 1 day of infusion (figure 1), whereas weight loss did occur as early as 6 hrs after 2 days of infusion (figure 2); an even greater loss in body weight was seen when the animals were infused on the 3-day schedule (figure 3). The 6-day infusion schedule presented in table 1 is used to produce the greatest level of physical dependence to morphine (figure 4).

As can be seen to the left of the dotted vertical line, the rats in each group either maintained their body weight or gained slightly during the last 2 days of the infusion period. The data from the right of the vertical line indicates that rats infused with morphine for 6 days and then given saline lost more than 20% of their body weight during the first 24 hrs after infusion. This was a greater weight loss than was presented in figure 3 for rats which had been infused with morphine on the 3-day schedule. This decrease in body weight persisted throughout the 96-hr observation period. Signs, such as a loss in body weight, were most pronounced 24 hrs after opiate infusion.

In similar studies measuring a longer period of withdrawal, following the end of chronic morphine infusion, rats do gain weight, but not to the degree of controls up to 20 days after withdrawal. The results of the 6-day experiment indicated infusion of saline or naloxone did not induce reduction in body weight following the end of the infusion period. Also, the exposure to naloxone with morphine completely blocks the loss in body weight and other signs of opiate withdrawal in these rats.

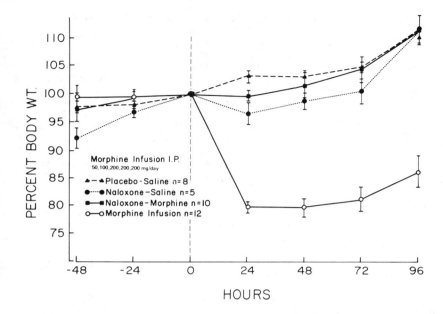

FIGURE 4. Loss in body weight following schedule 4. Placebo or
naloxone (75 mg) pellets were implanted immediately prior to the
start of the infusion. The end of the 6-day infusion period is
represented by the dotted vertical line indicated on the abscissa
as 0 hrs. All percent changes in body weight are calculated
based on the body weight of each rat at the end of the infusion.
In general, the rate of appearance of the other signs of
withdrawal correlate with the decrease in body weight.

It is our hypothesis that the constant infusion of naloxone
competitively inhibited access of the morphine to the opiate
receptors, thus blocking the initial step required for the
development of physical dependence. Naloxone has a shorter
duration of action than morphine and must be given in a fashion
similar to this in order to maintain proper levels at the opiate
receptors. This portion of the experiment also shows that
tolerance did not develop to the antagonistic effect of the
narcotic antagonist. These observations and hypotheses have
interesting implications. We are proposing that morphine causes
physical dependence and tolerance (see below) during constant
infusion by constantly or at least repeatedly interacting with
opiate receptors. When naloxone is infused simultaneously with
morphine, it too has an effect at the opiate receptors. That is,
it blocks the ability of morphine to induce physical dependence.
Tolerance does not develop to naloxone but does develop to the
constant exposure of another drug, morphine. Does this mean that
tolerance at the receptor level is specific for different drugs?
These data, like considerable data generated from binding assays

43

and other in vitro experiments, are explained by the purported lack of efficacy of naloxone at the opiate receptor.

Patrick et al. (1978) reported that during the induction of tolerance and physical dependence on morphine using the 6-day infusion procedure described in table 1, antinociceptive activity correlated quite well with brain levels of morphine. The antinociceptive activity, as well as the level of morphine in brain following the 6-day infusion (that is, the 4th day of the 200 mg/kg/day dose) was significantly less than after the first day of infusion of the 200 mg/kg/day dose of morphine. These authors also reported that the brain level of morphine fell precipitously after the end of its ip infusion. Yet tolerance to subsequent injections of morphine remained for many hours beyond the time they could measure levels of morphine in whole brain. It was apparent from these results that the duration of the phenomenon of tolerance far exceeded the presence of morphine in the brain. Two possibilities exist to explain these results. Either the analytical technique used in these experiments was not sensitive enough to measure the low levels of morphine in the brain at the end of the infusion, or morphine is not required in the brain to manifest tolerance.

In other experiments using mice, the brain level of morphine correlated closely with the antinociceptive activity as measured by the tail-flick test after the implantation of a 75 mg morphine pellet (Patrick et al. 1975; Way et al. 1969). Again, the antinociceptive activity somewhat paralleled the brain level of morphine as described in the rat experiments above; the peak analgesic activity preceded peak brain levels in mice. When the pellet was removed 72 hrs after implantation, the level of morphine fell dramatically in mice as it did at the end of the ip infusion of morphine in rats. Again, tolerance to an injection of morphine lasted well beyond the time we could measure levels of morphine in mouse brain. Taken together, the data generated suggest that there is a temporal component to tolerance development in animals and that once tolerance has formed the duration of the phenomenon outlasts detectable levels of morphine in brain.

In a further attempt to investigate the characteristics of the temporal phenomena involved with tolerance development, we injected a dose of 160 mg/kg of morphine or saline in many groups of mice and determined the ED50 values for subsequent injections of morphine in the mouse tail-flick test at 16, 24, 48 hrs and at 4 and 8 days after the initial injection. Morphine injected in the saline-treated mice served as controls for the animals that were pretreated with 160 mg/kg morphine. The ED50 values for these groups were not significantly different at any time, showing that tolerance did not develop in these experiments. It can be inferred from these data that the pharmacokinetics of opiates are such that one injection of a very high dose does not induce tolerance. However, when we injected mice with 10 mg/kg of morphine every 12 hrs for 10 days and then determined an ED50

TABLE 2

Activity in the Mouse Tail-Flick Test

Injection schedule of 10 mg/kg morphine s.c.	Percent analgesia		
1 injection	Group 1	-	83%
	Group 2	-	83%
every 12 hrs for 10 days	Group 1	-	10%
	Group 2	-	10%
every 12 hrs for 10 days (each given 10 mg/kg morphine, s.c. 10 min after 1 mg/kg naloxone, s.c.)	Group 1	-	59%
	Group 2	-	56%

value for morphine in the tail-flick test, we found pronounced tolerance to the antinociceptive action of morphine in mice. These data are presented in table 2. The results obtained in these mouse experiments were similar to those in the rat infusion experiments, in that pretreatment with naloxone blocked the development of tolerance to the chronic effects of morphine. Thus, a total dose of 200 mg/kg morphine injected at regular intervals over a 10-day period induced tolerance, whereas an acute dose of 160 mg/kg did not. These data suggest the necessity for a temporal relationship for the development of tolerance to the antinociceptive effect of morphine in mice. It is important to point out that these data do not indicate the best temporal rate of injection of morphine to produce tolerance to the antinociceptive activity of morphine in other species nor do they tell us anything about the frequency of injection of morphine to demonstrate the development of tolerance to any effect of morphine in mice other than antinociception. Clearly, tolerance develops to the same effect in various species at different rates and also develops at different rates to different effects in the same species.

In the next series of experiments, we compared the development of tolerance and dependence to two other narcotic analgesics, methadone and l-α-acetylmethadol (LAAM). The antinociceptive potencies of these drugs in mice and rats are presented in table 3.

TABLE 3

The Potency of Methadone and LAAM in Tail-Flick Test

Species	ED50 in mg/kg	
	Methadone	LAAM
Mouse	10.8 (6.3-18.5)	10.8 (5.0-23.6)
Rat	14	2

As can be seen in this table, methadone is equally potent to LAAM in mice but 1/7 as potent as LAAM in rats. Rats were injected chronically with oral doses of LAAM and methadone according to the dosage schedule presented in table 4.

TABLE 4

Oral Dosage Schedule for Methadone and LAAM in Rats

Methadone   (every 0-12 hrs or 2 times/day)

Days	Dose (mg/kg)
1 - 3	14
4 - 7	28
8 - 12	56

LAAM   (every 0-24 hrs or once daily)

Days	Dose (mg/kg)
1 - 3	2
4 - 7	4
8 - 12	8

Considerable tolerance developed to the antinociceptive activity of LAAM, whereas tolerance did not develop to the same effect of methadone following the injection schedule presented in table 4. Methadone was given twice a day, whereas LAAM was injected only once a day. Tolerance developed to LAAM much more rapidly than to methadone. We next investigated the characteristics of the temporal phenomena involved in the ability of these two agents to produce physical dependence, using the oral administration schedule in table 5.

TABLE 5

Oral Dosage Schedule for Mouse Jumping Test (mg/kg)

Day	Methadone*	LAAM
1	20	2
2	40	4
3	80	4
4	160	8

*Methadone was administered at these doses twice a day and LAAM was administered once a day.

The dose of naloxone required to produce jumping in 50% of the mice was used as an index of physical dependence. The lower the dose of naloxone required to induce jumping, the greater the level of physical dependence. The results of these experiments are presented in table 6.

TABLE 6

Naloxone ED50 (s.c.) in the Mouse Jumping Test

Methadone	LAAM
74.5 mg/kg	0.47 mg/kg
(58.9-94.2)	(0.16-1.36)

(Potency Ratio = 158)

Methadone-treated mice appeared normal, LAAM-treated mice lost weight and some died.

Physical dependence was more pronounced with LAAM than with methadone in these experiments. There appears to be a correlation between the temporal aspects of the development of tolerance and the development of physical dependence for these two substances. An explanation for this similarity becomes quite apparent when one looks at the data obtained on the duration of antinociceptive action of methadone and LAAM in mice and rats. Rats treated orally with 6 mg/kg LAAM showed significant analgesic activity up to 14 hrs after medication. The duration of antinociceptive action of 16 mg/kg methadone given orally was less than 2 hrs. These experiments were repeated in mice. Methadone at a oral dose of 25 mg/kg produced significant analgesia, but its duration of action was less than 2 hrs. The duration of action of LAAM exceeded 12 hrs. These data suggest a similar mechanism is involved in both species, and it seems reasonable to suggest that this is so. In order to induce tolerance, methadone must be in contact with brain receptors for a longer period of time than is possible with this treatment schedule. Equianalgesic injections of LAAM given half as frequently as the injections of methadone are sufficient to develop tolerance and physical dependence.

Since tolerance and dependence can develop to a particular effect at different rates with two drugs in the same class, it is not surprising that they can develop at different rates for a number of drugs of abuse from different classes. We have previously reported (Dewey et al. 1972, McMillan et al. 1971, 1972) several characteristics of tolerance to Δ^9-THC. Tolerance is pronounced, develops rapidly, and lasts for many days after the drug is withdrawn. It is also important to note that withdrawal symptoms do not develop following the cessation of chronic treatment with cannabinoids in many species. Tolerance develops to the cannabinoids even if the injections are given at infrequent intervals. Tolerance develops to most of the effects of cannabinoids that have been studied, and cross-tolerance among a number of cannabinoids has been reported.

The major portion of this article has been devoted to the characteristics of tolerance and physical dependence that occur with opiates. Also mentioned are some of the most important aspects of tolerance and dependence to the cannabinoids. The most important point is that tolerance and dependence develop to different effects of drugs at different rates. Tolerance and dependence are not interchangeable. The terms tolerance and/or dependence should only be used to describe the state of an animal when both characteristics have been quantitated in that animal. An animal may be tolerant to a specific effect of an opiate and not be physically dependent. Conversely, an animal may be physically dependent and not be tolerant to a specific effect of the drug. This is even more obvious for non-opiate drugs.

REFERENCES

Aceto, M.D., Flora, R.E., and Harris, L.S. The effects of naloxone or nalorphine during the development of morphine dependence in rhesus monkeys. Pharmacol, 15:1-9, 1977.
Dewey, W.L., Jenkins, J., O'Rourke, T., and Harris, L.S. The effects of chronic administration of trans-Δ^9-tetrahydro-cannabinol on behavior and cardiovascular system of dogs. Arch Int Pharmacodyn, 198(1):118-131, 1972.
McMillan, D.E., Dewey, W.L., and Harris, L.S. Characteristics of tetrahydrocannabinol tolerance. Ann NY Acad Sci, 191:83-100, 1971.
McMillan, D.E., and Dewey, W.L. On the mechanism of tolerance to Δ^9-THC. In: Lewis, M.F., ed. Current Research in Marijuana. New York and London: Academic Press, 1972. pp. 97-114.
Patrick, G.A., Dewey, W.L., Spaulding, T.C., and Harris, L.S. Relationship of brain morphine levels to analgesic activity in acutely treated mice and rats and in pellet-implanted mice. J Pharmacol Exp Ther, 193:876-883, 1975.
Patrick, G.A., Dewey, W.L., Huger, F.P., Daves, E.D., and Harris, L.S. Distribution of morphine in chronically infused rats: Relationship to antinociception and tolerance. J Pharmacol Exp Ther, 205:556-562, 1978.
Teiger, D.G. Induction of physical dependence on morphine, codeine, and meperidine in the rat by continuous infusion. J Pharmacol Exp Ther, 190:408-415, 1974.
Ternes, J.W., Ehrman, R., and O'Brien, C.P. Cynomolgus monkeys do not develop tolerance to opioids. Behav Neurosci, 97(2):327-330, 1985.
Way, E.L., Loh, H.H., and Shen, F.H. Simultaneous quantitative assessment of morphine tolerance and physical dependence. J Pharmacol Exp Ther, 167:1-8, 1969.

ACKNOWLEDGEMENTS

The work reported in this article was supported in part by USPHS grants DA-01647, DA-00490, and T32 DA-07027 from the National Institute on Drug Abuse.

AUTHOR

William L. Dewey, Ph.D., Department of Pharmacology, Medical
College of Virginia, Virginia Commonwealth University, MCV
Station, Box 613, Richmond, Virginia   23298-0001

Genetic Determinants of Responses to Drugs of Abuse: An Evaluation of Research Strategies

Louis Shuster

The use of certain genetically defined animal models can be very helpful in studies of drugs of abuse. The choice of model will be influenced by the aims of the study. This overview is intended to indicate the kind of information that can be obtained and some of the strategies that can be employed.

GOALS OF GENETIC ANALYSIS

1. To explain individual variations in response. About 25% of post-operative patients do not experience appreciable pain relief when injected with a standard dose of morphine sulfate. Another 35% obtain substantial relief from a placebo injection of saline (Lasagna and Beecher 1954). Sorting out the relative contributions of environment and heredity to such variability is very difficult to accomplish with human subjects. However, it is now widely appreciated that genetic determinants can affect the responses of animals to psychopharmacologic agents in many ways, ranging from altered metabolic inactivation to variations in population of neurons and neuronal receptors. Differences between inbred strains when all are raised and tested in the same environment are assumed to indicate the contribution of a genetic component. For example, Brase et al. (1977) measured five different responses to morphine in six inbred strains of mice and found variations of as much as 12-fold in some of them, such as the ED_{50} of naloxone for precipitated abstinence. The heritability or relative genetic contribution to a drug response can be calculated by testing the offspring of a few crosses and comparing them to the parents (Falconer 1960).

There are still some workers who continue to document drug responses obtained with "rats" or "white mice" or "laboratory mice." A larger number persist in using random-bred (outbred) populations which may exhibit wide ranges of response. Such animals, e.g. Swiss-Webster, may give results which vary with the supplier (Way et al. 1969), and compound the difficulty of reproducing values obtained in other laboratories. In general, however, it is widely appreciated that responses to ethanol, morphine or cocaine can vary with the genetic background of the test animal. Establishing this fact should no longer by itself be a major goal of pharmaco-genetic investigations.

2. To separate different components of the response to a given drug. By using different inbred strains of mice it can be shown that motor stimulation by morphine can be dissociated from the analgesic response (Castellano and Oliverio 1975). One can also separate some manifestations of physical dependence, such as naloxone-induced withdrawal jumping, from the development of tolerance (Brase et al. 1977).

Comparison of different rat strains has revealed similarities between some actions of morphine and ethanol on the central nervous system which are not shared by barbiturates (Mayer et al. 1983). Genetic evidence has also been advanced from correlations between the number of D_2 dopamine receptors in the brain and several drug responses (Helméste et al. 1981).

3. To develop models that differ quantitatively in a given drug response. These models may be two or more inbred strains. For example, strain F344 rats and Buffalo rats differ in responses to dopaminergic drugs (Helmeste 1983); low doses of ethanol stimulate the motor activity of BALB/c and DBA mice, but not C57Bl/6 mice (Kiianmaa and Tabakoff 1983); morphine stimulates the motor activity of C57Bl/6 mice but not DBA mice (Oliverio and Castellano 1974).

An alternative approach is to breed selectively high-responding and low-responding lines from a heterozygous foundation stock--for example, mice that sleep for a longer or a shorter time after a given dose of ethanol (McClearn and Anderson 1979).

4. To establish neurochemical mechanisms of drug action. A common aim is to develop meaningful correlations between a drug response and variables such as the amount or turnover of a neurohormone, or the number of receptors. For example, F344 rats, which exhibit greater spontaneous locomotor activity and more inhibition of locomotion by apomorphine than Buffalo rats, also have greater numbers of D_2-dopamine receptors in the striatum and olfactory tubercle (Helmeste 1983). There are also striking differences between these strains in the epinephrine content, rate of epinephrine synthesis, and number of alpha adrenergic receptors in certain brain regions (Perry et al. 1983).

5. To identify the genetic determinants of particular responses. Does a single gene control narcotic analgesia, or are there multiple genes? Are they dominant, recessive, autosomal? Which chromosomes and which particular loci are involved? Do the same genes modulate the responses to several different classes of drugs? Can useful linkage be established between certain drug responses and pleotropic markers such as coat color? For instance, there is a report that the albino locus in mice is associated with decreased responsiveness to morphine (Katz 1980).

STRATEGIES

Several useful strategies are now available to investigators who are interested in the goals described here.

1. Selective breeding. A defined drug response, such as analgesia, sleep time, motor activity, etc. is chosen, and a program is developed to produce strains characterized by the two extremes of this response. The foundation stock should exhibit considerable genetic variability. McClearn started by intercrossing eight purebred strains of mice. Selective breeding of high-responding and low-responding individuals has continued for over 25 generations. This selection has produced a long sleep (LS) line of mice, which sleep several hours, and a short sleep (SS) line of mice, which sleep several minutes, in response to a test dose of ethanol (McClearn and Anderson 1979).

Ideally, up to several hundred animals should be started in such a selection program in order to avoid premature inbreeding, and the entire process, including maintenance of a control line, should be replicated. A recent example of properly executed selective breeding is that carried out by Crabbe et al. (1983a) for the severity of withdrawal from ethanol.

The difference between LS and SS lines of mice seems to reflect a difference in the sensitivity of the central nervous system rather than a difference in ethanol metabolism (Heston et al. 1974). Cerebellar Purkinje cells from LS mice are 10-20 times more sensitive to depression by ethanol than those from SS mice (Sorennsen et al. 1980). The latter's cells also develop tolerance to ethanol much more readily. The fluidizing effect of ethanol on synaptic membranes from LS mice is more pronounced than on those from SS mice (Goldstein et al. 1982).

The main advantage of selective breeding is that it provides animals which were chosen specifically because of an inherited difference in a particular drug response. All other strategies yield animals which were found to differ in a drug response only after they had been selected or bred for other qualities such as coat color or susceptibility to tumor growth. However, this method also has some serious disadvantages. Selective breeding is cumbersome, expensive and slow. Repeating or comparing experiments is almost impossible until homozygosity has been achieved--a matter of 40 generations or about 15 years.

Selective breeding for only a few generations in order to reveal that a given drug response has a genetic component is usually not worth the effort. For example, showing that mice could be selectively bred on the basis of their running response to levorphanol (Judson and Goldstein 1978) did not reveal any more than had already been established by comparing inbred lines (Oliverio and Castellano 1974). Correlations which develop during the first few generations of selection can be misleading. When Wimer and Wimer (1982) bred mice for high and low brain weight, the initial parallelism between brain weight and ability to achieve certain learning tasks disappeared by generation 14.

2. The Use of Inbred Strains. A large number of inbred (purebred) strains of mice are now available commercially. They are essentially homozygous, being derived from over 40 generations of brother-sister matings (Heiniger and Dorey 1980). The choice of which strains to compare can be based on a genetic similarity matrix (Taylor 1972). As can be seen from figure 1, C57 Black mice and related strains differ in a large number of loci from BALB/c, A/J and DBA/2 mice. Furthermore, there are already numerous examples in the literature of drug-related differences between C57 and the other three strains.

Selections can also be made on the basis of neurochemical differences. For example, C57Bl/6 mice have more choline acetyltransferase and tyrosine hydroxylase, but less glutamate decarboxylase, in certain brain regions than A/J mice (Waller et al. 1983). They also have fewer dopamine receptors in the corpus striatum and olfactory tubercle (Boehme and Ciaranello 1981). Crabbe et al. (1981) found that C57Bl/6 mice have twice as much beta endorphin in their pituitaries as BALB/c or DBA/2 mice. The striatum of CBA/J mice is 20% smaller than that of BALB/cJ mice. There is a corresponding difference in the activities of striatal tyrosine hydroxylase and choline acetyltransferase (Baker et al. 1980). BALB/cJ mice have half as many benzodiazepine receptors in the brain as C57Bl/6J mice (Robertson 1979). A compilation of neurochemical values for different mouse strains has been published by Ingram and Corfman (1980).

Extensive comparisons of the pharmacologic and biochemical responses of C57Bl/6, BALB/C, and DBA/2 mice to morphine has been carried out by Castellano, Oliverio and their colleagues. Morphine produces analgesia in both strains, but increases the locomotor activity of only the C57Bl/6 mice (Castellano and Oliverio 1975). Diallel analysis of crosses and backcrosses suggests that the C57 trait is dominant (figure 2). Morphine increases the release of dopamine from the striatum and limbic forebrain in C57 mice but not in DBA mice (Racagni et al. 1979).

Reggiani et al. (1980) found that C57 mice have more receptors in the striatum for enkephalins than DBA mice. On the other hand, contraction of the vas deferens of DBA mice is more readily inhibited by normorphine than that of C57Bl mice (Szerb and Vohra 1979). Another interesting difference between these two strains is that it takes much less naloxone to produce withdrawal jumping in DBA mice than in C57 mice (Brase et al. 1977).

An additional response to morphine that displays interesting strain differences is sensitization, or reverse tolerance to motor stimulation. C57Bl/6J mice are sensitized more than A/J mice, and the F_1 hybrid gives an intermediate response (Shuster et al. 1975a) (figure 3).

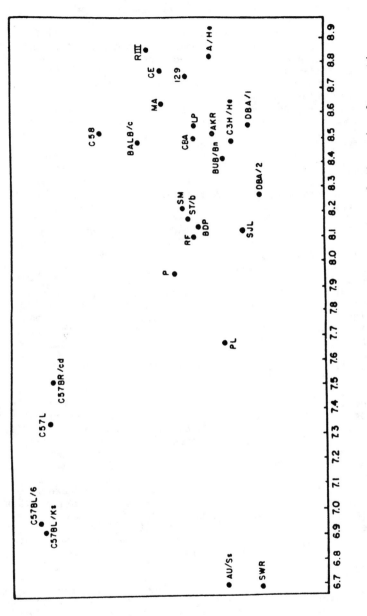

FIGURE 1. Positions of 27 inbred mouse strains in a 2-dimensional genetic similarity matrix. Reproduced, by permission, from Taylor 1972. Copyright 1972, by the American Genetic Association.

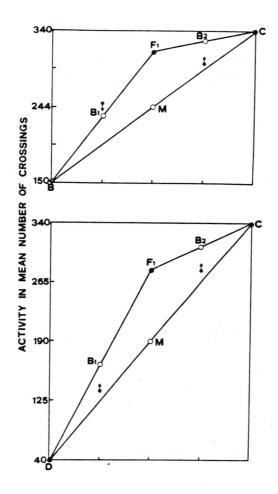

FIGURE 2. Genetic triangles depicting the observed and expected population means for the running activity, in response to morphine, of BALB/cJ, C57Bl/6J, and DBA/2J mice and their crosses. The corner points of the triangle represent the mean values for the parental lines. The expected mean for the F_1 generation (M) is halfway between the parental values. The expected means for backcrosses of F_1 to each parent (B_1 and B_2) are halfway between the parental and F_1 values. Observed values are indicated by filled circles, with arrows pointing to the expected values. B and C and D refer to BALB/cJ, C57Bl/6J and DBA/2J respectively. Reproduced, by permission, from Castellano and Oliverio (1975). Copyright 1975, Springer Verlag New York, Inc.

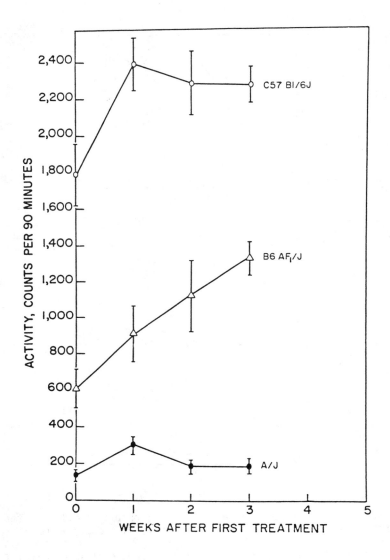

FIGURE 3. Changes in the running response of C57Bl/6J, A/J, and the B6AF1/J hybrid male mice to repeated weekly i.p. injections of morphine sulfate, 25 mg/kg. Each point represents 10 mice + SEM. Reproduced, by permission, from Shuster, Webster, and Yu (1975). Copyright 1975, American Society for Pharmacology and Experimental Therapeutics.

Crabbe et al. (1983b) have examined several responses to ethanol in 19 different inbred strains of mice. They found that the severity of withdrawal was inversely correlated to the initial sensitivity and the degree of tolerance to ethanol hypothermia. C57Bl/6 mice are less sensitive to the activating and hypnotic effects of ethanol than BALB/c or DBA/2 mice. (Kiianmaa and Tabakoff 1983). Low doses of ethanol release less dopamine from the striatum of C57Bl/6 mice than from the striatum of the other two strains (ibid).

It is unlikely that the kinds of differences and correlations de-scribed here can lead to the identification of the genetic deter-minants of the responses to morphine or ethanol. The inbred strains that are compared in these studies may differ in hundreds or thousands of genes. However, they can suggest which neuro-chemical mechanisms are worth pursuing. They also provide readily available animal models which can yield consistent, reproducible results in different laboratories.

3. Recombinant-Inbred and Congenic Lines. Even elementary genetic analysis of differences in drug responses between inbred lines requires time-consuming crossing and backcrossing. The purpose of these crosses is to shift around the genetic determinants in order to establish which ones might be associated with the drug re-sponse. Bailey (1971) has developed a method for randomizing and fixing the genes from two inbred lines in a replicable, homozygous form. A battery of recombinant-inbred (RI) lines is derived by repeated sib matings for 40 generations or more from the F_2 gene-ration of the original cross. Because the distribution of histo-compatibility loci among the lines has been defined by skin-graft-ing, it is possible to ascribe linkage of drug responses to these loci on the basis of a pattern of similarity to one or other of the progenitor strains. Every time a different drug is tested, the drug response itself becomes a new linkage marker for a given chromosome region.

As the number of markers increases, so does the probability of linking new chracteristics. The seven RI lines derived from C57Bl/6 and BALB/c have been typed for about 80 loci, so that the probability of detecting linkage with these lines is 0.37. For the 24 RI lines derived from C57Bl/6 and DBA/2, the identification of 80 markers would bring this probability to about 0.7 (Taylor 1978).

The availability of a test battery of congenic lines enhances the usefulness of the RI lines (Bailey, 1975). Repeated backcrossing from the F1 generation to one progenitor strain (A) produces ani-mals in which only a small portion of the genome is derived from the other progenitor (B). This portion can be identified by his-tocompatibility testing. If the histocompatibility follows the same distribution pattern across the R1 lines (e.g. AABABBA) as a drug response, then one can identify the genetic locus which governs that response.

RI analysis is most useful when a large difference in response exists between the two progenitor strains, and this difference is controlled by a single gene. If more than one gene is involved, then the phenotype of some RI lines may be unlike that of either progenitor. This situation seems to describe running and analgesia in response to morphine (Shuster et al. 1975b; Oliverio et al. 1975). Furthermore, the strain distribution pattern for analgesia was different with the hot-plate assay than with the tail-flick assay (Shuster 1975).

Other responses that have been examined in RI mice include the development of narcotic tolerance (Oliverio and Castellano 1974), acute naloxone-induced withdrawal jumping (figure 4) and the motor response to d-amphetamine (Oliverio et al. 1973). There are interesting differences in the elimination of d-amphetamine (figure 5). We have observed marked differences in cocaine-induced liver damage (table 1). The strain distribution pattern varies with sex as well as with the inducer which serves to stimulate the conversion of cocaine to a hepatotoxic metabolite. At least part of the

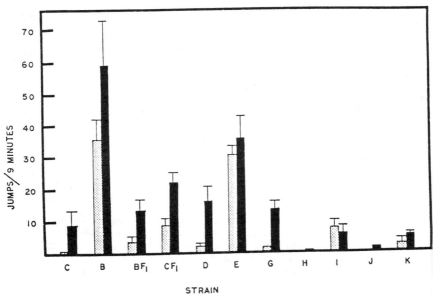

FIGURE 4.   Naloxone-precipitated jumping in morphine-treated recombinant-inbred mice.   Twelve mice of each RI line were injected daily for 5 days with 12.5 mg/kg morphine sulfate i.p. On the first day and on the fifth day they were injected 2 hours later with naloxone-HCl, 10 mg/kg i.p.   The number of jumps was counted during the first 9 minutes after naloxone injection.   Each bar represents the mean value for 12 mice.   Stippled bars - first day; solid bars - fifth day.   B,C,BF$_1$ and CF$_1$ represent progenitors C57Bl/6By, BALB/cBy and the 2 reciprocal hybrids, respectively.

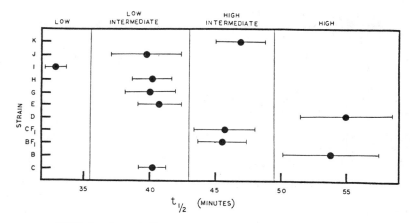

FIGURE 5. Rate of disappearance of tritium-labeled d-amphetamine from the blood of RI mice. Mice were injected i.p. with 5 mg/kg of generally labeled tritiated d-amphetamine sulfate (10 micro-curies per mouse). At 15-minute intervals during the following 2 hours each mouse was warmed under an infra-red lamp for 1 minute, and 25 microliters of blood was collected from the tail into a heparinized micropipette. The blood was transferred to 1 ml of 1 M K_2HPO_4 in a scintillation vial. Fifteen ml of toluene-based scintillation fluid was added and the labeled amphetamine was ex-tracted into the scintillation fluid for counting. The rate of disappearance of d-amphetamine from the blood between 15 and 120 minutes after injection followed first order kinetics. Each point represents the mean value for from 4 to 6 mice. The groups separated by vertical lines showed a statistically significant difference in half-time.

TABLE I

HEPATOTOXICITY OF COCAINE IN R.I. MICE

STRAIN		SGOT, K.U./ML X 10^3		
		Pine-Induced Male	Phenobarbital-Induced Male	Female
BALB/cBy		0.2 + 0.02	0.1 + 0.03	4.6 + 1.6
C57Bl/6By		16.8 + 9.8*	10.9 + 1.4*	24.0 + 1.7*
CXB	D	8.2 + 0.6	2.2 + 0.4	8.1 + 1.1
	E	3.5 + 1.7	12.0 + 3.9*	9.1 + 1.6
	G	28.7 + 13.0*	3.6 + 1.0	16.1 + 0.8*
	H	31.1 + 6.6*	7.2 + 1.4*	19.0 + 1.1*
	I	23.3 + 10.6*	8.8 + 3.9*	12.4 + 1.9*
	J	2.8 + 1.6	7.2 + 1.3	2.7 + 0.7
	K	3.0 + 1.6	3.3 + 1.0	12.6 + 2.4*

Microsomal enzymes were induced by exposing the mice to pine bed-ding for at least 7 days, or by giving phenobarbital in drinking water (0.8 g/l). The mice were injected with 50 mg/kg cocaine HCl i.p. and bled from the tail after 18 hrs. Each value is the mean + S.E. for a group of 5 mice (on pine) or from 5-19 mice (pheno-barbital induced).

*Significantly different from BALB/c progenitor, p < .05

difference between the progenitor strains can be attributed to differences in some of the metabolic steps involved (Thompson et al. 1984).

RI analysis has turned up some interesting differences in narcotic receptors. One of the Bailey lines, CXBK, has a decreased number of naloxone binding sites in the brain associated with a decreased analgesic response to morphine (Baran et al. 1975), to acupuncture (Pomeranz 1978), D-amino acids (Cheng and Pomeranz 1979) and to stress (Miczek et al. 1982). The binding of several ligands at a single concentration to brain membranes from the same R1 lines was examined by Reith et al. (1981). The lowest binding of naloxone, dihydromorphine and ethyl ketocyclazocine was obtained with CXBK membranes, and the highest with progenitor BALB/cBy. There were no significant genetic differences in the binding of D-ala^2-D-leu^5-enkephalin, which was assumed to be specific for delta receptors.

Where a drug response shows a clear-cut difference between two progenitor strains, it should be possible to define a chromosomal locus by surveying all of the existing congenic lines. If these lines each contain only a small chromosomal segment from progenitor A, most of them will respond like strain B. The exception, which responds like strain A, can be defined as having a genetic determinant for the drug response located in a known fragment of a single chromosome. However, sufficient numbers of congenic mice for testing are not readily available. Furthermore, there is still a 50% chance that the chromosome segment which has been isolated in any given congenic line may contain more than one histocompatibility locus (Johnson 1981).

4. Defined Mutants. The use of defined point mutations avoids any uncertainties which may be encountered with congenic lines. A large number of such mutants are available on a C57Bl/6J background (Heiniger and Dorey 1980; Green 1981). A survey of some of these mutants has revealed at least three which differ in one or more responses to morphine from the progenitor strain. The mutant Pallid shows more running activity and hypothermia (Katz and Doyle 1980). We have found that mutants Sepia and Gunmetal display more analgesia and running activity (figures 6 and 7). There was much less naloxone-precipitated withdrawal jumping of Gunmetal (Gm) mice than either C57Bl/6J or Sepia (figure 8). A comparison of heterozygotes and homozygotes revealed dominance in some cases. Other mutants which we tested resembled C57Bl/6J. These included Brown, Pearl, Viable Dominant Spotting, Black and Tan 33J, Ragged and Ruby Eye (Heiniger and Dorey 1980).

It is intriguing that the mutations which affect the responses to morphine do not seem to be directly related. The respective chromosomes bearing the mutations Pallid, Gunmetal and Sepia, are 2, 14 and 1 (Heiniger and Dorey 1980). These mutations are assumed to be pleiotropic, because they have been identified by a change in coat color, or some other characteristic unrelated to drug responses. The Pallid mutant is known to have a defect in manganese

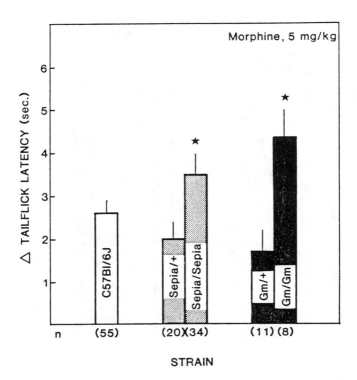

FIGURE 6. Analgesic response to morphine sulfate of C57BL/6J mice
and homozygous and heterozygous single gene mutant mice. Sepia/+
and Gm/+ refer to heterozygotes. Bars indicate mean $\pm$ SEM change
in tailflick latency 30 min after injection of morphine. The cut-
off was 8.0 sec. The number (n) of mice in each group is indicated in parentheses below the bars. A star indicates significant
difference from C57B1/6J, p<.05.

metabolism (Erway et al. 1970). Mutants which exhibit defective
development of the central nervous system may display multiple
abnormalities (Nussbaum et al. 1969). This situation makes it
difficult to interpret the decreased responsiveness of Jimpy mice
to morphine as proof that cerebroside sulfate is an important constituent of narcotic receptors (Law et al. 1978).

5. Sublines of Inbred Strains. The maintenance of separate
colonies in different laboratories has given rise to sublines that
differ in a small number of genes from the original breeding
stock. These differences can be attributed either to new mutations or to residual heterozygosity. According to Bailey (1978)
sublines that have been maintained for 50 generations (20 years)
after branching should have only 14 gene differences due to new

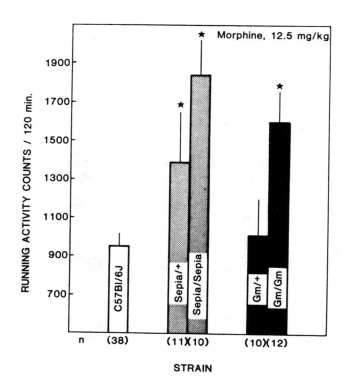

FIGURE 7. Running response to morphine sulfate of C57Bl/6J mice and homozygous and heterozygous single gene mutants.. Bars indicate mean number of photocell interruptions accumulated during a 2-hour test session following the injection of morphine. Each mouse was tested individually. Mice were allowed to habituate to the test cage for 1 hour prior to the injection of morphine. The number of mice in each group is indicated in parentheses. A star indicates significant difference from C57Bl/6J, p<.05.

mutations. Because the original lines have been inbred for 40 generations or more, the extent of residual heterozygosity is also very low--for example, 14 gene differences after 30 generations.

We have encountered clear-cut differences in drug response between the Bailey (By) subline of C57Bl/6 mice and the original Jackson (J) line. The By mice were separated from the J line after the latter had undergone 75 generations of inbreeding. The lines have been separate for 62 generations and differ in less than 50 gene pairs (Bailey 1978). In an animal possessing 30,000 structural genes (Green 1981), it is extremely unlikely that as much as 1% of these would be associated with one particular trait such as the analgesic response to morphine. Hence, any difference between the two sublines with respect to this trait can reasonably be attributed to a single gene difference.

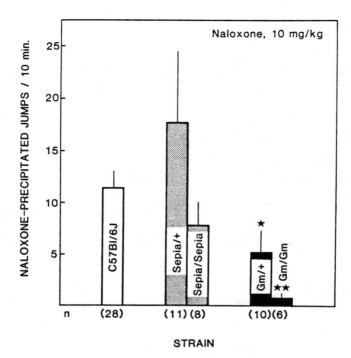

FIGURE 8. Naloxone-precipitated acute withdrawal jumping in C57Bl/6J mice and homozygous and heterozygous single gene C57Bl/6J mutant mice. Sepia/+ and Gm/+ refer to heterozygotes. Bars reflect mean $\pm$ SEM number of jumps per mouse observed during a 10-min period after the injection of naloxone. Naloxone was injected 2 hrs after an injection of morphine sulfate, 12.5 mg/kg i.p. A star indicates significant difference from C57Bl/6J, $p < .05$; two stars, $p < .01$. The number of mice in each group is indicated in parentheses.

The By subline shows a greater analgesic response to morphine than J mice (Shuster 1982). Analysis of dose-response curves by the method of Litchfield and Wilcoxon (1949) gave ED_{50} values of 2.5 mg/kg morphine sulfate for By and 8.0 mg/kg for J mice. The By mice also showed more analgesia by the hot plate assay. Experiments with tritiated morphine showed no difference between the two lines in the rate of elimination of morphine from the blood.

Whole brain homogenates from the two sublines were used to measure the specific binding of several ligands. Scatchard analysis revealed that brain membranes from each subline had the same number of low affinity receptors for dihydromorphine, but a marked difference in the number of high affinity receptors (22.5 $\pm$ 3 vs. 12.0 $\pm$ 2 fmoles/mg protein for By vs J, p=.01). There was no difference in K_D (about 0.6 nM). When other tritiated ligands were used, both sublines had similar B_{max}'s and K_D's for D-ala^2-met-enkephalinamide, ethyl ketocyclazocine and naloxone (Cremins and

Shuster 1982). The B_{max} for dihydromorphine binding to brain homogenates from F1 mice was not significantly different from that of the By parent, and the analgesic response was also inherited as dominant trait (Shuster and Cremins, in preparation).

These findings suggest that there is a single gene difference between By and J mice which controls both the analgesic response to morphine and the number of high affinity mu receptors in the brain. The situation in other parts of the body may be different. Our preliminary experiments indicate that the By subline may actually have fewer mu receptors in the spinal cord than J mice.

We also examined the running response of By and J mice to morphine, and found that J mice showed a greater response (Shuster 1982). The narcotic receptors which mediate the running response appear to be different from the mu receptors which are believed to mediate analgesia. An indication of the nature of these receptors comes from the work of Reggiani et al. (1980). They compared the binding of several ligands in different brain regions from C57/Bl (high running response to morphine) and DBA/2 mice (no running response). They found a greater number of binding sites for tritiated D-ala^2-met-enkephalin and leu-enkephalin in the striatum of C57 mice, with no difference in affinity. The binding of dihydromorphine and naloxone was the same in both strains. These observations suggest that delta receptors may be involved in the running response.

The subline differences in narcotic receptors also appear to affect the responses of mice to endogenous opiates. One kind of stress-induced, naloxone-reversible analgesia which we have examined is that seen when one mouse is attacked and defeated by another mouse (Miczek et al. 1982). Here, too, By mice show more analgesia than J mice (figure 9).

By mice also have more fatty liver damage after high doses of morphine than J mice (Needham et al. 1981). There are indications that a good part of this response can be attributed to morphine-induced release of epinephrine from the adrenals. Here, also, genetic comparisons suggest that mu receptors may be involved.

The Jackson subline of C57Bl/6 mice shows a greater stimulant response to amphetamine than the Bailey subline. In this case, too, the By gene is dominant (Moisset 1977).

Additional subline differences await closer investigation. For instance, the vasa deferentia from the Biobreeding subline of C57Bl/6 mice are about 3 times as sensitive to inhibition by normorphine or by met-enkephalin as those from the Jackson line (Szerb and Vohra 1979). Balb/cJ mice have higher levels of enzymes for synthesizing epinephrine than the NIH subline (Ciaranello et al. 1974). Moisset (1978) found that BALB/cBy mice sleep over twice as long after an injection of ethanol, four g per kg, as mice of the Jackson subline.

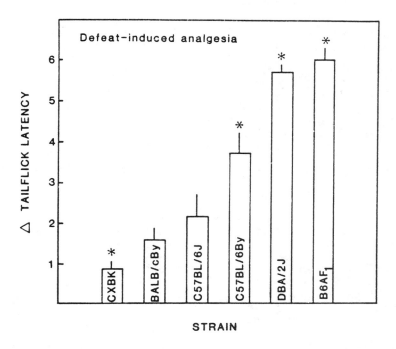

FIGURE 9. Defeat-induced analgesia in mice of 6 different strains. Bars indicate mean ± SEM change in tailflick latency following 70 bites. An asterisk indicates significant difference from C57Bl/6J, p<.05.

CONCLUSIONS

Genetic differences in responses to drugs of abuse can be found if one looks for them. The particular model system which is most useful will depend to a great extent on the goals of pharmacogenetic analysis. There is still a great need for systematic surveys of the drug responses of available inbred strains, sublines and mutants. These surveys should also extend to the assay of drug receptors, drug metabolism, and the mapping of brain proteins by two-dimensional gel electrophoresis. The heroic labors of selective breeding also pose a tremendous challenge. Eventually one should be able to identify specific genes that determine drug responses and relate these to the mechanism of action.

REFERENCES

Bailey, D.W. Recombinant inbred strains. Transplantation, 11:325-327 1971.
Bailey, D.W. Genetics of histocompatibility in mice. I. New loci and congenic lines. Immunogenetics, 2:249-256 1975.

Bailey, D.W. Sources of subline divergence and their relative importance for sublines of six major inbred strains of mice. In: Morse, H.C., III, ed. Origins of Inbred Mice, New York, Academic Press, 1978. pp. 197-215.

Baker, H., Joh, T.H., and Reis, D.J. Genetic control of number of midbrain dopaminergic neurons in inbred strains of mice: Relationship to size and neuronal density of the striatum. Proc Nat Acad Sci USA, 77:4369-4373, 1980.

Baran, A., Shuster, L., Eleftheriou, B.E., and Bailey, D.W. Opiate receptors in mice. Genetic differences. Life Sci, 17:633-640, 1975.

Boehme, R.R., and Ciaranello, R.D. Dopamine receptor binding in inbred mice: Strain differences in mesolimbic and nigrostriatal dopamine binding sites. Proc Nat Acad Sci USA, 78:3255-3259, 1981.

Brase, D., Loh, H.H., and Wa, E.L. Comparison of the effects of morphine on locomotor activity, analgesia and primary and protracted physical dependence in six mouse strains. J Pharmacol Exp Ther, 201:768-374, 1977.

Castellano, C., and Oliverio, A. A genetic analysis of morphine-induced running and analgesia in the mouse. Psychopharmacol, 41:197-200, 1975.

Cheng, R.S.S., and Pomeranz, B. Correlation of genetic differences in endorphin systems with analgesic effects of D-amino acids in mice. Brain Res, 177:583-587, 1979.

Ciaranello, R.D., Hoffman, H.J., Shire, J.G.M., and Axelrod, J. Genetic regulation of catecholamine biosynthetic enzymes. II Inheritance of tyrosine hydroxylase, dopamine hydroxylase and phenylethanolamine methyl transferase. J Biol Chem, 249:4520-4536, 1974.

Crabbe, J.C., Jr., Allen, R.G., Gaudette, N.D., Young, E., Kosobud, A., and Stack, J. Strain differences in pituitary-endorphin and ACTH content in inbred mice. Brain Res, 219:219-223, 1981.

Crabbe, J.C., Kosobud, A., and Young, E.R. Genetic selection for ethanol withdrawal severity: Differences in replicate mouse lines. Life Sci, 33:955-962, 1983a.

Crabbe, J.C., Jr., Young, E.R., and Kosobud, A. Genetic correlations with ethanol withdrawal severity. Pharmacol Biochem Behavior, 18:541-547, 1983b.

Cremins, J., and Shuster, L. A genetically controlled difference in morphine analgesia and narcotic receptors in mice. Fed Proc, 41:1314, 1982.

Erway, L., Hurley, L.S., and Fraser, A.S. Congenital ataxia and otolith deficits due to manganese deficiency in mice. J Nutrit, 100:643-654, 1970.

Falconer, D.S. Introduction to Quantitative Genetics. New York: Ronlad Press, 1960.

Goldstein, D.B., Chin, J.H., and Lyon, R.C. Ethanol disordering of spin-labeled mouse brain membranes: correlation with genetically determined ethanol sensitivity of mice. Proc Nat Acad Sci USA, 79:4231-4233, 1982.

Green, M.C. Genetic Variants and Strains of the Laboratory Mouse. Stuttgart, Gustav Fischer Verlag, 1981.

66

Heiniger, H.J., and Dorey, J.J., eds. Handbook on Genetically Standardized JAX Mice, 3rd edition. Bar Harbor, Me: The Jackson Laboratory, 1980.

Helmeste, D.M., Seeman, P., and Coscina, D.V. Relation between brain catecholamine receptors and dopaminergic stereotypy in rat strains. Eur J Pharmacol, 69:465-470, 1981.

Helmeste, D.M. Spontaneous and apomorphine-induced locomotor changes parallel dopamine receptor differences in two rat strains. Pharmacol Biochem Behavior, 19:153-155, 1983.

Heston, W.D.W., Erwin, V.G., Anderson, S.M., and Robbins, H. A comparison of the effects of ethanol on mice selectively bred for differences in ethanol sleep time. Life Sci, 14:365-370, 1974.

Ingram, D.K., and Corfman, T.P. An overview of neurobiological comparisons in mouse strains. Neurosci Biobehav Rev, 4:421-435, 1980.

Johnson, L.L. At how many histocompatibility loci do congenic mouse strains differ? Probability estimates and some implications. J Hered, 72:27-31, 1981.

Judson, B.A., and Goldstein, A. Genetic control of opiate-induced locomotor activity in mice. J Pharmacol Exp Ther, 206:56-60, 1978.

Katz, R.J. The albino locus produces abnormal responses to opiates in the mouse. Eur J Pharmacol, 68:229-232, 1980.

Katz, R.J., and Doyle, R.L. Enhanced responses to opiates produced by a single gene substitution in the mouse. Eur J Pharmacol, 67:301-303, 1980.

Kiianmaa, K., and Tabakoff, B. Neurochemical correlates of tolerance and strain differences in the neurochemical effects of ethanol. Pharmacol Biochem Behavior, 18, Suppl. 1: 383-388, 1983.

Lasagna, L., and Beecher, H.K. The optimal dose of morphine. J Am Med Assoc, 156:230-234, 1954.

Law, P.Y., Harris, R.A., Loh, H.H., and Way, E.L. Evidence for the involvement of cerebroside sulfate in opiate receptor binding: Studies with Azure A and Jimpy mutant mice. J Pharmacol Exp Ther, 207:458-468, 1978.

Litchfield, J., and Wilcoxon, F. A simplified method of evaluating dose-effect experiments. J Pharmacol Exp Ther, 96:99-113, 1949.

Mayer, J.M., Khanna, J.M., Kim, C., and Kalant, H. Differential pharmacological responses to ethanol, pentobarbital and morphine in rats selectively bred for ethanol sensitivity. Psychopharmacol, 81:6-9, 1983.

McClearn, G.E., and Anderson, S.M. Genetics and ethanol tolerance. Drug Alcohol Depend, 4:61-76, 1979.

Miczek, K.A., Thompson, M.L., and Shuster, L. Opioid-like analgesia in defeated mice. Science, 215:1520-1522, 1982.

Moisset, B. Genetic analysis of the behavioral response to d-amphetamine in mice. Psychopharmacology, 53:263-267 (1977).

Moisset, B. Subline differences in behavioral responses to pharmacological agents. In: More, H.C. III ed. Origins of Inbred Mice, New York, Academic Press, 1978. pp. 483-484.

Needham, W.P., Shuster, L., Kanel, G.C., and Thompson, M.L. Liver damage from narcotics in mice. Toxicol Appl Pharmacol, 58:157-170, 1981.

Nussbaum, J.L., Nescovic, N., and Mandel, P. A study of lipid components in the brain of the "Jimpy" mouse, a mutant with myelin deficiency. J Neurochem, 16:927-934, 1969.

Oliverio, A., and Castellano, C. Genotype-dependent sensitivity and tolerance to morphine and heroin: dissociation between opiate-induced running and analgesia in the mouse. Psychopharm, 39:13-22, 1974.

Oliverio, A., Eleftheriou, B.E., and Bailey, D.W. Exploratory activity: Genetic analysis of its modification by scopolamine and amphetamine. Physiol Behav, 10:893-899, 1973.

Oliverio, A., Castellano, C., and Eleftheriou, B.E. Morphine sensitivity and tolerance. A genetic investigation in the mouse. Psychopharmacologia, 42:219-224, 1975.

Perry, B.D., Stolk, J.M., Vantini, G., Guchhart, R.B., and U'Prichard, D.C. Strain differences in rat brain epinephrine synthesis: Regulation of alpha-adrenergic receptor number by epinephrine. Science, 221:1297-1299, 1983.

Pomeranz, B. Do endorphins mediate acupuncture analgesia? Adv in Biochem Psychopharm, 18:351-360, 1978.

Racagni, G., Bruno, F., Juliano, E., and Paoletti, R. Differential sensitivity to morphine-induced analgesia and motor activity in two inbred strains of mice: Behavioral and biochemical correlations. J Pharmacol Exp Ther, 209:111-116, 1979.

Reggiani, A., Battaini, F., Kobayashi, H., Spano, P., and Trabucchi, M. Genotype-dependent sensitivity to morphine: Role of different opiate receptor populations. Brain Res, 189:289-294, 1980.

Reith, M.E.A., Sershen, H., Vadasz, C., and Lajtha, A. Strain differences in opiate receptors in mouse brain. Eur J Pharmacol, 74:377-380, 1981.

Robertson, H.A. Benzodiazepine receptors in "emotional" and "non-emotional" mice: Comparison of four strains. Eur J Pharmacol, 56:163-166, 1979.

Shuster, L. Genetic analysis of morphine effects: Activity, analgesia, tolerance and sensitization. In: Eleftheriou, B.E., ed. Psychopharmacogenetics, New York: Plenum Press, 1975. pp. 73-98.

Shuster, L., Webster, G.W., and Yu, G. Increased running response to morphine in morphine-pretreated mice. J Pharmacol Exp Ther, 192:64-72, 1975a.

Shuster, L., Webster, G.W., Yu, G., and Eleftheriou, B.E. A genetic analysis of the response to morphine in mice: analgesia and running. Psychopharmacol, 42:249-254, 1975b.

Shuster, L. A pharmacogenetic approach to the brain. In: Lieblich, I., ed. Genetics of the Brain. Amsterdam, Elsevier Biomedical Press, 1982. pp. 157-176.

Sorenssen, S., Palmer, M., Dunwiddie, T., and Hoffer, B. Electrophysiological correlates of ethanol-induced sedation in differentially sensitive lines of mice. Science, 210:1143-1145, 1980.

Szerb, J.C., and Vohra, M.M. Potencies of normorphine and met-en-
kephalin in the vas deferens of different strains of mice.
Life Sci, 24:1983-1988, 1979.
Taylor, B.A. Genetic relationships between inbred strains of mice.
J. Heredity, 63:83-86, 1972.
Taylor, B.A. Recombinant-inbred strains: Use in gene mapping. In:
Morse, H.C. III, ed. Origins of Inbred Mice. New York,
Academic Press, 1978. pp 423-438.
Thompson, M.L., Shuster, L., and Casey, E. Sex and strain differ-
ences in response to cocaine. Biochem Pharmacol, in press.
Waller, S.B., Ingram, D.K., Reynolds, M.A., and London, E.D. Age
and strain comparisons of neurotransmitter synthetic enzyme
activities in the mouse. J Neurochem, 41:1421-1428, 1983.
Way, E.L., Loh, H.H., and Shen, F.H. Simultaneous quantitative as-
sessment of morphine tolerance and physical dependence. J
Pharmacol Exp Ther, 167:1-8, 1969.
Wimer, R.E., and Wimer, C.C. A geneticists map of the mouse
brain. In: I. Lieblich, ed. Genetics of the Brain. Amsterdam,
Elsevier Biomedical, 1982, pp. 395-420.

ACKNOWLEDGMENTS

The research described here was supported by grants DA-01626 and
DA-01885 from the National Institute on Drug Abuse. Guy
Webster, Peter H. Short, Allison Wood, and Michell Hoffman
assisted with breeding and pharmacological assays. Drs. Earl
L. Green, Don W. Bailey, and Michael L. Thompson provided
helpful discussions.

AUTHOR

Louis Shuster, Ph.D.
Department of Biochemistry and Pharmacology
Tufts University School of Medicine
Boston, MA 02111

Opioid Tolerance and Dependence in Light of the Multiplicity of Opioid Receptors

Rüdiger Schulz and Albert Herz

Opioid tolerance and dependence are the consequence of chronic activation of opioid receptors. To explain these phenomena, several theories have been advanced to account for the respective adaptational mechanisms (Collier 1980, Shuster 1961, Goldstein and Goldstein 1968). A common postulate of these is the appearance of tolerance and dependence in a unitary manner. They, thus, take into consideration the well-known observations in man and animals that tolerance and dependence appear in parallel. Within this framework, the existence of cross-tolerance has been exploited as an essential criterion for the characterization of opioid agonists. That is, tolerance to one opioid is accompanied by cross-tolerance to another opioid.

In recent years, these concepts have been seriously challenged. It has become clear that the absence or the presence of cross-tolerance is by no means a prerequisite to judge whether or not a drug is a narcotic. These findings are closely associated with the concept of the multiplicity of opioid receptors, as originally proposed by Martin et al. (1976). Indications for the existence of different types of opioid receptors have come from experiments with intact animals (Martin et al. 1976) but also from studies with isolated tissues (Lord et al. 1977). Investigations with the isolated mouse vas deferens and guinea-pig ileum, which have been employed to study the development of tolerance and cross-tolerance (Wüster et al. 1981a), proved very successful.

The mouse vas deferens represents an isolated tissue preferentially employed to study tolerance and cross-tolerance (Schulz et al. 1980). This preparation seems to be unique as it contains at least each of the classical opioid receptors, such as the μ-, κ- and δ-type. It was the aim of several investigations to test whether chronic stimulation of, for example, the μ-receptors is associated with an adaptation of other receptor types. In other words, is tolerance to a specific receptor type associated with cross-tolerance to a different type of opioid receptor? Mice were treated with an opioid, e.g., a μ-agonist, for several days, using osmotic minipumps for the application of the drug. The vasa deferentia of these animals were set up in vitro for electrical stimulation in the presence of the opioid applied in vivo. This procedure allows for maintenance of tolerance in vitro. According to this schedule, vasa deferentia were rendered tolerant in vivo to μ-, κ- or δ-receptor agonists. The preparations were challenged in vitro for the degree of tolerance and cross-tolerance.

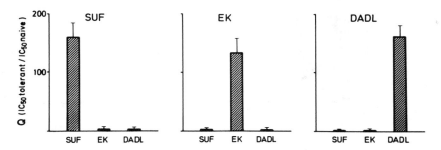

FIGURE 1: Tolerance and cross-tolerance studies of opioids on the isolated mouse vas deferens. Vasa deferentia were rendered tolerant in vivo to sufentanil (SUF), ethylketazocine (EK) and D-Ala^2,D-Leu^5-enkephalin (DADL), respectively. The degree of tolerance, measured by calculation of the quotient (Q) of the IC$_{50}$ values of tolerant and naive preparations is plotted on the ordinate. Q=1 indicates lack of tolerance. The drug chronically applied is indicated in each panel. Abscissa: opioids tested for tolerance and cross-tolerance. Each column represents the quotient of mean IC$_{50}$ values. For details see Wüster et al. (1981a).

Figure 1 depicts the degree of tolerance and cross-tolerance of vasa deferentia rendered tolerant to the μ-agonist sufentanil (SUF), the κ-agonist ethylketazocine (EK), and the δ-agonist D-Ala^2-D-Leu^5-enkephalin (DADL), respectively. Apparently, preparations highly tolerant to SUF display an almost unchanged sensitivity to the κ- or the δ-agonist. Analogous results were obtained with preparations rendered tolerant to EK or DADL.

These data clearly reveal the existence of a state of tolerance and non-tolerance in the same vas deferens preparation. In principle identical results were obtained with the isolated guinea-pig ileum (Wüster et al. 1981a) and in experiments with intact animals (Schulz et al. 1981). Thus, these results do not favor the notion that cross-tolerance between opioids is an essential criterion to classify a drug as an opioid.

This demonstration of "selective tolerance" does not-in itself-conflict with theories claiming a "unitary mechanism" for tolerance and dependence. The question arises, however, whether those highly "tolerant receptors" also display a high degree of dependence, and whether those receptors lacking tolerance also lack dependence. If such assumptions are correct, each binding site for a specific opioid should be firmly linked to a subsequent system and such an entity should function independently from other opioid

71

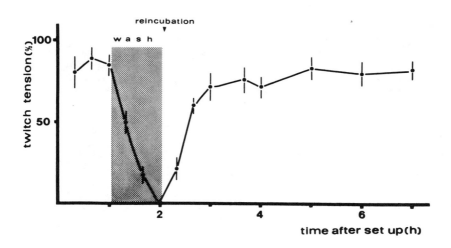

FIGURE 2: Naloxone-induced contracture (twitch tension) of longitudinal muscle-myenteric plexus preparations taken from a morphine
tolerant/dependent guinea pig. The preparations were kept in
Krebs-Ringer solution containing normorphine (200 nM), except
during the time indicated by the hatched field. Washes were conducted in the presence and absence of the opiate every 5-10 min.
Naloxone was added to the bath 1 min after electrical stimulation
was turned off. The ordinate represents tension (contracture)
expressed as percent of the preceding electrically induced twitches.
For details see Schulz and Herz (1976).

receptor entities. A different situation would occur if one adapts
the "mobile-receptor hypothesis" (Cuatrecasas 1974) to the functioning of opioid receptors. In this case, the binding site is
suggested not to be linked to a single transducer system. That is,
the different opioid binding sites would have access to a common
subsequent system floating in the membrane. One may assume, thus,
that even those receptors which were not chronically exposed to an
opioid in a tolerant preparation should display dependence. This
argumentation remains vague, as the definition for "the receptor"is
still under discussion. It is generally accepted that the receptor
consists of a recognition site for its ligand and a subsequent
transducer system. While the interaction of the recognition site
with its ligand is well described, the function of the "subsequent
transducer system" is not. Since opioid tolerance and dependence
may find their expression at different sites of the receptor
entity, an understanding of the molecular mechanism is highly de-
sired. Basically, an association of tolerance and dependence development with the "opioid receptor" does not exclude adaptational
mechanisms down-or upstream-from the neuron primarily affected by
the opioid.

These considerations prompted investigations into opioid dependence
and cross-dependence, extending, thereby, studies of tolerance and

cross-tolerance. Since highly tolerant vasa deferentia of mice fail
to display any sign of dependence (Gillan et al. 1979), the studies
were conducted with the isolated longitudinal muscle-myenteric
plexus preparation of the guinea pig ileum. This preparation has
been widely used to study both opioid tolerance and dependence.

The demonstration of dependence in tolerant preparations requires
the displacement of the agonist (Schulz and Herz 1976). Thus, administration of the narcotic antagonist naloxone may uncover dependence; that is, it elicits a withdrawal contracture. A serious problem relates to the fact that naloxone covers the different types of
opioid receptors with only minor differences in affinity. This im-
plies that naloxone alone cannot be employed as a drug to study
dependence associated with a specific type of receptor. Since a
withdrawal sign can be precipitated by naloxone only by displacing
an agonist, dependence and cross-dependence were therefore studied
by use of highly selective μ- or κ-agonists. A withdrawal contracture caused by naloxone under these conditions would reveal dependence of the specific opioid receptor occupied by the agonist.

In the light of the above considerations, the experiments were designed as follows: The ilea of guinea pigs, which had been chronically treated with low concentrations of morphine or EK, were set
up in vitro for electrical stimulation. The preparations were withdrawn by washing in order to unmask all opioid receptors. A successful removal of the agonist from its receptor is manifested in the
failure of naloxone to precipitate a withdrawal contracture. Thereafter, the strips were re-exposed for 30 min to a specific opioid
receptor agonist of a very low concentration. Subsequently,
naloxone was added to the bath to test for dependence (figure 2).
Figure 3, upper panel, displays the results obtained with preparations rendered in vivo dependent on the μ-agonist morphine (10 and
100 μg/h, 6 days).•After the preparations were withdrawn, they were
re-exposed to either the μ-agonist normorphine (NORM) or to the κ-
agonists dynorphin A_{1-13} (DYN_{1-13}) or α-neoendorphin$_{1-8}$ (ANE_{1-8}).
Tests for dependence revealed a similar intensity of withdrawal
contracture in all preparations, regardless of whether a μ- or κ-
agonist was employed for reexposure. Essentially identical results
were obtained with preparations taken from guinea pigs chronically
treated with EK (lower panel, 5 and 50 μg/h, 6 days). Taken together, dependence cannot be allocated to a specific opioid receptor type. The preparations chronically exposed to a μ-agonist
display dependence, but a sign of dependence can equally well be
demonstrated after the μ-agonist has been exchanged with a κ-
agonist. This phenomenon may be called cross-dependence.

However, any overlap of the agonist employed for reexposure in
vitro to a different receptor type may affect the interpretation
of these above-mentioned results. Thus, the aim of further experiments was to rule out the possibility that the naloxone-induced
withdrawal contracture could relate to more than a single receptor
population. To accomplish this aim, the irreversible μ-receptor
antagonist ß-funaltrexamine (ß-FNA) (Ward et al. 1982) was employed
in these studies. The experimental design followed that described
above with the exception that the withdrawn preparations were ex-

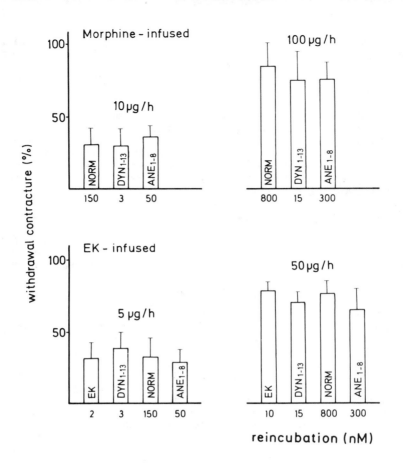

FIGURE 3: Opioid dependence and cross-dependence in the isolated guinea pig ileum. The preparations were rendered dependent by infusing guinea pigs with morphine or ethylketazocine (EK). After withdrawal of the preparations, they were reincubated with opioids with a high receptor selectivity, such as normorphine (NORM) for μ-receptors, and EK, dynorphin A_{1-13} (DYN_{1-13}) and α-neo-endorphin$_{1-8}$ (ANE_{1-8}) for κ-receptors. The reincubation concentrations of the drugs are indicated on the abscissa and the elicited strength of the withdrawal interaction is given on the ordinate. For details see Schulz et al. (1982).

posed to ß-FNA (Seidl and Schulz 1983). This treatment provides preparations containing κ-receptors only. The intensity of the withdrawal contractions of preparations exposed in vivo to fentanyl (FEN) and treated in vitro with ß-FNA are given in figure 4. The left panel (A) illustrates the data of preparations exposed in vitro to different concentrations of FEN. In preparations not exposed to ß-FNA, the contracture evoked by naloxone amounts in all tissues to about 50 percent of the electrically evoked contractions.

In the presence of ß-FNA, the response was greatly reduced, although the intensity of the contractions increased as the concentration of FEN increased. The fact that ß-FNA-exposed preparations
responded to naloxone in the presence of FEN most likely relates
to an incomplete inactivation of μ-receptors upon ß-FNA treatment.
Under analogous experimental conditions, but exposing the preparations in vitro to the κ-agonist EK instead to FEN, the withdrawal
contractions were of similar intensity in both the ß-FNA-exposed
and non-exposed preparations (panel B). Thus, the studies employing
the irreversible antagonist ß-FNA, which interacts selectively with
μ-receptors, confirm previous results. They indicate the development of dependence at μ- and κ-receptors (cross-dependence), although only a single type of receptor has been chronically activated
in vivo.

A different issue relates to the assumption that tolerance and
dependence are phenomena of a common mechanism. It would follow
that these phenomena should both be displayed together under appropriate conditions. Applying these considerations to the isolated
mouse vas deferens, opioid tolerance has never, in fact, been

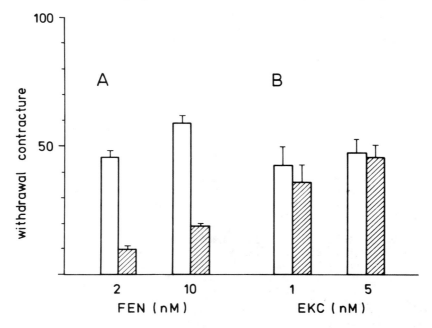

FIGURE 4:   Withdrawal contractions precipitated by naloxone in
isolated guinea pig ileum preparations rendered dependent to fentanyl (FEN) in vivo. Open columns are data from preparations not
exposed to ß-FNA in vitro; hatched columns indicate data from
preparations exposed in vitro to ß-FNA. The ordinate reflects the
tension of the withdrawal contracture. The abscissa reflects the
concentrations of FEN and ethylketazocine (EKC) employed to expose
the preparations in vitro. For details see Seidl and Schulz (1983).

demonstrated to be associated with any sign of dependence. Although electrophysiological data have been reported indicating that the neuronal firing rate increases in the tolerant mouse vas deferens upon naloxone exposure (North and Vitek 1980), the question under discussion remains whether or not this observation, in fact, represents a sign of dependence or an overshoot reaction subsequent to the disinhibition of the opioid effect. In contrast to the mouse vas deferens, both tolerance and dependence are commonly observed in the isolated guinea-pig ileum. However, a detailed analysis of the development of both parameters casts doubts on the principle of a simultaneous and parallel appearance.

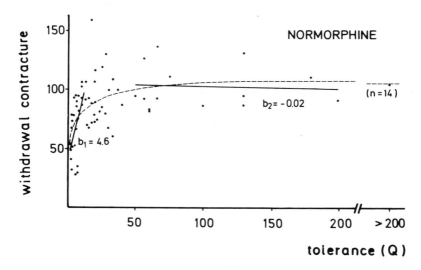

FIGURE 5:   Correlation between tolerance and dependence in the isolated guinea pig ileum. Guinea pigs were treated with different dosages of morphine. The isolated preparations taken from these guinea pigs were maintained in vitro at different concentrations of normorphine. Each dot represents data from a single strip which was used once to assay tolerance and dependence. The dotted line indicates the tolerance/dependence curve obtained by best-fit computer analysis. The solid lines indicate the regression lines for the degree of tolerance (Q) ranging from 1 to 10 and from 50-200. b_1 and b_2 reflect the respective regression coefficients. Abscissa: degree of tolerance (Q) calculated from IC_{50} values of tolerant and naive preparations. Ordinate: intensity of withdrawal contracture expressed as percent of the preceding electrical stimulation. For details see Schulz et al. (1982).

In order to investigate this matter, guinea pigs were infused chronically with different amounts of morphine (10 to 100 µg/h, 6 days). The strips were set up in vitro at corresponding concentrations of morphine in plasma and were tested for tolerance to morphine and for dependence by addition of naloxone to the organ bath. Figure 5 correlates the degree of tolerance with the intensity of withdrawal contracture (dependence). Apparently, a very steep slope of the curve at low degrees of tolerance is followed by an extremely flat slope at high degrees of tolerance. In fact, dependence was observed already in preparations which did not display a measurable degree of tolerance. From these experiments, it became obvious that the degree of tolerance and the degree of dependence do not appear in a parallel fashion in the isolated guinea pig ileum.

While the aforementioned experiments do not always demonstrate a separation between tolerance and dependence, a clear-cut dissociation of these phenomena can be obtained by experimental manipulations. Cholera toxin, a neurotoxin which interferes with the receptor mechanism, specifically with the guanyl regulatory unit (Rodbell 1980), has been shown to reduce the expression of dependence in the isolated guinea-pig ileum without changing the degree of tolerance to opioids (Lux and Schulz 1983). This result, thus, represents a further hint for a dissociation of tolerance from dependence.

CONCLUSIONS

Theoretical considerations have intimately linked opioid tolerance with dependence and provided the conceptual basis for a postulated "unitary mechanism" underlying these phenomena. Several recent findings are not in correspondence with this notion. Similarly, it has become clear that cross-tolerance between opioids is not a criterion for the classification of a drug as an opioid.

The studies with the mouse vas deferens reviewed here exemplify the above-mentioned issues in two respects. First, a highly opioid-tolerant vas deferens fails to display any sign of dependence. Second, a lack of cross-tolerance between different opioid receptor agonists has been convincingly demonstrated. A plausible explanation of these phenomena may be derived from studies of adaptational mechanisms observed in neuroblastoma cells. These cultured hybrid cells respond to chronic opioid exposure with a "down regulation" of the binding sites for opioids (Chang et al. 1982, Law et al. 1982). Thus, assuming a sufficiently high degree of "down regulation," the tolerance phenomenon could be explained by this mechanism. On the other hand, an uncoupling of the opioid binding site from its subsequent system has already been suggested (Rubini et al. 1982) as being responsible for tolerance. Such a mechanism may, in fact, occur in neuroblastoma hybrid cells (Wüster et al. 1983, Wüster and Costa, this volume). Both mechanisms would imply a disruption of the receptor function and could, thus, explain tolerance. In contrast, however, the expression of dependence demands a functioning opioid receptor. Since the highly tolerant mouse vas deferens fails to display any sign of dependence, the mechanisms underlying tolerance in the neuroblastoma cells and the vas deferens may be similar. Thus, both tolerance and dependence may dissociate in the vas deferens. This would suggest that only tolerance develops in the nerve terminals of the mouse vas deferens. Attempts, however, to demonstrate alterations of opioid binding sites in the tolerant mouse vas deferens have not, as yet, proven successful (Rubini et al. 1982). In contrast to the cellular development of tolerance (Collier 1980), adaptive processes may occur in transmission between neurons, that is, subsequent to the primary opioid-affected cell (Williams and North 1983).

An analysis of the findings with the isolated ileum would suggest multiple adaptational mechanisms. Since dependence has been demonstrated in all preparations chronically exposed to an opioid, a functional opioid receptor must be assumed to exist under these conditions. However, there appears to be a discrepancy between the degree of tolerance and the intensity of dependence. A maximal withdrawal sign is observed already at a low degree of tolerance. As tolerance gradually increases, dependence does not develop to the same degree. Apparently, two adaptive mechanisms may be involved. One involves tolerance and dependence, the second mainly the development of tolerance. If the second mechanism is due to a disturbance of the function of the opioid receptor, only a certain fraction may be affected. The remaining receptors must be intact since a withdrawal sign is still precipitated under these conditions. One may argue that the extremely high degree of tolerance seen in this preparations may be due to mechanisms similar to those assumed to account for the tolerant mouse vas deferens, or those manifested in neuroblastoma cells (Chang et al. 1982, Law et al. 1982, Wüster et al. 1983). Then the discrepancy mentioned above between tolerance and dependence could be explained. Promising tools for the further investigation of these mechanisms seem to be neurotoxins, such as pertussis toxin and cholera toxin. Both toxins have already been employed for studies of opioid tolerance/dependence in the guinea-pig ileum (Collier et al. 1983, Lux and Schulz 1983).

Of considerable interest is the observed cross-dependence between different opioid receptors in the isolated guinea-pig ileum (Schulz et al. 1982, Seidl and Schulz 1983). This finding may imply that all receptor binding sites are somehow linked to a common transducer system which adapts to chronic stimulation. A theoretical basis for such a mechanism would be subsumed in the "mobile receptor theory" (Cuatrecasas 1974).

ACKNOWLEDGEMENT

This work has been supported by Deutsche Forschungsgemeinschaft, Bonn.

REFERENCES

Chang, K.-J., Eckel, R.W., and Blanchard, S.G. Opioid peptides induce reduction of enkephalin receptors in cultured neuroblastoma cells. Nature, 296:446-448, 1982.
Collier, H.O.J. Cellular site of opiate dependence. Nature, 283: 625-629, 1980.

Collier, H.O.J., Plant, N.T., and Tucker, J.F. Pertussis vaccine inhibits the chronic but not acute action of normorphine on the myenteric plexus of guinea-pig ileum. Europ J Pharmacol, 91:325-326, 1983.

Cuatrecasas, P. Membrane receptors. Ann Rev Biochem, 43:169-214, 1974.

Gillan, M.G.C., Kosterlitz, H.W., Robson, L.E., and Waterfield, A.A. The inhibitory effects of presynaptic α-adrenoceptor agonists on contractions of guinea-pig ileum and mouse vas deferens in the morphine-dependent and withdrawn states produced in vitro. Br J Pharmacol, 66: 601-608, 1979.

Goldstein, D.B., and Goldstein, A. Enzyme expansion theory of drug tolerance and physical dependence. Assoc for Res of Nervous and Mental Diseases, Res Publications, 46:265-267, 1968.

Law, P.Y., Hom, D.S., and Loh, H.H. Loss of opiate receptor activity in neuroblastoma x glioma NG108-15 hybrid cells after chronic opiate treatment. A multiple-step process. Mol Pharmacol, 22:1-4, 1982.

Lord, J.A.H., Waterfield, A.A., Hughes, J., and Kosterlitz, H.W. Endogenous opioid peptides: Multiple agonists and receptors. Nature, 267:495-499, 1977.

Lux, B., and Schulz, R. Cholera toxin selectivity affects the expression of opioid dependence in the tolerant myenteric plexus of the guinea-pig. Europ J Pharmacol, 96:175-176, 1983.

Martin, W.R., Eades, C.G., Thompson, J.A., Huppler, R.E., and Gilbert, P.E. The effect of morphine- and nalorphine-like drugs in the non-dependent and morphine-dependent chronic spinal dog. J Pharmacol Exp Ther 197:517-532, 1976.

North, R.A., and Vitek, L.V. The effect of chronic morphine treatment on excitatory junction potentials in the mouse vas deferens. Br J Pharmacol, 68:399-405, 1980.

Rodbell, H. The role of hormone receptors and GTP-regulatory proteins in membrane transduction. Nature, 284:17-22, 1980.

Rubini, P., Schulz, R., Wüster, M., and Herz, A. Opiate receptor binding studies in the mouse vas deferens exhibiting tolerance without dependence. Naunyn-Schmiedeberg's Arch Pharmacol, 319:142-146, 1982.

Schulz, R., and Herz, A. Aspects of opiate dependence in the myenteric plexus of the guinea-pig. Life Sci, 19:1117-1128, 1976.

Schulz, R., Wüster, M., Krenss, H., and Herz, A. Lack of cross-tolerance on multiple opiate receptors in the mouse vas deferens. Mol Pharm, 18: 395-401, 1980.

Schulz, R., Wüster, M., and Herz, A. Differentiation of opiate receptors in the brain by the selective development of tolerance. Pharmacol Biochem Behav, 14:75-79, 1981.

Schulz, R., Seidl, E., Wüster, M., and Herz, A. Opioid dependence and cross-dependence in the isolated guinea-pig ileum. Europ J Pharmacol, 84:33-40, 1982.

Seidl, E., and Schulz, R. Selective opiate tolerance in the guinea-pig ileum is not associated with selective dependence. Life Sci, 33:357-360, 1983.

Shuster, L. Repression and depression of enzyme synthesis as a possible explanation of some aspects of drug action. Nature, 189:314-315, 1961.

Ward, S.J., Portoghese, P.S., and Takemori, A.E. Improved assays for the assessment of κ- and δ-properties of opioid ligands. Europ J Pharmacol, 85:163-170, 1982.

Williams, J.T., and North, R.A. Tolerance to opiates in locus coeruleus neurones. Life Sci, in press, 1983.

Wüster, M., Costa, T., and Gramsch, Ch. Uncoupling of receptors is essential for opiate-induced desensitization (tolerance) in neuroblastoma x glioma hybrid cells NG 108-15. Life Sci, in press, 1983.

Wüster, M., Rubini, P., and Schulz, R. The preference of putative pro-enkephalins for different types of opiate receptors. Life Sci 29:1219-1227, 1981a.

Wüster, M., Schulz, R., and Herz, A. Multiple opiate receptors in the peripheral tissue preparation. Biochem Pharmacol, 30: 1883-1887, 1981b.

AUTHORS

Dr. R. Schulz
Prof. Dr. A. Herz
Max-Planck Institut für Psychiatrie, Department of Neuropharmacology, Am Klopferspitz 18A, D-8033 Martinsried, FRG.

Sites and Mechanisms of Dependence in the Myenteric Plexus of Guinea Pig Ileum

H. O. J. Collier and J. F. Tucker

INTRODUCTION

The understanding of drug dependence mechanisms has probably
reached its highest point so far with opioids. This is due to
several factors, including: (1) the availability of a specific
opiate antagonist, naloxone; (2) the feasibility of inducing and
measuring opiate dependence in two in vitro preparations (a) neuroblastoma-glioma hybrid cells in culture and (b) guinea pig ileum;
and (3) a better understanding of the complex processes regulating
adenylate cyclase activity.

The isolated guinea pig ileum has been used frequently in the study
of the long-term effects of opiates (Paton 1957; Ehrenpries et al.
1972; Goldstein and Schultz 1973; Hammond et al. 1976; Schultz and
Herz 1976; Villarreal et al. 1977; Lujan and Rodriquez 1978;
Gintzler 1979; Collier et al. 1981b). Tolerance and dependence in
this tissue and in the whole animal have many characteristics in
common (table 1).

Two recent developments have enabled the analysis of the problem of
opiate dependence to be carried forward using the guinea pig ileum
model. One is the demonstration that dependence on adenosine can
be induced in the isolated ileum (Collier and Tucker 1983). The
other is the demonstration that pertussis vaccine, through its
content of islet activating protein, can selectively interfere with
the inhibitory regulation of adenylate cyclase (Katada and Ui 1980,
1981; Hildebrandt et al. 1983).

SITE OF DEPENDENCE IN THE ILEUM

Subsequent to the demonstration that prolonged in vivo or in vitro
exposure of the guinea pig ileum to opiates results in dependence,
it has been shown that a similar phenomenon is associated with both
clonidine (Collier et al. 1981a) and adenosine (Collier and Tucker
1983). Exposure of guinea pig ileum to either clonidine (10^{-6}M)
or adenosine (4×10^{-6}M) for 18-24 hr induces in the tissue a
dependence, the withdrawal from which is expressed as a contracture

TABLE 1. Characterization of Opiate Dependence in Both Guinea Pig Isolated Ileum and Experimental Animals (based on work in Collier et al. 1981 a,b)

1. Dependence does not appear immediately, but requires a period of continued exposure to opiate.

2. Dependence is accompanied by tolerance to the acute effects of opiate.

3. Withdrawal of opiate elicits a "spontaneous" behavioral disturbance that can be suppressed by retreatment with opiate.

4. Withdrawal disturbance can be precipitated with a specific antagonist, the potency of which is related to the degree of dependence.

5. Induction of dependence requires the activation of a specific and stereospecific opiate receptor.

6. Precipitation of withdrawal requires a specific and stereospecific opiate antagonist.

7. Clonidine inhibits the opiate withdrawal disturbance.

in response to α-adrenoceptor antagonists or adenosine receptor antagonists respectively.

Although normorphine, clonidine, and adenosine each induce dependence in the ileum, there are reasons for believing that the dependencies are distinct. Firstly, the three agents induce dependence by interaction with different receptors, activation of which inhibits the release of acetylcholine from neurons of the myenteric plexus (table 2).

Secondly, withdrawal from these drugs can only be precipitated with a selective antagonist of the dependence-inducing agent (Collier et al. 1981a; Collier and Tucker 1983). For example, neither yohimbine nor naloxone will produce a response in tissues previously incubated for 18-24 hr in adenosine, but challenge with the adenosine antagonist 8-phenyltheophylline produces a marked withdrawal contracture (figure 1).

All the evidence to date suggests that the site of dependence in the ileum is within neurons of the myenteric plexus. This is illustrated by the fact that normorphine, clonidine, and adenosine withdrawal contractures can all be blocked with tetrodotoxin (Collier et al. 1981a,b; Collier and Tucker 1983). Additionally, North and Karras (1978) have demonstrated that after continued

Table 2. Selective Agonists and Antagonists at Specific Receptors Inhibiting Acetylcholine Release From the Final Cholinergic Motoneuron of Guinea Pig Ileum

Receptor	Agonist example	Antagonist example	Reference
Opioid, Mu	Normorphine	Naloxone	Lord et al. 1977 Schultz et al. 1981
Kappa	Ethylketo-cyclazocine	---	Chavkin & Goldstein 1981
	dynorphins		Paterson et al. 1983
Adrenoceptor, alpha$_2$	Clonidine, noradrenaline	Yohimbine	Kosterlitz et al. 1970
	adrenaline		Tanaka & Starke 1979
			Malta et al. 1981
Purinoceptor, Al (Ri)	Adenosine, 2-chloro-adenosine	8-Phenyl-theo-phylline	Paton 1981

Collier 1984. Copyright 1984, by Taylor Francis Ltd.

exposure to morphine, a burst of impulse production can be elicited with naloxone in neurons of the myenteric plexus. In this last study, electrical activity was recorded from cell bodies via suction electrodes, suggesting that dependence develops in the soma of neurons of the myenteric plexus rather than in the axon or nerve terminal.

MEDIATORS OF THE WITHDRAWAL CONTRACTURE

Early studies of the withdrawal response in the guinea pig ileum supported the contention that the consequence of neuronal firing, occasioned by naloxone-precipitated morphine withdrawal, was acetylcholine release. Recently it has been shown that a second transmitter, first observed by Gintzler (1980) and later by Tsou et al. (1982), also participates in the normorphine withdrawal contracture. Experiments with capsaicin, densensitization to substance P (SP), and SP antagonists have shown that this second transmitter is SP. Chahl (1983) has shown that the relative contributions by acetylcholine and SP to the [Met]enkephalin withdrawal contracture in the guinea pig ileum vary depending on the duration of exposure to enkephalin. Short periods of exposure

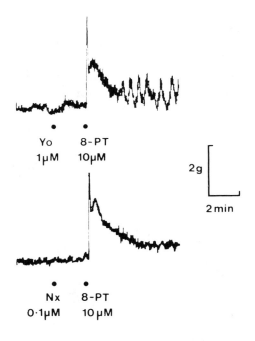

FIGURE 1. Lack of Responsiveness to Yohimbine (YO) and Naloxone
(Nx) of 8-Phenyltheophylline (8-PT)-Sensitive Guinea Pig Ileum.
Pieces of ileum were incubated in 4×10^{-6}M adenosine for 18-24
hr at 19-21° and for 30-40 min at 37°C.

appear to be associated with a withdrawal contracture due to both
acetylcholine and SP, whereas the withdrawal contractures associated with longer periods of contact are predominantly due to SP
alone.

We have extended these observations and shown that the same neuron
or neurons that are involved in opiate withdrawal in the ileum are
also likely to be involved in adenosine and clonidine withdrawal
contractures. That is, in the ileum, withdrawal from these agents
can only be completely antagonized by abolishing responses to both
acetylcholine and SP. For example, figure 2 shows that after
adenosine withdrawal, a hyoscine-resistant component of the
withdrawal contracture remains which can be abolished by SP
desensitization. Similar results have been obtained by using a
combination of hyoscine and the SP antagonist D Pro^2-D Trp^{7,9}
SP.

CONVERGENT DEPENDENCE IN THE ILEUM

Since the dependencies on normorphine, clonidine, and adenosine
appear not to differ in character other than in the nature of the

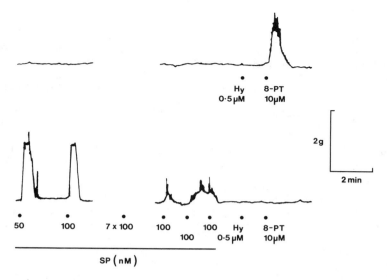

FIGURE 2.   Prevention by Substance P (SP) [Desensitization] of the
Hyoscine (Hy)-Resistant 8-Phenyltheophylline (8-PT)-Precipitated
Adenosine Withdrawal Contracture.   Upper strip shows effect of Hy
alone; lower strip shows effect of Hy and SP-desensitization.
Details as in figure 1.

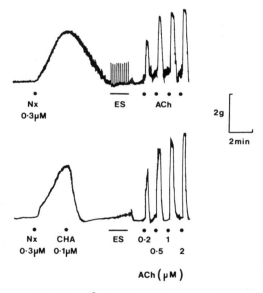

FIGURE 3.   Suppression by N^6-Cyclohexyladenosine (CHA) of
Withdrawal Contracture Precipitated With Naloxone (Nx).   Pieces of
ileum were incubated in 10^{-6}M normorphine for 18-24 hr at 4°C
and for 30-40 min at 37°C.   ES : electrical stimulation with 0.5
ms pulses at 0.1 Hz; ACh: acetylcholine (Tucker et al. 1983).

85

inducing drug and its selective antagonist, these dependencies have been termed convergent (Collier 1983). That is, dependence can be induced through binding of a particular drug with a specific recognition site on the neuron, but beyond this point the mechanisms converge, so that withdrawal of all three is expressed through liberation of the same transmitters, and any one of the three agonists can suppress withdrawal of the other two (Collier et al. 1981a,b; Collier and Tucker 1983). For example, activation of purinoceptors with N^6-cyclohexyladenosine (CHA), a stable derivative of adenosine, can abruptly terminate naloxone- precipitated normorphine withdrawal contractures in the ileum (figure 3).

A possible useful consequence of convergent dependence is that not only clonidine but also adenosine derivatives might be useful in inhibiting opiate withdrawal symptoms in man. We have previously shown that 2-chloroadenosine (2-CA), a stable derivative of adenosine, potently suppresses morphine withdrawal signs in the mouse (Tucker et al. 1983). Recently we have compared CHA, with clonidine with respect to inhibition of jumping, diarrhea, and weight loss in naloxone-precipitated morphine withdrawal in mice. Mice were made dependent by implanting one 50 mg pellet of morphine subcutaneously under ether anesthesia. Three days later, mice were treated ip with CHA, clonidine, or saline; 25 min later, withdrawal was precipitated with 1 mg/kg ip naloxone.

TABLE 3. Inhibition with N^6-Cyclohexyladenosine (CHA) and Clonidine (CLON) of Withdrawal Effects Precipitated With Naloxone in Morphine-Dependent Mice

Drug	Dose (mg/kg)	n	Jumps/15 min ± SE	Incidence of Diarrhea	Weight Loss (mg ± SE)
Control		58	177 ± 10	78	743 ± 55
CHA	0.1	17	91 ± 11*	24*	468 ± 62*
	0.5	6	77 ± 25*	0*	143 ± 76*
	3.125	6-7	35 ± 12*	0*	63 ± 32*
CLON	0.05	10	121 ± 20*	10*	441 ± 80*
	0.2	11	125 ± 11*	0*	325 ± 90*

* $P < 0.01$ for significance of difference from control value

From table 3 it is evident that clonidine is about equipotent with CHA in suppressing naloxone-precipitated diarrhea and weight loss but less potent in suppressing jumping. This may be explained by van der Laan's finding (1983) that at higher doses than those shown here clonidine can in fact potentiate naloxone-precipitated morphine withdrawal jumping.

The demonstration that, in the ileum at least, dependence can develop to adenosine has important consequences. It has recently been demonstrated in mice that interference with adenosine uptake or antagonism of its effects can modify the action of acutely and chronically administered alcohol (Dar et al. 1983). This raises the possibility that adenosine might mediate some of the effects of alcohol and might be involved in the dependence phenomenon associated with its chronic use.

There is as yet no evidence that chronic administration of adenosine or its derivatives induces dependence in the whole animal, but after repeated administration of CHA to mice, tolerance to some of its actions develops (unpublished observation).

Adenosine has also been implicated as a mediator of some of morphine's actions (Sawynok and Jhamandas 1976; Stone 1981). Additionally, in NG 108-15 cells, enhanced sensitivity of adenylate cyclase to the excitatory action of adenosine has been reported to occur after prolonged incubation with morphine (Griffin et al. 1983). Moreover, adenosine has been identified as the cytosolic component responsible for the enhanced activity of adenylate cyclase in morphine-dependent NG 108-15 cells. It is difficult to equate the work with NG 108-15 cells with that in the ileum, as in the latter it is believed that adenosine inhibits rather than stimulates adenylate cyclase activity.

CYCLIC AMP HYPOTHESIS

The adenylate cyclase/cAMP system and its involvement in the mechanisms of drug dependence has been the subject of extensive work over the past 10 years. Collier and Roy (1974) showed that opiates specifically inhibit prostaglandin E_1 (PGE_1) stimulated cAMP production and proposed that opiate tolerance and dependence represent a compensating hypertrophy of a part of the inhibited PGE_1/cAMP mechanism. At about the same time, Sharma et al. (1975) demonstrated that cultivation of NG 108-15 cells in the presence of morphine slowly increases PGE_1-stimulated and basal adenylate cyclase activity. Their observations led them to propose that late positive regulation of adenylate cyclase counteracts the inhibitory action of morphine and is responsible for narcotic dependence and tolerance. Recently, further evidence supporting this theory has come from work with pertussis toxin and NG 108-15 cells (Wuster et al. 1983).

Until recently it has been difficult to test the cAMP hypothesis of dependence in normal neurons, but the demonstration of dependence on normorphine, clonidine, and adenosine in the ileum now makes that possible.

The general concept that dependence arises in normal neurons in response to inhibition of adenylate cyclase is supported by the fact that all three agonists that induce dependence in the ileum have been shown to inhibit adenylate cyclase in other biological preparations as a consequence of binding with their distinct recognition sites (table 4).

TABLE 4. Inhibition of Adenylate Cyclase by Activation of Various Receptors

Receptor	Agonist	Site	Reference
Opioid, mu	Morphine	Mammalian brain	Collier & Roy 1974
			Collier 1980
			Barchfeld et al. 1982
			Pay & Bhoola 1983
kappa	Ethylketo-cyclazocine	Rat brain	Barchfeld et al. 1982
delta	(Leu)^5-enkephalin	NG 108-15 cells	Lampert et al. 1976 Brandt et al. 1976
		rat brain	Law et al. 1981
Adreno-ceptor, alpha$_2$	Clonidine, noradrenaline	Thrombo-cytes	Garcia-Sainz & Fain 1982
		Adipocytes	Burns et al. 1982
			Limbird 1983
		NG 108-15 cells	Sabol & Nirenberg 1979
Purino-ceptor, Al (Ri)	Adenosine	Adipocytes	Londos et al. 1980
	2-chloro-adenosine	brain membranes	Bruns et al. 1980
		Brain glial cells in culture	van Calker et al. 1979

Collier 1984. Copyright 1984, by Taylor Francis Ltd.

Because of the difficulty of separating nervous from muscular tissue in the ileum, it has so far proved impossible to test directly whether normorphine, clonidine, and adenosine inhibit adenylate cyclase in the cholinergic neurons of the myenteric plexus. Recently, however, some indirect evidence relevant to this matter has been obtained.

Katada and Ui (1980, 1981) and Hildebrandt et al. (1983) demonstrated that pertussis vaccine through the islet-activating protein-toxin can inactivate an inhibitory regulator of adenylate cyclase. More recently, Costa et al. (1983) have shown that pertussis toxin can reduce opiate inhibition of adenylate cyclase in NG 108-15 cells, possibly due to an uncoupling of the opiate receptor and the inhibitory regulator (Ni) of adenylate cyclase. We have explored the cAMP hypothesis of dependence by determining the effect of pertussis vaccine on the actions of normorphine on the myenteric plexus of the ileum (Collier et al. 1983). Initially we looked at the effect of pertussis vaccine on the acute effects of normorphine.

The IC_{50} values for normorphine in vaccine-treated tissues and nontreated tissues were not significantly different, being 36 and 37 nM respectively for in vitro treatment, and 21 and 23 nM respectively for in vivo treatment. However, in normorphine-dependent ileum, treatment with vaccine affects contraction (table 5).

TABLE 5. Inhibition by Pertussis Vaccine of Normorphine Dependence in the Guinea Pig Isolated Ileum

Vaccine treatment	n	Mean response to Nx ± SEM	
		Treated	Control
In vitro	14 + 14	19.2 ± 2.7*	36.1 ± 5.7
In vivo	5 + 5	21.1 ± 4.9**	49.7 ± 4.9

Responses expressed as per cent maximal response to acetylcholine.
Nx, 0.3 x 10^{-6}M Naloxone.
*P < 0.02; **P < 0.01 for difference from control.
Collier et al. 1983. Copyright 1983, Elsevier Science Publishers BV.

In vitro treatment with vaccine reduced the withdrawal response by about 47%. In ilea from guinea pigs treated with vaccine, the withdrawal contracture was reduced by nearly 60% when compared to control. In both sets of determinations, responses to electrical stimulation and acetylcholine were unaffected by vaccine treatment. We have also shown that pertussis vaccine has similar inhibitory effects on adenosine dependence in the ileum.

We conclude from this that although pertussis vaccine does not change the acute potency of normorphine it profoundly inhibits the dependence mechanism, possibly by inactivating the inhibitory regulator of adenylate cyclase which opiates and adenosine normally activate.

It has recently been reported that cholera toxin, a nonspecific
activator of adenylate cyclase, inhibits the expression of opioid
dependence in the myenteric plexus of the guinea pig (Lux and
Schulz 1983). This complements the work with pertussis vaccine.
The latter prevents the prolonged inhibition of adenylate cyclase
by morphine by inactivating the inhibitory regulator of adenylate
cyclase (Katada and Ui 1980, 1981; Hildebrandt et al. 1983), and
cholera toxin opposes the prolonged inhibition of adenylate cyclase
by direct activation of its excitatory regulator (Gill and Meren
1978). Thus both agents prevent the prolonged inhibition of
adenylate cyclase which is proposed to be central to the
development of dependence on opiates.

SUMMARY

The isolated guinea pig ileum provides a model in which drug
dependence can be induced in normal neurons.

The characteristics of opiate dependence in the ileum closely
resemble those of dependence in whole animals.

Convergent dependence on normorphine, clonidine, and adenosine can
be separately induced in the ileum in vitro.

Use of selective antagonists indicates that both acetylcholine and
substance P participate in the withdrawal response associated with
all three of these dependencies.

The demonstration that adenosine derivatives suppress opiate
withdrawal in the guinea pig ileum and in mice raises the
possibility that they might act similarly in man.

The point at which the dependencies on normorphine, clonidine, and
adenosine converge is probably below their separate recognition
sites and is possibly at the level of adenylate cyclase
regulation.

REFERENCES

Barchfeld, C.C., Maassen, Z.F., and Medzihradsky, F.
    Receptor-related interactions of opiates with PGE-induced
    adenylate cyclase in brain. Life Sci, 31:1661-1665, 1982.
Brandt, M., Fischer, K., Moroder, L., Wunsch, E., and Hamprecht,
    B. Enkephalin evokes biochemical correlates of opiate tolerance
    and dependence in neuroblastoma X glioma hydrid cells. FEBS
    Lett, 68:38-40, 1976.
Bruns, R.F., Daly, J.W., and Snyder, S.H. Adenosine receptors in
    brain membranes: Binding of N^6-cyclo-hexyl (^{3}H) adenosine
    and 1,3-diethyl-8-(^{3}H) phenylxanthine. Proc Natl Acad Sci
    USA, 77:5547-5551, 1980.
Burns, T.W., Langley, P.E., Bylund, D.B. and Forte, L.R. Alpha-2
    adrenergic activation inhibits forskolin-stimulated adenylate
    cyclase activity and lipolysis in human adipocytes. Life Sci,
    31:815-821, 1982.

Chahl, L.A. Contracture of guinea-pig ileum on withdrawal of methionine[5]-enkephalin is mediated by substance P. Br J Pharmacol, 80:741-751, 1983.

Chavkin, C., and Goldstein, A. Demonstration of a specific dynorphin receptor in guinea pig ileum myenteric plexus. Nature Lond, 291:591-593, 1981.

Collier, H.O.J. Cellular site of opiate dependence. Nature Lond, 283:625-629, 1980.

Collier, H.O.J. Cellular aspects of opioid tolerance and dependence. In: Hughes, J., Collier, H.O.J., Rance, M.J., and Tyers, M.B., eds. Opioids; Past, Present and Future. London: Taylor Francis Ltd., 1984. pp. 109-125.

Collier, H.O.J., Cuthbert, N.J., and Francis, D.L. Clonidine dependence in the guinea-pig isolated ileum. Br J Pharmacol, 73:443-453, 1981a.

Collier, H.O.J., Cuthbert, N.J., and Francis, D.L. Model of opiate dependence in the guinea-pig isolated ileum. Br J Pharmacol, 73:921-932, 1981b.

Collier, H.O.J., Plant, N.T., and Tucker, J.F. Pertussis vaccine inhibits the chronic but not acute action of normorphine on the myenteric plexus of guinea-pig ileum. Eur J Pharmacol, 91:325-326, 1983.

Collier, H.O.J., and Roy, A.C. Morphine-like drugs inhibit the stimulation by E prostaglandins of cyclic AMP formation by rat brain homogenate. Nature Lond, 248:24-27, 1974.

Collier, H.O.J., and Tucker, J.F. Novel form of drug-dependence - on adenosine in guinea pig ileum. Nature Lond, 302:618-621, 1983.

Costa, T., Aktories, G., Schultz, G., and Wuster, M. Pertussis toxin decreases opiate receptor binding and adenylate cyclase inhibition in a neuroblastoma x glioma hybrid cell line. Life Sci, 33:219-223, 1983.

Dar, M.S., Mustafa, S.J., and Wooles, W.R. Possible role of adenosine in the CNS effects of ethanol. Life Sci, 33:1363-1374, 1983.

Ehrenpries, S., Light, I., and Schonbuck, G.H. Use of the electrically stimulated guinea pig ileum to study potent analgesics. In: Singh, J.M., Miller, L.H., and Lal, H., eds. Drug Addiction: Experimental Aspects. New York: Futura, 1972. pp. 319-342.

Garcia-Sainz, J.A., and Fain, J.N. Regulation of adipose tissue metabolism by catecholamines: Roles of alpha$_1$, alpha$_2$ and beta-adrenoceptors. TIPS, 3:201-203, 1982.

Gill, D.M., and Meren, R. ADP - ribosylation of membrane proteins catalyzed by choleratoxin: Basis of the activation of adenylate cyclase. Proc Natl Acad Sci USA, 75:3050-3054, 1978.

Gintzler, A.R. Serotonin participation in gut withdrawal from opiates. J Pharmacol Exp Ther, 211:7-12, 1979.

Gintzler, A.R. Serotonin-substance-P pathway in the manifestation of gut withdrawal. In: Way, E.L., ed. Endogenous and Exogenous Opiate Agonists and Antagonists. Oxford: Pergamon, 1980. pp. 497-500.

Goldstein, A., and Schultz, R. Morphine-tolerant longitudinal muscle strip from guinea-pig ileum. Br J Pharmacol 48:644-666, 1973.

Griffin, M.T., Law, P.Y., and Loh, H.H. Modulation of adenylate cyclase activity by a cytosolic factor following chronic opiate exposure in neuroblastoma X glioma NG 108-15 hybrid cells. Life Sci, 33:365-369, 1983.

Hammond, M.D., Schneider, C., and Collier, H.O.J. Induction of opiate tolerance in isolated guinea pig ileum and its modification by drugs. In: Kosterlitz, H.W., ed. Opiates and Endogenous Opioid Peptides. Amsterdam: Elsevier, 1976. pp. 169-176.

Hildebrandt, J.D., Sekura, R.D., Codina, J., Iyengar, R., Manclark, C.D., and Birnbaumer, L. Stimulation and inhibition of adenyl cyclases mediated by distinct regulatory proteins. Nature Lond, 302:706-708, 1983.

Katada, T., and Ui, M. Slow interaction of islet-activating protein with pancreatic islets during primary culture to cause reversal of alpha-adrenergic inhibition of insulin secretion. J Biol Chem, 255:9580-9588, 1980.

Katada, T., and Ui, M. Islet-activating protein: A modifier of receptor-mediated regulation of rat islet adenylate cyclase. J Biol Chem, 256:8310-8317, 1981.

Kosterlitz, H.W., Lydon, R.J., and Watt, A.J. The effects of adrenaline, noradrenaline and isoprenaline on inhibitory alpha and beta-adrenoreceptors in the longitudinal muscle of the guinea-pig ileum. Br J Pharmac, 39:398-413, 1970.

Lampert, A., Nirenberg, M., and Klee, W.A. Tolerance and dependence evoked by an endogenous opioid peptide. Proc Natl Acad Sci, USA, 73:3165-3167, 1976.

Law, P.Y., Wu, J., Koehler, J.E., and Loh, H.H. Demonstration and characterization of opiate inhibition of the striatal adenylate cyclase. J Neurochem 36: 1834-1836, 1981.

Limbird, L.E. Alpha$_2$-adrenergic systems: Models for exploring hormonal inhibition of adenylate cyclase. TIPS, 4:135-138, 1983.

Londos, C., Cooper, D.M.F., and Wolff, J. Subclasses of external adenosine receptors. Proc Natl Acad Sci USA, 77:2551-2554, 1980.

Lord, J.A.H., Waterfield, A.A., Hughes, J., and Kosterlitz, H.W. Endogenous opioid peptides: Multiple agonists and receptors. Nature Lond, 267:495-499, 1977.

Lujan, M., and Rodriquez, R. Further characterization of opiate physical dependence in the isolated guinea-pig ileum. Pharmacologist, 20:268, 1978.

Lux, B., and Schulz, R. Cholera toxin selectively affects the expression of opioid dependence in the tolerant myenteric plexus of the guinea-pig. Eur J Pharmacol, 96:175-176, 1983.

Malta, E., Raper, C., and Tawa, P.E. Pre- and postjunctional effects of clonidine- and oxymetazoline-like compounds in guinea-pig ileal preparations. Br J Pharmacol, 73:355-362, 1981.

North, R.A., and Karras, P.J. Opiate tolerance and dependence induced in vitro in single myenteric neurones. Nature Lond, 272:73-75, 1978.

Paterson, S.J., Robson, L.E. and Kosterlitz, H.W. Classification of opioid receptors. Br Med Bull, 39:31-36, 1983.

Paton, D.M. Structure-activity relations for presynaptic inhibition of noradrenergic and cholinergic transmission by adenosine: Evidence for action on A$_1$ receptors. J Auton Pharmacol, 1:287-290, 1981.

Paton, W.D.M. The action of morphine and related substances on contraction and on acetylcholine output of coaxially stimulated guinea-pig ileum. Br J Pharmacol, 12:119-127, 1957.

Pay, S., and Bhoola, K.D. Inhibition of rat striatal membrane adenylate cyclase by opiates. 5th Int. Conf. Cyclic Nucleotides and Protein Phosphorylation, Milan, 1983. Abstract, in press.

Sabol, S.L., and Nirenberg, M. Regulation of adenylate cyclase of neuroblastoma X glioma hybrid cells by alpha-adrenergic receptors. J Biol Chem, 254:1913-1920, 1979.

Sawynok, J., and Jhamandas, K.H. Inhibition of acetylcholine release from cholinergic nerves by adenosine, adenine nucleotides and morphine: Antagonism by theophylline. J Pharmacol Exp Ther, 197:379-390, 1976.

Schultz, R., and Herz, A. Aspects of opiate dependence in the myenteric plexus of the guinea-pig. Life Sci, 19:1117-1128, 1976.

Schultz, R., Wuster, M., Rubini, P., and Herz, A. Functional opiate receptors in the guinea-pig ileum: Their differentiation by means of selective tolerance development. J Pharmacol Exp Ther, 219:547-550, 1981.

Sharma, S.K., Klee, W.A., and Nirenberg, M. Dual regulation of adenylate cyclase accounts for narcotic dependence and tolerance. Proc Natl Acad Sci, USA, 72:3092-3096, 1975.

Stone, T.W. The effects of morphine and methionine-enkephalin on the release of purines from cerebral cortex slices of rats and mice. Br J Pharmacol, 74:171-176, 1981.

Tanaka, T., and Starke, K. Binding of ^{3}H-clonidine to an a-adrenoceptor in membranes of guinea-pig ileum. Naunyn-Schmiedebergs Arch Pharmacol, 309:207-215, 1979.

Tsou, J., Louie, G., and Way, E.L. Manifestations of gut opiate withdrawal contracture and its blockade by capsaicin. Eur J Pharmacol, 81:377-383, 1982.

Tucker, J.F., Plant, N.T., von Uexkull, A., and Collier, H.O.J. Inhibition by adenosine analogs of opiate withdrawal effects. In: Harris, L.S., ed. Problems of Drug Dependence, 1983. National Institute on Drug Abuse Research Monograph 49. DHHS Pub. No. (ADM) 84-1316. In press. pp. 85-91.

van Calker, D., Muller, M., and Hamprecht, B. Adenosine regulates via two different types of receptors, the accumulation of cyclic AMP in cultured brain cells. J Neurochem, 33:999-1005, 1979.

van der Laan, J.W. Potentiation of jumping in precipitated morphine withdrawal by alpha$_2$-agonists: Adrenergic and dopaminergic mechanisms. International Narcotic Research Conference, Garmisch Partenkirchen, 1983. Abstract.

Villarreal, J.E., Martinez, J.N., and Castro, A. Validation of a new procedure to study narcotic dependence in the isolated guinea-pig ileum. In: Harris, L.S., ed. Problems of Drug Dependence, 1977. Washington, D.C.: National Academy of Sciences, 1977. pp. 305-314.

Wuster, M., Costa, T., and Gramsch, C.H. Uncoupling of receptors is essential for opiate induced desensitization (tolerance) in neuroblastoma x glioma hybrid cell NG 108-15. Life Sci, 33:341-345, 1983.

ACKNOWLEDGEMENT

The Committee on Problems of Drug Dependence, Inc., provided financial support.

AUTHORS

The late Harry O.J. Collier, B.A., Ph.D., Sc.D., F.I.Biol.
John F. Tucker, B.Sc., Ph.D.
Department of Pharmacology, Chelsea College, University of London, Manresa Road, London, SW3 6LX, U.K.

Biochemical Reactions Between Opiate Receptor Binding and Inhibition of Neurotransmission

Doris H. Clouet and Norifumi Yonehara

An account of the mechanisms by which opiate tolerance develops at the molecular level should begin with two caveats: there is no reason to assume (1) that all opioids act through the same mechanisms in all neural tissues (although a general response of a depression of neuronal firing when an opioid is applied to a cell suggests a commonality of mechanisms) or (2) that all subtypes of opioids produce the same states of biochemical tolerance (the lack of cross-tolerance among the different subtypes suggests that there are differences in the tolerant state).

One aspect of this review will be to note similarities and differences in the molecular events leading to tolerance among opioid subtypes and also among various nervous tissues. The studies from this laboratory have been carried out exclusively in the rat nigrostriatal system, both because the relationship between behavior and the dopaminergic system has been examined rigorously and because opiate receptors and endogenous opioids have a relatively enriched distribution in rat striatum. In the nigrostriatal dopaminergic(DA) pathways, the cell bodies, located in the substantia nigra, have long axons with extensive terminal arborization in the caudate nucleus of the striatum. The very numerous nerve terminals make synapses with GABA, acetylcholine and probably enkephalin-containing neurons, leading to the presence of large numbers of pre- and postsynaptic DA-responsive neurons. Important neurochemical effects induced by acute or chronic opioid treatment that have been found in neuronal cells in culture, in peripheral nerve, or in brain areas other than striatum, will be included in this review.

EFFECTS OF ACUTE OPIOID TREATMENT

The binding of an opioid agonist to a presynaptic receptor on the DA terminal leads to a sequence of biochemical events that are disrupted by the administration of an opioid. In table 1, some of the biochemical steps between opiate receptor binding and impulse transport between striatal neurons are listed, together with the effects produced at these steps by acute opioid administration. The inhibition

95

TABLE 1

Biochemical Reactions Between Opiate Receptor Binding and the Inhibition of Neurotransmission in Rat Striatum: Responses to Acute Opiate Administration

Biochemical Step	Responses
Binding of Ligand to Receptor	* Coupling of signal from binding to amplifier impaired (Childers et al. 1983)
Formation of cAMP GTP-binding	* Decreased GTP binding due to enhanced GTPase activity (Koski and Klee 1981; Parenti et al. 1983)
Adenylate cyclase	* Inhibition of adenylate cyclase (Collier and Roy 1974; Sharma et al. 1977; Barchfeld et al. 1982; Gentleman et al. 1983)
Stimulation by DA	* DA binding inhibited (Gentleman et al. 1983) * Levels of cAMP and cyclase activity in striatum back to normal by 120 minutes (Clouet et al. 1975).

Ion Fluxes
  Influx of K+, Ca++
  Efflux of Na+
  Depolarization
	Retention of intraterminal Ca++ and increased Ca++ dep. K+ conductance (North and Williams 1983)
	Hyperpolarization and inhibition of firing of most neurons (Zieglgansberger and Fry 1978)
	* Increased firing of nigrostriatal DA neurons (Iwatsubo and Clouet 1977)

Protein Phosphorylation	* Increased phosphorylation of some membrane proteins (Williams & Clouet 1982) * Increases in calmodulin-Ca++ dep. protkinase activity (phosphorylation of tyrosine hydroxylase, Ca++ATPase, etc.) (Williams and Clouet 1982)
Calmodulin	* Movement from cytosol to membranes increased (Clouet and Williams 1982b) * Inhibition "in vitro" by opioids of Ca++- dep. kinase not due to interaction between calmodulin and opioid (Clouet et al. 1983)
Synthesis and Release of Neurotransmitters	Generally inhibited by opioids * DA biosynthesis increased (Clouet and Ratner 1970; Gauchy et al. 1973) * Delta inhibition of DA release (Wood et al. 1980; Yonehara and Clouet, in press)

*·Effect shown in rat striatum

of adenylate cyclase activity by an opiate was first reported by
Collier and Roy (1974), who found that prostaglandin-stimulated
adenylate cyclase activity was inhibited by morphine in brain homogenates. In neuroblastoma-glioma (NG) hybrid cells in culture, Klee
and his colleagues reported that DA-stimulated adenylate cyclase
activity was inhibited by β-endorphin (Sharma et al. 1977). Later,
the inhibition of cyclase was shown to be related to a destruction
of the GTP required in the coupling of opiate receptor and adenylate
cyclase by an increased GTPase activity induced by opioids (Koski
and Klee 1981). The same changes in DA-dependent adenylate cyclase
and GTPase activities have been found in rat striatal membranes
(Gentleman et al. 1983; Parenti et al. 1983). Both cyclase activity
and cAMP levels in striatum are restored to control levels 30 to 120
minutes after opiate administration (Clouet et al. 1975).

Ion fluxes change during the passage of a nerve impulse from neuron
to neuron: the influx of calcium ions and potassium ions is increased while the efflux of sodium ions is also increased. Opiate
treatment can produce a hyperpolarization that prevents subsequent
firing of the cell in most neuronal systems (Zieglgansberger and Fry
1978). The nigrostriatal DA system is one that is highly regulated
by both presynaptic and feedback controls, so that neuronal firing
is increased by opiates due to the inhibition of an inhibitory neuron
(Iwatsubo and Clouet 1977). Thus, there are opposing forces regulating DA release during acute opioid treatment, an increased propagation of the nerve impulse to the nerve terminals that promotes neurotransmitter release, and presynaptic opiate effects that promote
decreased neurotransmitter release. In many species (cat, mouse) DA
release in striatum is stronger than any presynaptic inhibitory
effect and opioids induce DA release (Chesselet et al. 1981; Wood et
al. 1980). In rats, the presynaptic inhibitory effect predominates
and there is no release of DA when opiopeptides or narcotic drugs
are administered (Yonehara and Clouet, in press). In these studies,
the delta opiopeptides had greater effect on DA turnover than the
mu opiopeptides.

The two "second messengers" are involved in opiate actions. The
formation of cAMP is decreased when an opioid is introduced into a
neuron, or a NG cell in culture, in an"in vitro" tissue preparation
or into an animal. All of the consequences of a limited cAMP supply
come into play, including decreased Ca++ influx into nerve terminals,
decreased phosphorylation by cAMP-dependent protein kinases, etc.
The role of the other "second messenger" calcium, in impulse conduc-
tion is well known. Other sites of calcium activity involve a number
of enzymes that are phosphorylated by Ca++/calmodulin-dependent protein kinases or Ca++/phospholipid-dependent protein kinases (Greengard 1978; Takai et al. 1979). We have found that the increased phosphorylation of striatal SPM proteins following the acute administration of an opioid had a protein pattern after gel electrophoresis
that was very similar to that produced by Ca++/calmodulin stimulation
of phosphorylation, in terms of increased radioactivity in certain
protein bands after phosphorylation with ATP[32] (Williams and Clouet
1982). We examined the levels and intracellular site of calmodulin
after opioid administration to see whether calmodulin availability

was the cause of the opioid-induced effect. Calmodulin is a Ca++ binding protein primarily localized in nervous tissue. While localized in the cytosol, it is relatively inactive. Its movement into membranes seems to be related to increased cellular activity in many forms: a capping of cell wall prior to endocytosis (Salisbury et al. 1981); an activation of the red cell calcium pump (Hinds et al.1978); and the binding of soluble proteins to membranes (Geisow and Burgoyne 1983). The acute administration of either etorphine or met-enkephalin to rats resulted in a significantly higher level (60-80% above control) of calmodulin in both striatal synaptic membranes and in synaptosomal cytosol, with the ratio of cytosolic to membranal calmodulin remaining at about 3:7 (Clouet and Williams 1982b). It is possible that the excess calmodulin was sequestered so effectively in control animals that it was not removed by homogenization in detergent, but was mobilized by increasing levels of Ca++ in the neurons. The acute effects of opioids in increasing the endogenous phosphorylation of striatal membrane proteins could be ascribed completely to the increased calmodulin available in the preparation to activate Ca++-calmodulin-dependent protein kinases found in SPM preparations.

EFFECTS OF CHRONIC OPIOID TREATMENT

A common consequence of repeated stimulation of many neurohormone receptors is a down-regulation that decreases the number of active receptors. Such a phenomenon has been demonstrated for the opiate receptor after chronic opioid exposure. Hippocampal slices incubated with d-ala^{2}d-leu^{5}enkephalin for 4 hours had decreased numbers of delta (d-ala^2,d-leu^{5}enkephalin) receptors, but no changes in the number of mu receptors (Dingledine et al. 1983). The NG hybrid cells and fetal brain cells exposed to opiates or opiopeptides similarly showed a down-regulation of opiate receptors (Lenoir et al. 1983; Wuster et al. 1983). The levels of enkephalins in the striatum seem to be fairly stable and resistant to change during opiate treatment when examined at time periods from five to 180 minutes after opioid treatment. It is possible that the response to opiate receptor occupation related to enkephalin biosynthesis may be dependent temporally on the initial binding of opiates to receptors rather than on the period of pharmacological responses. Enkephalin levels are, however, responsive to treatment with other types of neuroactive drugs. Striatal enkephalin levels are increased by the administration of either benzodiazepines or neuroleptics (Duka et al. 1980; Hong et al. 1978). Long-term chronic treatment of rats with opiates did decrease both leu- and met-enkephalin levels in the striatum (Przewlocki et al. 1979). The chronic administration of an opiate antagonist, naltrexone, to rats produced an up-regulation of both delta and kappa receptors (Zukin et al. 1982) (table 2).

Adenylate cyclase activity was normal in brain areas of opiate-tolerant animals (Clouet et al. 1975). The enzyme, however, was supersensitive to both DA (Clouet and Iwatsubo 1975) and to GTP (Parenti et al. 1983). The increase in GTPase activity found after acute opioid administration was no longer seen in tolerant tissues including striatal synaptic plasma membranes (Parenti et al. 1983). The large increases in rat striatal DA turnover produced by an initial dose of an opioid no longer occur as tolerance develops. The release of DA in

TABLE 2

Biochemical Reactions Between Opiate Receptor (O.R.) Binding and the Inhibition of Neurotransmission in Rat Striatum: Responses to Chronic Opiate Administration

Biochemical Step	Responses
Binding of Ligand to Receptor	Down-regulation of O.R. in hippocampus or NG cells (Parenti et al. 1982) Up-regulation of O.R. after chronic antagonist treatment (Zukin et al. 1982)
Formation of cAMP GTP binding Adenylate Cyclase Stimulation	* GTPase decrease (Parenti et al. 1983) * Basal activity normal * Supersensitivity to DA (Clouet and Iwatsubo 1975) * Supersensitivity to GTP (Parenti et al. 1983)
Ion Fluxes Influx of K+ Ca++ Efflux of Na+ Depolarization	* Ca++ fluxes normal * Some tolerance to hyperpolarization (Zeiglgansberger and Fry 1978)
Protein Phosphorylation	* Decreased phosphorylation of some membrane proteins (O'Callaghan et al. 1979)
Calmodulin	* Calmodulin in cytosol (Clouet and Williams 1982b) * Chronic trifluperazine blocked effect of morphine on calmodulin levels (Williams et al. in press)
Synthesis and Release of Neurotransmitters	Generally normal in tolerant tissue * No increase in DA turnover * DA-receptor supersensitivity (Parenti et al. 1983)

* Effect shown in rat striatum

areas other than rat striatum is no longer inhibited.

In the striatum of morphine-tolerant rats, the levels of endogenous phosphorylation of SPM proteins are greatly reduced (O'Callaghan et al. 1979). When separated by SDS-gel electrophoresis, the many specific protein bands in which phosphorylation is reduced by chronic opioid treatment are the same as those in which phosphorylation is increased by acute opioid treatment or by Ca++-calmodulin stimulation. To remedy the defect in phosphorylation, supplementation of the protein kinase assay with calmodulin was examined. In contrast to the situation in acutely treated animals, when calmodulin supplementation was able to restore phosphorylation, extra calmodulin was never able to restore the rates of phosphorylation to those in the striata of placebo-treated rats (Clouet and Williams 1982a). A transfer of calmodulin from membranal to cytosolic sites was also seen in rat striata from morphine-tolerant rats (Clouet and Williams 1982a).

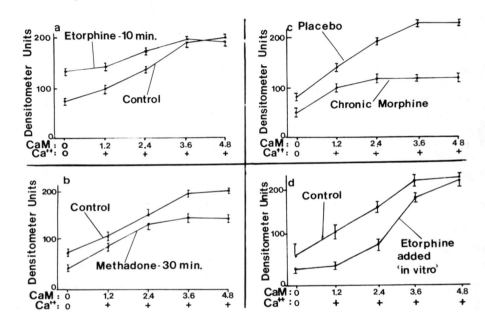

FIGURE 1. Effect of supplementation with calmodulin on the phosphorylation of striatal synaptic plasma membrane (SPM) proteins measured in densitometer units for autoradiographs.
Calmodulin (CaM) was added as units described in Clouet and Williams, 1982b. Optimal Ca++ levels were maintained in all assays except the zero control.
a= Acute etorphine vs. Saline-control; b= Acute methadone vs. Saline-control; c= Chronic morphine vs. Placebo pellets; d= Etorphine added to assay vs. Same preparation without drug.

100

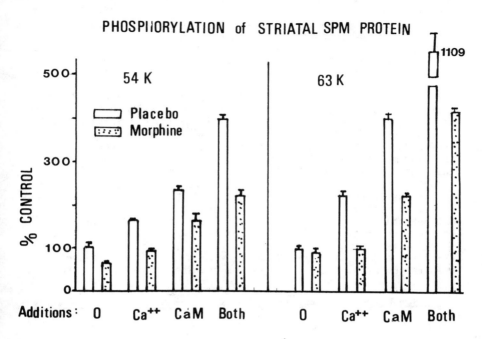

FIGURE 2.   Phosphorylation of two striatal SPM proteins.
Supplementation of striatal SPM proteins from morphine-tolerant (stippled) or control (clear) rats with Ca++ and/or CaM in assays of protein kinase activity.   The proteins have apparent M.W. in SDS-gel of 54 kilodaltons (left panel) or 63 kilodaltons (right panel).

The effect of calmodulin supplementation in the protein kinase assay is shown in figure 1.   As described above, control levels of total phosphate incorporated into protein can be brought to the increased levels found 10 minutes after the injection of etorphine by adding calmodulin (1a).   The decreased levels found 30 minutes after metha-done administration were not brought to control levels by adding calmodulin (1b), nor were the levels found in SPM proteins from mor-phine-tolerant rats (1c).   The effect of an opioid in reversing the inhibition of Ca++-calmodulin stimulation is shown in 1d.   It should be noted that different effects of calmodulin supplementation can be seen between individual protein bands (figure 2).   After SDS gel electrophoresis of SPM proteins from the striata of tolerant rats, a protein band with an apparent M.W. of 54 kilodaltons was increasing-ly phosphorylated with the addition of Ca++, calmodulin or both to the assay, maintaining a constant ratio with a sample from placebo-treated rats (left panel).   A protein with a M.W. of 63 kilodaltons was phosphorylated more in response to calmodulin than to Ca++, al-though the protein from placebo-treated rats responded to both co-factors (right panel).   Yamauchi and Fujisawa (1980) attributed the phosphorylation of the 63K protein to protein kinase III, that acts

on only two proteins in brain. One is believed to be a protein kinase
subunit. The band at 54 K is probably a mixture of proteins such as
a tubulin subunit, an adenylate cyclase subunit, etc. Four soluble
Ca++-calmodulin-dependent protein kinases have been found in rat
cerebral cortex (Yamauchi and Fujisawa 1980) and membranal kinases
are also activated by the same cofactors. These enzymes may be un-
equally affected by opioid treatment.

A phenomenon that we noted several years ago is a reversal of the
stimulation of protein kinase activity by Ca++-calmodulin by adding
opioids to the assay tubes (Clouet et al. 1978). Using a rapid flow
multi-mixer to conduct short-time assays of protein kinase activity,
we found that the inhibitory effect of opioids was apparent in less
than 200 milliseconds (Clouet and Williams 1982a). The possibility
that opioids, like neuroleptics, interact directly with calmodulin,
removing it from the enzyme assay, was examined. The stimulation of
endogenous phosphorylation of striatal SPM proteins by Ca++-calmodu-
lin is inhibited by etorphine, methadone, beta-endorphin and d-ala^2
met enkephalin with K_is of 5×10^{-7}M (Clouet et al. 1983) (figure 3).
The constant ratio for inhibition of calmodulin to opioid suggested a
direct interaction. As shown in figure 1c, additional calmodulin can
reverse the opioid effect. However, when a calmodulin-free purified
preparation of phosphodiesterase was examined in the same paradigm,

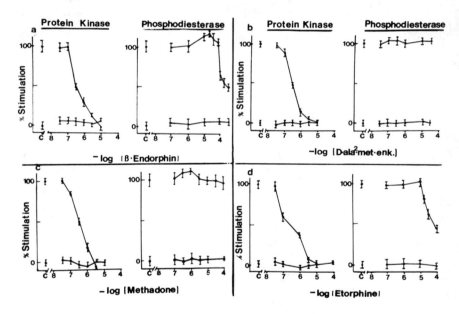

FIGURE 3. The effect of opioids on CaM-dependent enzyme activity
The basal (lower curves) and Ca++-CaM stimulated (upper curves)
activity of protein kinases in striatal SPM preparations and of a
purified phosphodiesterase are shown. The dose-dependent effects of
(a) beta-endorphin, (b) d-ala^{2}met enkephalin, (c) methadone and (d)
etorphine are depicted as inhibition of stimulated enzyme activity.

stimulated phosphodiesterase activity was inhibited by beta-endorphin and etorphine with K_is of 2×10^{-4}M and not inhibited by methadone or d-ala^{2}met enkephalin. Thus, a direct interaction of calmodulin and opioids may be ruled out as obligatory for this "in vitro" inhibition of Ca++-calmodulin dependent enzyme, although it may play a role in some effects of beta-endorphin. The importance of changes in the state of phosphorylation of proteins, particularly enzymes, may be assessed by tentatively identifying some of the proteins in a striatal SPM preparation that are phosphorylated by Ca++-calmodulin-dependent protein kinases, and are affected by opioid treatment. Needless to say, a protein can not be identified by M.W. in SDS gel alone, but a consensus is beginning to be formed concerning certain brain proteins (table 3). Some protein kinases are relatively non specific as to substrate preference (e.g., protein kinase II (table 3). Others like protein kinase III have only two substrates that seem to be subunits of another protein kinase (Yamauchi and Fujisawa 1980). In depolarized neurons or in synaptosomal preparations from depolarized cells, Ca++ uptake into the cell stimulated both neurotransmitter release and phosphorylation of two proteins in synaptic vesicles (DeLorenzo et al. 1979). These proteins of 55 and 62K M.W. are believed to participate in the endocytotic process. Synapsin I, a neuron-specific protein, also participates

TABLE 3

Molecular weights and possible identities of brain proteins of their subunits that are phosphorylated by Ca++-calmodulin dependent protein kinases

Approximate M.W.	Protein	References
**185	Clathrin	A
96	Ca++ATPase SU	B
** 87-82	Synapsin I	B
74	Protein Kinase SU	C
68	Neurofilament SU	B
***63	Protein kinase	A
62	Synaptic vesicle SU	C
60	Tyrosine hydroxylase	B
55	Synaptic vesicle protein	C
54	Adenylate cyclase SU	D
**52	Tublin SU	D
50	Protein kinase SU	A
**45	(Substrate)	A
**37	"	A
*21	"	A
18	Myelin basic protein	B
**17		A
16.5	GABA modulin	B
***15		A
14	Myeline basic protein	B

Proteins may be phosphorylated by Ca++-calmodulin-dependent protein kinases I (*), II (**) or III (***) SU=Subunit. References are to: A= Yamauchi and Fujisawa 1980; B= Nestler and Greengard 1983; C= DeLorenzo et al. 1979; D= Burke and DeLorenzo 1981.

in endocytosis since its phosphorylation decreases its affinity to proteins on the outer wall of the vesicles (Forn and Greengard 1976). The
total amount of Synapsin I is regulated by various hormones, and also
by morphine (Nestler and Greengard 1983). Also, in depolarized neurons,
the biosynthesis of neurotransmitter is accelerated by the activation
of tyrosine hydroxylase through a Ca++-calmodulin-dependent process
(Mestikawy et al. 1983). The phosphorylation of GABAmodulin decreases
its affinity for the GABA receptor leaving the receptor free to bind
GABA (Wise et al. 1983).

Interconnections in the striatum between the DA system and other neurotransmitter systems make it possible for opioid effects to be extended to other systems. Both morphine and β-endorphin injections into rat
striatum cause a decreased turnover of GABA in the caudate nucleus and
an increased turnover in the globus pallidus (Moroni et al. 1979).
Since an activation of caudate DA neurons by electrical stimulation or
by apomorphine does not change GABA turnover, it seems that enkephalinergic neurons may impinge directly on GABA cells (Oertel et al. 1983).
Similarly, a direct correlation between opioid effects on cholinergic
neurons and on DA in the striatum has been ruled out by studies in
which acetylcholine turnover and binding were not affected by opioid
treatment (Schurr et al. 1983). In other areas of the central and
peripheral nervous system opioid effects on GABA and acetylcholine
have been shown.

CONCLUSIONS

In the striatum a variety of responses to chronic opioid exposure have
been discovered. Some phenomena are merely reversals of activations
or inhibitions that were produced as part of the response to the initial exposure to the opioid; e.g., the reversal of GTPase activation
in samples from tolerant rats, thereby increasing the GTP supply for
opiate receptor binding and adenylate cyclase activation. Other molecular effects of chronic opioid exposure involve changes in the sensitivity of receptors; e.g., the down- and up- regulation of opiate
receptors in response to chronic treatment with opioid agonists or
antagonists, respectively; or the supersensitivity of DA receptors to
DA in tolerant rat striatum.

The reversal during tolerance to the initial responses to opioid treatment in the phosphorylation of striatal SPM proteins does not seem to
be simple, since the acute effects are reversed by the addition of
calmodulin to the assay, suggesting a lack of active calmodulin, while
the lack of complete activity after supplementation of the assay with
calmodulin and Ca++ in assays of protein kinase activity in striatal
samples from tolerant animals suggests a decreased amount of active
enzymes. Calmodulin is active as a Ca++ cofactor when at least two
out of four Ca++ binding sites are occupied by Ca++. The same Ca++
binding is required for calmodulin to be localized on the inner surface
of neuronal membranes or the outer side of synaptic vesicles (Means
and Dedman 1980). Thus, the availability of Ca++ regulates calmodulin
effectiveness and determines its intracellular site to some extent. The

movement of calmodulin to SPM after acute opioid treatment and to the cytosol during chronic treatment is probably a consequence of opioid effects on the levels and localization of Ca++.

We conclude, in common with other participants in this symposium, that the biochemical mechanisms of opiate tolerance are diverse. The biochemical effects produced by an initial exposure of nervous tissue to opioids are largely specific to each tissue, although a common response is inhibition of neurotransmission. Neurochemical changes following chronic opioid exposure tend to result in a diminution of disturbance of neuronal cell function with succeeding doses of drug by an available mechanism (change in number or sensitivity of receptors, in activation or inhibition of biosynthetic enzymes or in cellular localization of cofactors, etc.). Thus, the usual ways in which biochemical events are regulated are evoked during the development of tolerance to enable the nervous system to limit the aberrations produced by opioid exposure. It is possible that in largely unexplored systems psychic dependence may result from a series of biochemical responses tending to limit the wide mood swings due to sequential euphoria and withdrawal.

REFERENCES

Barchfeld, C.C. Maassen, F.A. and Medzihradsky, F. Receptor-related interactions of opiates with PGE-induced adenylate cyclase in brain. Life Sci 31:1661-1665, 1982
Burke, B.E. and DeLorenzo, R.J. Ca++ and calmodulin-stimulated endogenous phosphorylation of neurotubulin. Proc Natl Acad Sci 78: 991-995, 1981.
Chesselet, M.F. Cheramy, A. Reisine, T.D. and Glowinski, J. Morphine and delta opiate agonists locally stimulate in vivo dopamine release in rat caudate nucleus. Nature 291:320-322, 1981.
Childers, S.R. Lambert, S.M. and LaRiviere, G. Selective alterations in guanine nucleotide regulation of opiate receptor binding and coupling with adenylate cyclase. Life Sci 33:215-218, 1983.
Clouet, D.H. and Iwatsubo, K. Dopamine-sensitive adenylate cyclase of the caudate nucleus of rats treated with morphine. Life Sci 17: 35-40, 1975.
Clouet, D.H. and Ratner, M. Catecholamine biosynthesis in the brains of rats treated with morphine. Science 168:854-856, 1970.
Clouet, D.H. and Williams, N. The role of calmodulin in opioid-induced changes in the phosphorylation of rat striatal synaptic membrane proteins. Neurochem Res 7:1135-1148, 1982a.
Clouet, D.H. and Williams, N. The effect of opioids on striatal calmodulin levels. Life Sci 31: 2283-2286, 1982b.
Clouet, D.H. Gold, G.J. and Iwatsubo, K. Effects of narcotic analgesic drugs on the cyclic AMP- adenylate cyclase system in rat brain. Br J Pharmac 54: 541-548, 1975.
Clouet, D.H. Williams, N. and Yonehara, N. Is a calmodulin-opiopeptide interaction related to the mechanism of opioid action? Life Sci 33:727-730, 1983.

Clouet, D.H., O'Callaghan, J.P. and Williams, N. The effect of opiates on calcium-stimulated phosphorylation of synaptic plasma membrane proteins in intact synaptosomes from rat striatum. In: VanRee, J and Terenius, L.eds. Characteristics and Functions of Opioids, Amsterdam, North-Holland, 1978, pp. 351-352.

Collier, H.O.J., and Roy, A.C. Morphine-like drugs inhibit the stimulation by E prostaglandins of cyclic AMP formation by rat brain homogenate. Nature 248:24-27, 1974.

DeLorenzo, R.J. Freedman, S.D. Yohe, W.B. and Maurer, S.C. Stimulation of Ca++-dependent neurotransmitter release and presynaptic nerve terminal protein phosphorylation by calmodulin and a calmodulin-like protein isolated from synaptic vesicles. Proc Natl Acad Sci 76:1838-1842, 1979.

Dingledine, R. Valentino, R.J. Bostock, E. King, M.E. and Chang, K-J. Down regulation of delta but not mu opioid receptors in hippocampal slice associated with loss of physiological response. Life Sci 33: 333-336, 1983.

Duka, T., Wuster, M., and Herz, A. Benzodiazepines modulate striatal enkephalin levels via a GABAergic mechanism. Life Sci 26:771-776, 1980.

Forn, J. and Greengard, P. Regulation by lipolytic and antilipolytic compounds of the phosphorylation of specific proteins in isolated intact fat cells. Arch Biochem Biophys 176(2): 721-733, 1976.

Gauchy, C. Agid, Y. Glowinski, J. and Cheramy, A. Acute effects of morphine on dopamine synthesis and release and tyrosine metabolism in the rat striatum. Eur J Pharmacol 22:311-319, 1973.

Geisow, M.J. and Burgoyne, R.D. Recruitment of cytosolic proteins to a secretory granule membrane depends on Ca++-calmodulin. Nature 301: 432-435, 1983.

Gentleman, S. Parenti, M. Neff, N.H. and Pert, C.B. Inhibition of dopamine-activated adenylate cyclase and dopamine binding by opiate receptors in rat striatum. Cell Mol Biol 3:17-26, 1983.

Greengard, P. Phosphorylated proteins as physiological effectors. Science 199:146-152, 1978.

Hinds, T.R. Larsen, F.L. and Vincenzi, F.F. Plasma membrane Ca^{2+} transport: Stimulation of soluble proteins. Biochem Res Commun 81(2): 455-61, 1978.

Hong, J.S. Yang, H-Y.T. Fratta, W. and Costa, E. Rat striatal methionine-enkephalin content after chronic treatment with cataleptogenic and non-cataleptogenic antischizophrenic drugs. J Pharm Exp Therap 202: 141-147, 1978

Iwatsubo, D. and Clouet, D.H. Effects of morphine and haloperidol on the electrical activity of rat nigrostriatal neurons. J Pharm Exp Therap 202: 429-436, 1977.

Koski, G. and Klee, W.A. Opiates inhibit adenylate cyclase by stimulating GTP hydrolysis. Proc Natl Acad Sci 78: 4185-4189, 1981

Lenoir, D. Barg, J. and Simantov, R. Down regulation of opiate receptors in serum-free cultures of aggregating fetal brain cells. Life Sci 33: 337-340, 1983.

Means, A.R. and Dedman, J.R. Calmodulin-an intracellular calcium receptor. Nature 285: 73-77, 1980.

Mestikawy, S.El., Glowinski, J. and Hamon, M. Tyrosine hydroxylase activation in depolarized dopaminergic terminals-involvement of Ca++ dependent phosphorylation. Nature 302: 830-832, 1983.

Moroni, F. Peralta, E. Cheney, D.L. and Costa, E. On the regulation of gamma aminobutyric acid neurons in caudatus, pallidus and nigra. Effects of opioids and dopamine agonists. J Pharm Exp Therap 208: 190-194, 1979.

Nestler, E.J. and Greengard, P. Protein phosphorylation in the brain. Nature 305: 583-588, 1983.

North, R.A. and Williams, J.T. Opiate activation of potassium conductance inhibits calcium action potential in rat locus coeruleus. Br J Pharm 80: 225-228, 1983

O'Callaghan, J.P., Williams, N. and Clouet, D.H. The effect of morphine on the endogenous phosphorylation of synaptic plasma membrane proteins of the rat. J Pharm Exp Therap 208: 96-106, 1979

Oertel, W. Riethmuller, G. Mugnaini, E. Schmechel, D.E. Weindl, A. Gramsch, E. and Herz, A. Opioid peptide like immunoreactivity localized in GABAergic neurons of rat neostriatum and central amygdaloid nucleus. Life Sci 33: 73-76, 1983

Parenti, M. Gentleman, S. Olianas, M.C. and Neff, N.H. The dopamine receptor adenylate cyclase complex: Evidence for a post recognition site involvement for the development of supersensitivity. Neurochem Res 7:115-124, 1982.

Parenti, M. Gazzotti, G. Tirone, F. and Groppetti, A. Opiate tolerance and dependence is associated with a decreased activity of GTPase in rat striatal membranes. Life Sci 33: 345-348, 1983

Przewlocki, R. Hollt, V. Duka, T. Kleber, G. Gramsch, C. Haarmann, I. and Herz, A. Long time morphine treatment decreases endorphin levels in rat brain and pituitary. Brain Res 174: 357-361, 1979

Salisbury, J.L. Condeelis, J.S. Maihle, N.J. and Satir, P. Calmodulin localization during capping and receptor-mediated endocytosis. Nature 294: 163-166, 1981

Sharma, S.K. Klee, W.A. and Nirenberg, M. Endorphin from pituitary inhibits cyclic AMP formation in homogenates of neuroblastoma x glioma hybrid cells. Nature 265: 362-363, 1977

Schurr, A. Rigor, B.M. Strong, R. and Gottesfeld, A. The cholinergic system in rat striatum during morphine tolerance and dependence Life Sci 33: 2521-2525, 1983.

Takai, Y. Kishimoto, A. Iwasa, Y. Kawahara, Y. Mori, T. and Nishizuka, Y. Calcium-dependent activation of a multifunctional protein kinase by membrane phospholipids. J Biol Chem 254: 3692-3695, 1979.

Williams, N. and Clouet, D.H. The effect of acute opioid administration on the phosphorylation of rat striatal membrane proteins. J Pharmacol Exp Therap 220: 278-286, 1982.

Williams, N. Yonehara, N. and Clouet, D.H. Synergistic effect of trifluoroperazine on analgesia and turnover of dopamine responses induced by morphine in rats. Ann N Y Acad Sci (in press).

Wise, B.C. Guidotti, A. and Costa, E. Phosphorylation induces a decrease in the biological activity of the protein inhibitor (GABA-modulin) of gamma-aminobutyric acid binding sites. Proc Natl Acad Sci 80: 880-890, 1983.

Wood, P.L. Stotland, M. Richard, J.W. and Rackham, A. Actions of
mu, kappa, sigma, delta and agonist/antagonist opiates on striatal
dopamine function. J Pharmacol Exp Therap 215:697-703, 1980.

Wuster, M., Costa, T. and Gramsch, Ch. Uncoupling of receptors is
essential for opiate-induced desensitization (tolerance) in
neuroblastoma x glioma hybrid cells:NG 108-15. Life Sci 33:341-
344, 1983.

Yamauchi, T. and Fujisawa, H. Evidence for the distinct forms of
calmodulin-dependent protein kinases from rat brain. FEBS Lett
116: 141-144, 1980.

Yonehara, N. and Clouet, D.H. The effects of delta and mu opiopeptides on the turnover and release of dopamine in rat striatum.
J Pharmacol Exp Therap (in press).

Zieglgansberger, W. and Fry, J.P. In: Developments in Opiate Research.
Herz, A. ed. New York: Marcel Dekker, 1978, pp 192-299.

Zukin, R.S. Sugarman, J.R. Fitz-Syage, M. Gardner, E.L, Zukin, S.R.
and Gintzler, A.R. Naloxone-induced opiate receptor supersensitivity. Brain Res 245:285-297, 1982.

ACKNOWLEDGEMENT

The experimental work was supported in part by Research Grant DA00087
from the National Institute on Drug Abuse.

AUTHORS

Doris H. Clouet, Ph.D.
New York State Division of Substance Abuse
Services Research Laboratory
80 Hanson Place
Brooklyn, New York 11217 and
Professor of Psychiatry
Downstate Medical Center
Brooklyn, N.Y. 11203

Norifumi Yonehara, Ph.D.
New York State Division of Substance Abuse
Services Research Laboratory
80 Hanson Place
Brooklyn, New York 11217
now at
Osaka University School of Medicine
Osaka, Japan

The Role of Adenyl Cyclase in Opiate Tolerance and Dependence

Werner A. Klee, Graeme Milligan, William F. Simonds, and Bruno Tocque

The topic of this paper is one which was very important to H.O.J. Collier because it concerns an area of research in which he and his colleagues made pioneering contributions. It was with great sadness that I delivered it at a symposium dedicated to his memory rather than in his presence as originally planned. With Harry Collier's death, some of us have lost a good friend, and all of us have lost a clarifying and civilizing influence in our work. Harry Collier's contributions to the understanding of the relationships between the acute and chronic actions of opiates and the production of cyclic AMP are relatively well known and will be referred to in the body of this paper. His contributions to the understanding of the mechanisms of drug receptor action in general go much deeper and are, perhaps, even more profound and original. In 1972, at the International Pharmacology Congress in San Francisco, he predicted the existence of the endogenous opiates, long before most of the rest of us were thinking in such terms: "... the receptor for a foreign drug is really the receptor for a humoral substance, with which the foreign molecule also interacts. .... we do not yet know the natural function of the macromolecule with which morphine specifically interacts." (Collier 1973). In only 3 years the discovery of the enkephalins proved the correctness of this speculation (Hughes et al. 1975). If we were all to emulate the precision in thought and in language that Harry Collier demanded so successfully of himself, our studies of tolerance and dependence would undoubtedly progress much faster.

One well-established biochemical mechanism by which opiates exert their acute effects is by inhibition of adenylate cyclase in neuronal cell membranes. This action of opiates was first described by Collier and Roy (1974), and has since been demonstrated in a variety of systems including both cultured cells (Sharma et al. 1975), and, more recently, brain membranes (Wilkening et al. 1976; Law et al. 1981; Neff et al. 1981; Cooper et al. 1982). The immediate result of opiate-mediated inhibition of adenylate cyclase is a decrease in cellular cAMP levels. As a direct consequence of this decrease, the activity of cAMP-dependent protein kinase is diminished, so that many cellular proteins whose phosphorylation is effected by this kinase will remain unphosphorylated. Thus, opiate receptor occupancy is the first step in a cascade of processes leading to a panoply of effects on neuronal metabolism and excitability. The existence of such a cascade provides a powerful amplification mechanism in terms both of amounts and of rates.

A mechanism for tolerance and dependence is implicit in the above formulation of acute opiate actions, as Collier and Roy realized in their very first publication on the subject in 1974. Because opiates inhibit adenylate cyclase and lower cAMP levels in their acute actions, the homeostatic response of the cell to the chronic presence of opiates might well be to see to it that adenylate cyclase activity levels increase. Evidence that such a response actually occurs in neuroblastoma x glioma hybrid, NG 108-15, cells was supplied by the work of Sharma et al. (1975b) and of Traber et al. (1975). The NG 108-15 cell line is richly endowed with opiate receptors (Klee and Nirenberg 1974), and the adenylate cyclase activity of such cells is inhibited by up to about 50% when these receptors are occupied by opiate agonists (Sharma et al. 1975a). After culture of these cells for 12 or more hours in the presence of opiate agonists such as morphine (Sharma et al. 1975b) or enkephalin (Lampert et al. 1976), adenylate cyclase activity is increased. In these experiments enzyme activity was measured in the presence of naloxone to insure reversal of inhibition by any opiates remaining in the membranes of the washed cells. Interestingly, the increase in activity found after culture in the presence of morphine was such that, even though functional opiate receptors are present in undiminished amount, cAMP levels in the cells were normal. Thus, the cells had become tolerant to morphine, because they exhibited normal metabolism, growth, and morphology in the presence of amounts of morphine which greatly diminish the cAMP levels of control cells. They are also dependent upon morphine in the sense that addition of naloxone causes a dramatic rise in cAMP levels, a biochemical analogy of the withdrawal syndrome.

The increased levels of adenylate cyclase activity of chronically exposed cells are, in large part, reflections of changes in the state of the enzyme rather than in its amount. Thus, when the adenylate cyclase activities of control and opiate-treated cell membranes are compared in the presence of sodium fluoride, or of nonhydrolyzable GTP analogues, no differences are found (Sharma et al. 1977). Because much, if not all, of the regulatory apparatus for controlling adenylate cyclase activity is completely activated under these conditions, changed levels of the catalytic component of the enzyme should have resulted in changes in activity here too. Furthermore, it was found that simultaneous treatment of the cells with morphine and the protein synthesis inhibitor, cycloheximide, still allows the expression of opiate-induced increases in adenylate cyclase activity. The detailed nature of the regulatory changes taking place is an intriguing mystery, awaiting solution. Some experiments aimed at clarifying this mechanism will be reported below.

Important advances in the understanding of the mechanisms of receptor control of adenylate cyclase activity have been made in the past few years. It had been known since the work of Rodbell et al. (1971), that the presence of GTP is essential for hormone stimulation of adenylate cyclase. It is now clear that the GTP binding protein N_s (also called G_s or G/F), which is the substrate for cholera toxin catalyzed ADP-ribosylation, is the mediator of such stimulation (Ross and Gilman 1980). Agonists coupled to the appropriate receptors, such as β- adrenergic and glucagon, for example, facilitate the interaction of GTP and N_s, and this complex (or a component of it) activates the catalytic subunit of adenylate cyclase. A second GTP binding protein N_i (sometimes called G_i) mediates receptor-coupled inhibition of the enzyme. This protein is the substrate for pertussis toxin catalyzed ADP-ribosylation, a process which greately diminishes the ability of inhibitory hormones, including opiates, to attenuate adenylate cyclase activity (Katada and Ui 1979, 1982a, 1982b). These recent advances have laid the foundation for a deeper understanding of opiate actions at the molecular level.

Among the earliest observations made with NG 108-15 membranes was the lack of opiate inhibition when measured in the presence of the nonhydrolyzable GTP analogue, GppNHp (Sharma et al. 1975a). These observations have recently been repeated with highly purified membranes. In such a system it was also possible to show that opiate inhibition of adenylate cyclase is actually the reversal of GTP stimulation. Such observations led to the inference that GTP hydrolysis is a step necessary for opiate inhibition of adenylate cyclase. Cassel and Selinger (1977) had already demonstrated that a low K_m-GTPase is associated with the adenylate cyclase of turkey erythrocyte membranes. Using their methodology, Koski and Klee (1981) showed that opiates stimulate a low K_m-GTPase in NG 108-15 membranes. The GTPase stimulation is receptor mediated since it is blocked by naloxone, is observed only in cells known to posess opiate receptors, and the potencies of a series of opiate-stimulators of GTPase match exactly the same drugs inhibition of adenylate cyclase. Perhaps more tellingly, even the efficacies (intrinsic or maximal activities) of the opiates in the two types of assay match very well (Koski et al. 1982). Thus, the relative amounts of GTPase stimulation and of adenylate cyclase inhibition observed at saturating concentrations of opiates are very close to the same over the range from apparently full agonists such as dalamid (D-Ala[2], Met[5] - enkephalin amide) to the pure antagonist, naloxone (Table 1).

TABLE 1

Relative Efficacies of Opiates as Inhibitors of Adenylate Cyclase and as Stimulators of GTPase in NG 108-15 Membranes*

OPIATE	ADENYLATE CYCLASE	GTPase
Dalamid	100	100
Etorphine	99	95
Morphine	79	60
Levorphanol	79	67
Diprenorphine	61	52
Nalorphine	50	23
Buprenorphine	35	18
Naltrexone	21	12
Naloxone	0	0

*Efficacy was determined by measuring the inhibition of adenylate cyclase, or stimulation of GTPase produced by each opiate at concentrations high enough to be saturating. Data are expressed relative to those of dalamid. Linear regression analysis of the data results in a correlation coefficient of 0.94. Taken from Koski et al. (1982).

Opiate inhibition of adenylate cyclase requires the presence of both Na^+ and GTP as first shown by Blume et al. (1971). Importantly therefore, opiate stimulation of GTPase activity was also found to exhibit a similarly absolute requirement for Na^+ (Table 2). Surprisingly, perhaps, the effect of Na^+ is to inhibit GTPase (in the presence of Mg^{2+}) and opiates simply reverse this inhibition. These data are strongly supportive of the proposal that opiate inhibition of adenylate cyclase is the direct result of its stimulation of a GTPase component of the adenylate cyclase complex. Thus, in diagramatic fashion: adenylate cyclase shuttles between two states, an active one with bound GTP, and an inactive one with bound GDP. Stimulatory receptors facilitate exchange of GTP for bound GDP, whereas inhibitory

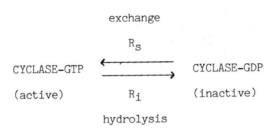

exchange

R_s

CYCLASE-GTP $\longleftarrow$ CYCLASE-GDP

(active) $\xrightarrow{\quad\quad}$ (inactive)

R_i

hydrolysis

receptors, including those for opiates, stimulate the GTPase activity which converts GTP, bound to the adenylate cyclase-N protein complex, to GDP.

TABLE 2

Effects of Na^+ and Mg^{2+} on Basal and Dalamid Stimulated GTPase in NG 108-15 Membranes*

Salt Added	GTPase Activity	
	Basal	1 μM Dalamid
none	64.8 ± 2.5	67.9 ± 3.4
100mM NaCl	63.1 ± 2.5	66.0 ± 3.6
5mM $MgCl_2$	51.0 ± 2.5	63.0 ± 0.7
100mM NaCl + 5mM $MgCl_2$	30.0 ± 1.5	64.8 ± 4.4

*GTPase is expressed as pmols of GTP hydrolyzed/min/mg protein. Data are means ± S.E. for triplicate determinations. Taken from Koski et al. (1982).

Because GTPase is an essential part of the adenylate cyclase mechanism and opiates stimulate its activity, it was natural to wonder whether chronic exposure of cells to opiates modifies the activity of the enzyme. Answering this question experimentally has been a surprisingly difficult undertaking because of the unfortunate fact that optimum conditions for the study of the GTPase require a relatively highly purified membrane. However, the stimulatory effects of opiate pretreatment upon adenylate cyclase activity are largely lost during the long times required to prepare such membranes. Table 3 shows data obtained with membranes prepared from control and opiate-treated NG 108-15 cells using a rapid preparative procedure to preserve some of the opiate-induced increase in adenylate cyclase activity. As shown in the table, treatment of cells with etorphine led to both increased adenylate cyclase activity and decreased GTPase activity. Neither of the structurally related partial agonists tested affected either enzyme activity. These data suggest that the chronic effects of opiates include a modification of N_i which lowers its GTPase activity in a manner analogous to that of pertussis toxin (Klee et al. 1984). Interestingly, only relatively pure agonists affect either adenylate cyclase or GTPase activities.

113

TABLE 3

Chronic Opiate Effects on Adenylate Cyclase and GTPase*

	Adenylate Cyclase	GTPase
Control	100 + 4	100 + 3
Etorphine	132 + 7	84 + 9
Diprenorphine	111 + 6	98 + 8
Buprenorphine	111 + 13	112 + 17

*NG 108-15 cells were cultured for 48 hours in the presence of 1 μ M drug. Membrane suspensions were assayed in the presence of 100 μ M naloxone. Data are expressed as per cent of control + S.E. of quadruplicate determinations.

Until recently, little attention has been paid to the quantitation of opiate agonist efficacy or to the question of the relationship between efficacy in acute experiments and the ability of a substance to produce tolerance and dependence. However, the precipitation of abstinence by partial agonists such as nalorphine, for example, clearly indicates a need for a more quantitative approach to the question. As already seen in Table 1, measurements of adenylate cyclase inhibition (or GTPase stimulation) by opiates at saturating concentrations of drug provide a reliable quantitative index of agonist efficacy. Because of the greater precision of adenylate cyclase assays, we prefer to base efficacy determinations on them. One immediately striking aspect of the data presented in Table 1 is that morphine is clearly a partial agonist, with less than 80% the efficacy of dalamid. In assessing the significance of this fact, it is important to remember that efficacy is defined so as to be independent of potency (the concentrations at which drugs bind to receptors or exert other actions) since it is based upon measurements made at saturating levels of the drugs.

Because morphine is a partial, rather than full, opiate agonist, much of the literature in which it was used as the inducer of tolerance and dependence may need to be reexamined. As a case in point, consider the effects of chronic opiate treatment upon receptor numbers. It had been quite well established that chronic morphine treatment has no measureable effect upon receptor numbers or specificity, both in animals (Klee and Streaty 1974; Hollt et al. 1975) and in NG 108-15 cells (Sharma et al. 1975a; Simantov et al. 1982). Recently it has become clear that agents such as the

114

enkephalins and etorphine effect dramatic decreases in the number of opiate receptors present in neuroblastoma cells (Simantov et al. 1982) and that chronic naloxone administration can result in an increased number of opiate receptors in rat brain (Zukin, this volume). Clearly, opiate receptor numbers can be regulated by the prolonged presence of some agonists but not by others. We asked whether there is a relationship between agonist efficacy and receptor down-regulation in NG 108-15 cells by exposing them to each of a series of opiates of defined efficacy for 48 hours and subsequently measuring receptor numbers. Following the opiate treatment, the cells were washed and homogenized and the membranes were washed further after exposure to GppNHp and Na^+ at 37° in order to maximize dissociation of the bound opiate. Receptor numbers were then measured by studying $^3[H]$-dalamid binding over a range of concentrations between 1 and 40 nM. Scatchard analysis of the data gave the results listed in Table 4. The results show that opiates with efficacies greater than 90% that of dalamid, and which are therefore considered to be full agonists, lead to marked receptor down-regulation. Enkephalin is apparantly somewhat weak in this respect, but its concentration is greatly diminished during the experiment by proteolysis (Lampert et al. 1976). Opiates, including morphine, with efficacies less than 80% that of dalamid do not produce significant down-regulation. Because chronic morphine administration leads to an increased adenylate cyclase activity and no receptor down-regulation, the two may be completely independent manifestations of chronic drug treatment.

TABLE 4

Opiate Regulation of Receptor Numbers

Opiate	Receptor Numbers Remaining	Efficacy
	% of control	%
None	100 (9)	–
Dalamid	9 (2)	100
Phenazocine	18 (2)	96
Etorphine	21 (4)	100
Enkephalin	55 (4)	100
Butorphanol	76 (1)	72
Naloxone	83 (2)	0
Diprenorphine	96 (4)	58
Morphine	96 (4)	79
Buprenorphine	123 (4)	35

It is of some interest that chronic morphine administration to animals does not lead to a loss of receptors. The implication of these findings is that the partial agonist character of morphine is not limited to the delta receptors of NG 108-15 cells, but applies to both the mu and delta populations of rat brain as well.

Although we have progressed in our understanding of the roles of cAMP metabolism in both the acute and chronic actions of opiates, much more remains to be done. The detailed mechanisms involved in these actions are not yet completely defined, at least in part because of gaps in our understanding of the structure and function of the adenylate cyclase complex. Furthermore, evidence is mounting to show that several mechanisms may be operating in parallel during the development of tolerance and dependence. Both the efficacy and potency of the drug may determine which of the pathways is predominantly followed.

Much of this paper has been concerned with tolerance and dependence in a cultured cell line of neuronal origin. To what extent are these results and concepts applicable to animals and man? This question does not have a simple answer. There is no reason to believe that the changes seen with NG 108-15 cells subsequent to opiate treatment do not also occur in brain. In fact some observations made with rats suggest that just as with NG 108-15 cells: "...adenylate cyclase activity is enhanced in opiate dependence." (Collier at al. 1975).

REFERENCES

Blume, A.J., Lichtshtein, D., and Boone, G. Coupling of opiate receptors to adenylate cyclase: requirement for Na$^+$ and GTP. Proc Natl Acad Sci USA 76:5626-5630, 1979.

Cassel, D., and Selinger, Z. Catecholamine-stimulated GTPase activity in turkey erythrocyte membranes. Biochim Biophys Acta 452:538-551, 1976.

Collier, H.O.J. Pharmacological mechanisms of drug dependence. In: Cochin, J., and Way. E.L., eds. Proc 5th Int Congr Pharmacol San Francisco, Vol. 1. Karger, Basel, 1973. pp 65-76.

Collier, H.O.J., and Roy, A.C. Morphine-like drugs inhibit the stimulation by E prostaglandins of cyclic AMP formation by rat brain homogenate. Nature 248:24-27, 1974.

Collier, H.O.J., Francis, D.L., McDonald-Gibson, W.J., Roy, A.C., and Saaed, S.A. Prostaglandins, cyclic AMP and the mechanism of opiate dependence. Life Sci 17:85-90, 1975.

Cooper, D.M.F., Londos, C., Gill, D.L., and Rodbell, M. Opiate receptor-mediated inhibition of adenylate cyclase in rap striatal plasma membranes. J. Neurochem 38:1164-1167, 1982.

Hollt, V., Dum, J., Blasig, J., Schubert, P., and Herz, A. Comparison of in vivo and in vitro parameters of opiate receptor binding in naive and tolerant/dependent rodents. Life Sci 16:1823-1828, 1975.

Hughes, J., Smith, T.W., Kosterlitz, H.W., Fothergill, L., Morgan, B., and Morris, H.R. Identification of two related pentapeptides from the brain with potent opiate agonist activity. Nature 258:577-579, 1975.

Katada, T., and Ui, M. Islet-activating protein: enhanced insulin secretion and cyclic AMP accumulation in pancreatic islets due to activation of native calcium ionophores. J Biol Chem 254:469-479, 1979.

Katada, T., and Ui, M. ADP-ribosylation of the specific membrane protein of C_6 cells by islet-activating protein associated with modification of adenylate cyclase activity. J Biol Chem 257: 7210-7216, 1982.

Katada, T., and Ui, M. Direct modification of the membrane adenylate cyclase system by islet-activating protein due to ADP-ribosylation of a membrane protein. Proc Natl Acad Sci USA 79: 3129-3133, 1982.

Klee, W.A., and Nirenberg, M. A neuroblastoma x glioma hybrid cell line with morphine receptors. Proc Natl Acad Sci USA 71:3474-3477, 1974.

Klee, W.A., Koski, G., Tocque, B., and Simonds. W.F. On the mechanism of receptor-mediated inhibition of adenylate cyclase. Advances in Cyclic Nucleotide and Phosphoprotein Research 17:153-159, 1984.

Klee, W.A., and Streaty, R.A. Narcotic receptor sites in morphine-dependent rats. Nature 248:61-63, 1974.

Koski, G., and Klee, W.A. Opiates inhibit adenylate cyclase by stimulating GTP hydrolysis. Proc Natl Acad Sci USA 78: 4185-4189, 1981.

Koski, G., Streaty, R.A., and Klee, W.A. Modulation of sodium-sensitive GTPase by partial opiate agonist: an explanation for the dual requirement for Na^+ and GTP in inhibitory regulation of adenylate cyclase. J Biol Chem 257: 14035-14040, 1982.

Lampert, A., Nirenberg, M., and Klee, W.A. Tolerance and dependence evoked by an endogenous opiate peptide. Proc Natl Acad Sci USA 73:3165-3167, 1976.

Law, P.Y., Wu, J., Koehler, J.E., and Loh, H.H. Demonstration and characterization of opiate inhibition of the striatal adenylate cyclase. J Neurochem 36:1834-1846, 1981.

Neff, N.H., Parenti, M., Gentleman, S., and Olianas, M.C. Modulation of dopamine receptors by opiates. In: Gessa, G.L. and Corsini G.U. eds. Apomorphine and Other Dopaminomimetics. Vol 1. New York: 1981. pp 193-200.

Rodbell, M., Birnbaumer, L., Pohl, S.L., and Krans, H.M. The glucagon-sensitive adenyl cyclase system in plasma membranes of rat liver. V. An obligatory role of guanyl nucleotides in glucogon action. J Biol Chem 246:1877-1882, 1971.

Ross, E.M., and Gilman A.G. Biochemical properties of hormone-sensitive adenylate cyclase. Ann Rev Biochem 49:533-564, 1980.

Sharma, S.K., Nirenberg, M., and Klee, W.A. Morphine receptors as regulators of adenylate cyclase activity. Proc Natl Acad Sci USA 72:590-594, 1975a.

Sharma, S.K., Klee, W.A., and Nirenberg, M. Dual regulation of adenylate cyclase accounts for narcotic dependence and tolerance. Proc Natl Acad Sci USA 72:3092-3096, 1975b.

Sharma, S.K., Klee, W.A., and Nirenberg, M. Opiate-dependent modulation of adenylate cyclase Proc Natl Acad Sci USA 74:3365-3369, 1977.

Simantov, R., Baram, D., Levy, R., and Nadler, H. Enkephalin and adrenergic receptors: evidence for both common and differentiable regulatory pathways and down-regulation of the enkephalin receptor. Life Sci 31:1323-1326, 1982.

Traber, G., Gullis, R., and Hamprecht, B. Influence of opiates on the levels of adenosine 3':5' cyclic monophosphate in neuroblastoma X glioma hybrid cells. Life Sci 16:1863-1868, 1975.

Wilkening, D., Mishra, R.K., and Makman, M.M. Effects of morphine on dopamine-stimulated adenylate cyclase and on cyclic GMP formation in primate brain amygdaloid nucleus. Life Sci 19: 1129-1138, 1976.

AUTHORS

Werner A. Klee, Ph.D.
Graeme Milligan, Ph.D.
William F. Simonds, M.D.
Bruno Tocque, Ph.D.

Laboratory of General and Comparative Biochemistry
National Institute of Mental Health
Bethesda, MD   20205

Mechanisms of Multiple Cellular Adaptation Processes in Clonal Cell Lines During Chronic Opiate Treatment

Ping-Yee Law, Michael T. Griffin, and Horace H. Loh

Among the various in vitro models for studies of opiate action, the clonal cell line, neuroblastoma x glioma NG 108-15 hybrid cells, represents the simplest model of brain origin in which the molecular basis of opiate action is being investigated. The hybrid cells possess many neuronal properties, such as having excitable membrane containing light and dense core vesicles; also the hybrid cells can be synapsed onto striatal muscle cells (Hamprecht 1977). Furthermore, the NG 108-15 cells possess a homogeneous opiate delta receptor system (Chang et al. 1978) and can synthesize opioid peptides (Glaser et al. 1983). The opiate receptor is coupled to a well-defined second messenger system, the adenylate cyclase. Opiate agonist inhibits the adenylate cyclase activity (Sharma et al. 1975) and the agonist inhibition requires the presence of Na+ and GTP (Blume et al. 1979). For this delta receptor system, enkephalin and its analogs possess the greatest potencies in regulating the adenylate cyclase activity (Law et al. 1983). Most interestingly, the hybrid cells exhibit adaptation processes in response to the chronic presence of opiates. Continuous exposure of the NG 108-15 cells to the agonists resulted in a gradual loss of opiate ability to inhibit adenylate cyclase activity. Eventually, the intracellular cAMP level in the presence of opiate returns to that in the control cells when the opiates are absent. At this point, addition of naloxone results in an increase in adenylate cyclase activity. This increase in the cAMP level in the hybrid cells could be the biochemical correlate for the proposed increase in cyclic nucleotide's metabolism during opiate withdrawal in the animal. Hence, the hybrid cells represent a good model for studies of the chronic opiate effect at the cellular level. In the current review, we will examine the multiple cellular adaptation processes which occur in the chronic presence of opiate agonists. The possible mechanisms for these adaptation processes will be discussed.

MULTIPLE CELLULAR RESPONSES TO CHRONIC OPIATE TREATMENT

The ability of naloxone to increase the adenylate cyclase activity in NG 108-15 cells after chronic opiate treatment led Sharma et al. (1977) to conclude that the loss of opiate ability to inhibit aden-

ylate cyclase activity was due to the concomitant increase of
the enzyme's activity. The opiate receptor remained coupled to
the adenylate cyclase after chronic agonist treatment. This hypothesis suggested that there was no desensitization of the
opiate receptor or uncoupling of receptor from adenylate cyclase.
Loss of opiate activity, or tolerance to the opiate drugs in
NG 108-15 cells, was simply due to the increase in production of
cAMP. In this model, the heterologous desensitization of other
receptors which inhibit the adenylate cyclase activity in NG 108-
15 cells is predicted, i.e., chronic exposure of the hybrid cells
to opiate agonist would eliminate or, at least, attenuate the
ability of muscarinic or alpha$_2$-adrenergic agonist to inhibit the
adenylate cyclase activity. However, when such experiments were
carried out, it could be shown that opiate receptor desensitization after chronic opiate treatment was homologous only (table
1). The ability of carbachol and norepinephrine to inhibit the
adenylate cyclase after 24 hrs of 10 nM etorphine treatment remained intact, even though the ability of etorphine to inhibit
the adenylate cyclase activity was completely abolished. This
observation does not support the notion of concomitant increase
in adenylate cyclase activity as the cause of the observed loss of
opiate activity in NG 108-15 cells.

There is other evidence to support the hypothesis that the opiate
receptor is indeed desensitized during chronic drug treatment.
If the model proposed by Sharma et al. (1977) is correct, then
treatment of an opiate drug would produce the loss of all opiate
ligands' ability to regulate adenylate cyclase. As shown in
figure 1, treatment of the hybrid cells with opiate ligands with
various intrinsic activities and potencies produces dissimilar
responses. Treatment of the NG 108-15 cells with enkephalin or
its analogs or an agonist such as etorphine results in a complete
loss of D-Ala^2-Met^5-enkephalin's (DAME) ability to inhibit adenylate cyclase activity. However, treatment of the NG 108-15
cells with a partial agonist, such as cyclazocine or morphine,
though completely abolishing the partial agonist's ability to
regulate the adenylate cyclase, did not completely abolish DAME's
activity. In all these treatments, the magnitude of adenylate
cyclase activity increase was the same. Furthermore, concentration-dependent studies revealed that the concentration of drugs
required to elicit these two effects, the loss of opiate inhibition and the increase of adenylate cyclase activity, was not
identical. The concentration of etorphine to produce 50% loss of
opiate inhibition after 24 hrs of chronic treatment was determined to be 14.3±5.0 nM. This was considerably higher than the
concentration required to elicit the increase of adenylate cyclase activity. As shown in figure 2, at 1 nM etorphine, the
increase of adenylate cyclase after chronic treatment for 24 hrs
was already at its maximum.

The separation of the loss of opiate receptor activity and the
increase in the adenylate cyclase activity after chronic treatment could be further demonstrated by the use of another cell

TABLE 1. Chronic Etorphine Treatment on Receptors' Activities in Neuroblastoma x Glioma NG 108-15 Hybrid Cells

Ligand-receptor binding

| | Specific binding, fmole/mg protein | |
Receptor	Control	Chronic etorphine
Opiate, 5.9 nM ^{3}H-diprenorphine	596.0±18.7	200.0±12 (−66.3)
Muscarinic, ^{3}H-QNB, 3.6 nM	38.6±1.3	34.5±1.2 (−10.2)
α_2-Adrenergic, ^{3}H-Rauwolscine, 1.5 nM	59.9±6.5	62.6±4.6 (+7.9)
Prostaglandin, ^{3}H-PGE$_1$, 1.2 nM	7.3±0.2	6.8±0.4 (−6.5)
Regulation of ^{3}H-cAMP level	**Control**	**Chronic etorphine**
α_2-Adrenergic, norepinephrine		
IC$_{50}$, uM	2.08±0.36	1.92±0.50
n$_H$	1.50±0.17	1.40±0.16
Maximal inhibition, %	50.0 ±1.9	41.0 ±2.3[a]
Muscarinic, carbachol		
IC$_{50}$, uM	0.99±0.31	2.12±0.04[a]
n$_H$	1.55±0.16	0.90±0.10[a]
Maximal inhibition, %	49.3 ±2.3	35.9 ±2.3[a]
Prostaglandin, PGE$_1$		
EC$_{50}$, uM	0.103±0.018	0.108±0.022
n$_H$	1.15±0.23	1.16±0.16
Maximal activity, cpm/mg prot/20 min	2.96±0.04 x 10^5	2.85±0.02 x 10^5

Neuroblastoma x glioma NG 108-15 hybrid cells were treated with 10 nM of etorphine for 24 hrs. Receptor binding was carried out with membrane preparations from the hybrid cells. Carbachol- or norepinephrine-inhibition of PGE$_1$-stimulated production in chronically treated cells was measured with 10 nM of etorphine present in incubation mixture to prevent the spontaneous increase of cAMP due to the absence of opiate agonist. The values presented are the average ± S.E.M. of determinations from 3 cell samples. The numbers in parentheses are the % changes in receptor binding after chronic etorphine treatment.

a = p values ≤0.05 when compared with control.

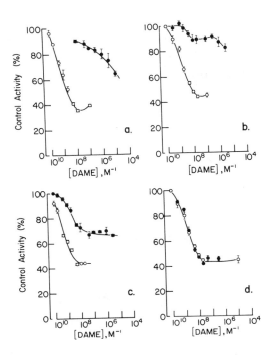

FIGURE 1. The relationship between the intrinsic activity of opiate ligands and opiate receptor desensitization in NG 108-15 cells. PGE_1 (5 uM)-stimulated cAMP production in suspensions of hybrid cells were inhibited by various concentrations of D-Ala[2], Met[5]-enkephalin (DAME) in control cells (-0-0-) or in cells treated chronically with opiates (-●-●-). Hybrid cells were treated for 24 hrs with (a) 5 nM DAME, (b) 1.0 uM Sandoz FK33824, (c) 100 nM cyclazocine or (d) 1.0 uM naloxone. Control activities in the absence of added opiates were 2.3 ± 0.09 x 10^5 cpm/ mg protein/ 20 min (n = 9).

line, neuroblastoma N 18TG2. In these neuroblastoma cells, one of the parents of NG 108-15 hybrids, opiate agonist also inhibits adenylate cyclase activity (Law et al. 1982). Chronic treatment of this cell line with etorphine also produced loss of etorphine's ability to inhibit adenylate cyclase. However, addition of naloxone after chronic treatment did not elicit an increase of the intracellular cAMP level (figure 3). Hence, in this cell - line, the loss of opiate activity after chronic treatment clearly is not due to the concomitant increase of adenylate cyclase activity.

During the chronic incubation of the neuroblastoma x glioma NG-108-15 hybrid cells with opiates, a third cellular adaptation process occurs. Incubation of the hybrid cells with opiate

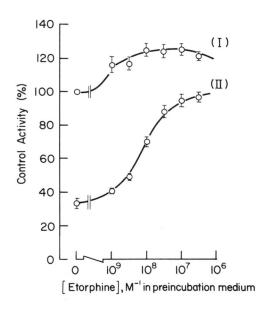

FIGURE 2. Etorphine concentration-dependent desensitization of the opiate receptor in NG 108-15 cells. Hybrid cells, cultured on 17 mm plates, were treated with various concentrations of etorphine for 24 hrs. PGE_1 (5 uM)-stimulated ^{3}H-cAMP production was determined in the presence of 100 uM naloxone (curve I) or in the presence of 1 uM etorphine (curve II). Values represent the average ± standard error of the mean of 3 cell samples. Quadruplicate 17 mm plates were used in each treatment. The control value for PGE_1-stimulated ^{3}H-cAMP production was $1.52\pm0.06 \times 10^5$ cpm/mg protein/ 10 min.

agonist resulted in a decrease in detectable opiate binding sites from the cell's surface, i.e., receptor down-regulation. It can be demonstrated that receptor desensitization is not due to receptor down-regulation, for both opiate agonists and partial agonists could desensitize the receptor. However, only opiate agonist could elicit receptor down-regulation. As shown in table 2, after treating the hybrid cells with approximately 5 X the K_d value of various ligands, the decrease in the ^{3}H-diprenorphine binding, a reflection of receptor density, was observed with ligands with intrinsic activities greater than 0.9. Some metabolically labile peptides did not elicit down-regulation in normal growth medium, which contains fetal calf serum. Replacement of the serum with chemically defined medium resulted in down-regulation by all opioid peptides following chronic treatment. Opiate partial agonists, such as cyclazocine, morphine, levorphanol, and diprenorphine did not cause a reduction in ^{3}H-diprenorphine binding. Cyclazocine, morphine and levorphanol could attenuate diprenorphine's ability to regulate adenylate cyclases. Furthermore, concentration-dependent studies

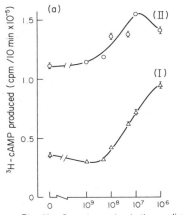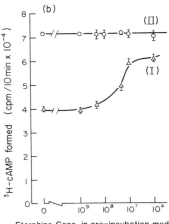

FIGURE 3. Effect of the concentration of etorphine during prein-cubation (2.5 hrs) on PGE$_1$-stimulated cyclic AMP production. (a) NG 108-15 cells (2.3 x 10^5 cells) were treated with various con-centrations of etorphine for 2.5 hrs. Sixty min before the assay, (^{3}H)adenine was introduced to the media containing varying concentrations of etorphine. The amounts of radioactivity being taken up by the cells in the presence and absence of etorphine were identical. During the enzyme assay (10 min at 37°C), after removal of (^{3}H)adenine from the preincubation mixture, 10 uM PGE$_1$ + 1 uM etorphine (curve I) or 10 uM PGE $_1$ + 100 uM naloxone (curve II) were added. (b) Neuroblastoma N 18TG2 cells were pretreated with etorphine as described in (a). The number of cells present in each assay was 9.5 x 10^5. Curve I represents the amount of ^{3}H-cyclic AMP formed during the 10 min assay in the presence of 10 uM PGE$_1$ + 1uM etorphine. Curve II represents the ^{3}H cyclic AMP formed in the presence of 10 uM PGE$_1$ + 100 uM naloxone.

also revealed the differences in the concentration of drug re-quired to elicit these two responses. The concentrations of drugs to promote down-regulation are analogous to the drugs' K_i values while the concentrations to promote desensitization are similar to the K_d values. Time-dependent studies also suggested differences in receptor desensitization and receptor down-regula-tion.

Receptor desensitization occurs prior to the appearance of re-ceptor down-regulation. Reappearance of opiate regulation of adenylate cyclase activity precedes the reappearance of opiate binding. Cycloheximide and tunicamycin both can prevent the reappearance of the binding sites after chronic treatment, but neither inhibitor prevents the desensitization of the opiate regulation of the adenylate cyclase. Therefore, it can be con-cluded that the receptor desensitization and receptor down-regula-tion are two separate cellular adaptation processes during chro-nic opiate treatment. It can be concluded, also, that there are multiple cellular processes in response to the presence of the opiate agonist.

TABLE 2. Chronic Treatment of NG 108-15 Hybrid Cells with Opiate Alkaloids and Opiate Peptides: Relationship Between Intrinsic Activity and Ability to Down-Regulate the Opiate Receptor

Opiate Alkaloids Incubation Concentration	Intrinsic Activity[a]		% Control Binding
Etorphine, 10 nM	1.00		41.0±7.7
Ethylketocyclazocine, 500 nM	0.96		41.3±1.3
GPA1657, 500 nM	0.96		64.9±7.9
Cyclazocine, 50 nM	0.62		91.8±2.9
Diprenorphine, 20 nM	0.70	95.7±13.7	108±8.0*
Levorphanol, 300 nM	0.65		96.8±6.7
Metazocine, 600 nM	0.69		105±3.4
Morphine, 100 uM	0.69	98.2±6.3	92.6±4.7*
N-allylnormetazocine, 200 nM	0.40	100±10	93.3±4.8
Nalorphine, 300 nM	0.18		103±2.9*
Oxymorphone, 400 nM	0.68		98.1±2.9
GPA2163, 500 nM	0		98.7±7.7
Naloxone, 20 uM	0	100±5.7	95.8±4.1*

Opioid Peptides			
Leu^5-enkephalin, 20 nM	0.94		50.6±2.4*
Met^5-enkephalin, 20 nM	0.95		47.6±5.8*
$D-Ala^2,Met^5$-enkephalin, 10 nM	0.98	78.8±3.5	50.6±2.6*
$D-Ala^2,Met^5$-enkephalinamide, 15 nM	0.98		53.3±8.9
$D-Ala^2,D-Leu^5$-enkephalin, 5 nM	0.92		51.5±8.9
Sandoz FK33824	1.01		41.4±3.7
$N-CH_3-D-Ala^2,D-Met^5$-enkephalin, 500 nM	0.94		50.4±4.9
$N-CH_3-D-Ala^2,D-Leu^5$-enkephalin, 500 nM	0.94		52.7±4.7
Dynorphin 1-13, 300 nM	0.96	83.9±1.9	65.1±2.7*
α-Neo-endorphin, 100 nM	0.97		27.9±2.6*
B_h-endorphin, 100 nM	0.99		65.2±3.2*

NG108-15 hybrid cells were incubated with various opiates or opioid peptides for 24 hrs at 37°C. Concentrations of ligands were approximately 5 x the K_d values for each ligand. Before assay, identical concentrations of opiate ligands were added to control plates and incubated at 37° C for 5 min, then washed free of ligands and incubated with ^3H-diprenorphine to measure binding. Control binding was 497.0±12.4 fmole/mg protein (n=39). Values are the average ± standard error SEM from three cell samples. * Denotes incubations were carried out in Sato medium (Law et al. 1983). [a] Intrinsic activities of opiate ligands were from Law et al. 1983.

As discussed in the previous section, loss of the opiate agonist's ability to regulate adenylate cyclase activity after
chronic opiate treatment is due to the homologous desensitization of the opiate receptor. To facilitate understanding the
mechanism involved, possibly involving the uncoupling of the
binding sites from the effector, it is necessary to investigate
agonist binding properties in the control membrane. In other
receptor systems, in which the agonist regulates adenylate cyclase activity (e.g., the beta-adrenergic receptor) the ability of
agonist to induce the receptor to change to a high affinity state
is a prerequisite for activity. The intrinsic activities of various beta-adrenergic agonist correlates with the percent of the
receptor in the high affinity states after agonist binding (Lefkowitz et al. 1980). Because this high affinity state is a
measurement of coupling, desensitization of the receptors would
result in the decrease in the percent of agonist-induced formation of the high affinity states (Lefkowitz et al. 1980). This
results in an overall reduction of the agonist affinity for the
binding sites.

Apparently, opiate receptor desensitization follows such a pathway. Computer analysis of competition binding data indicated
that opiate binding sites in the NG 108-15 cells could undergo
changes which represent multiple affinity states (table 3). In
the presence of Na+ and guanine nucleotides, the two components
which are required for coupling, DADL could change the receptor
from a single affinity state in the presence of Mg^{+2} to show at
least two affinity states. The K_d of the high affinity sites
compare favorably with that of the K_i value of DADL to inhibit
adenylate cyclase. If this altered affinity is related to receptor coupling, then it should be agonist specific. Opiate antagonist naloxone competes with ^{3}H-diprenorphine binding in a
single affinity manner, regardless of the condition of the binding
assays. As in the case of B-adrenergic receptor desensitization,
chronic opiate treatment of the NG 108-15 cells reduces the
percent of agonist-induced high affinity states. After exposing
the hybrid cells to 100 nM DADL for 3 hrs at 24°C, when there was
minimal receptor down-regulation but significant receptor desensitization, competition binding studies with DADL in the presence
of Na^+ revealed a reduction of the percent of binding sites in
the high affinity states (figure 4). There was a decrease from 75%
of the total binding sites in the high affinity states (K_d = 2.5
nM) to 45% in the DADL treated membrane. This resulted in an
overall reduction of the DADL affinity constant from 12.5 nM to
269 nM. Thus, chronic treatment of hybrid cells with opiate
agonists results in the uncoupling of the binding sites from the
effector systems. What causes this uncoupling remains to be
elucidated.

RECEPTOR INTERNALIZATION AS THE CAUSE FOR RECEPTOR DOWN-REGULATION

Another cellular response to the chronic opiate treatment is the
disappearance of detectable binding sites from the cell surface.

In other polypeptide hormone receptor systems (e.g., insulin, light-density-lipoprotein and epidermal growth factor), down-regulation of the receptor is due to the internalization of the receptor (Brown et al. 1983). Receptor internalization usually is accompanied by the internalization of the ligand. As a matter of fact, Chang and his coworkers (Chang et al. 1982), using neuroblastoma N4TG1, reported the accumulation of ^{3}H-DADL within the cells during chronic treatment with the radioactive peptides. However, chronic treatment of the cell with 10 nM ^{3}H-DADL did

TABLE 3. DADL Affinities for Opiate Receptor in NG 108-15 Cells under Various Conditions.

Additions	K_d, nM			R_H, %
	1-site analysis	2-site analysis		
		K_d^H	K_d^L	
Mg^{+2}, 10 mM	1.88±0.16	–	–	100%
+GppNHp, 10 uM	8.08±0.93	–	–	100%
+Na$^+$, 100 mM	10.8±0.4	2.59±0.18	170.2±20.9	61.4±3.0
+Na$^+$, +GppNHp	16.8±2.7	3.9±0.5	250.1±57.8	63.7±1.4

DADL affinities were determined by computer analysis of competition binding experiments carried out with P_2P_3 membrane preparations of NG 108-15 hybrid cells. Membranes equivalent to 0.25 mg protein were used per asssay. Opiate receptor was labelled with ^{3}H-diprenorphine, 2 nM. Binding assays were carried out at 24°C for 90 min.

not result in the accumulation of radioactivity. Rather, there was a time-dependent decrease in the ^{3}H-DADL associated with the cells, which paralleled that of the ^{3}H-diprenorphine binding decrease. These observations suggested that either down-regulation of opiate receptors in NG 108-15 cells did not involve receptor internalization or that internalization occurred without accumulation of the opiate ligands. These two possibilities were resolved by carrying out the chronic peptide exposure in the presence of chloroquine, a lysosomotropic agent. In the presence of 0.1 mM chloroquine, which inhibited the degradation process within the lysosomes, accumulation of ^{3}H-DADL within the lysosomes was observed during chronic treatment. The magnitude of increase in ^{3}H-DADL accumulated corresponded to the magnitude of receptor down-regulated. The intracellular location of the isotope could

127

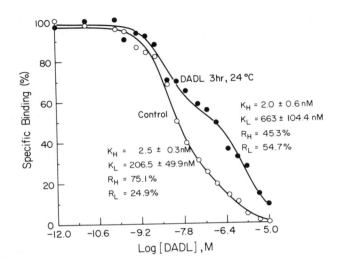

FIGURE 4. DADL affinities' alteration after chronic opiate treatment. NG 108-15 cells treated with 100 nM DADL for 3 hrs at 24°C were harvested and excess DADL was removed by repeated washing of membrane preparations. ^{3}H-Diprenorphine binding was carried out in the presence of various concentrations of DADL. Computer analysis of binding data was then carried out. (-O-O-) represents binding data with control membranes and (-•-•-) represents chronic opiate-treated membrane.

$$K_H = K_d \text{ for high affinity state}$$
$$K_L = K_d \text{ for low affinity state}$$
$$R_H = \text{receptor in high affinity state}$$
$$R_L = \text{receptor in low affinity state}$$

be demonstrated by insensitivity toward trypsin treatment, inability of excess diprenorphine to displace the accumulated ^{3}H-DADL, and by the Percoll gradient fractionation of the subcellular particles. There was a time-dependent translocation of the radioactivity from the plasma membrane-enriched fractions to the lysosome-enriched fractions in the Percoll gradients (figure 5). The translocation could be prevented by lowering the incubation temperature during chronic treatment. The accumulated ^{3}H-DADL can be demonstrated to be associated with macromolecules by the detergent extraction of the ^{3}H-DADL-macromolecular complexes and resolution of free ligand from the bound form using Sephadex G-50 chromatography. The accumulated ^{3}H-DADL was released into the medium upon removal of chloroquine and exhaustive washing of the cells. Hence, it is concluded that during chronic opiate agonist treatment, internalization of the ligand–receptor complexes occur with the delivery of the complexes to the lysosomes, where degradation of the receptors occurs. The free ligands are then released into the medium.

The mechanism for this overall decrease of receptor level in the cell surface is unknown. Although our chloroquine studies indicated that the receptor internalizes, our cycloheximide and tunicamycin studies indicated that the degradation, synthesis and processing of the receptor were not affected by the presence of agonist. Chronic opiate treatment of the hybrid cells must then interfere with the normal recycling process of the opiate receptor in order to elicit the observed down-regulation. At which step of the life cycle of the receptor does the agonist act remain to be determined?

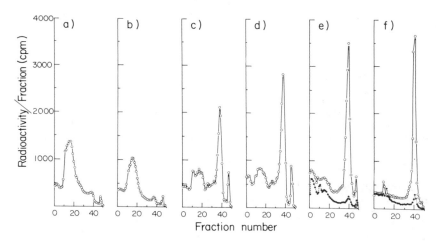

FIGURE 5. Time-dependent translocation of ^{3}H-DADL from the plasma membrane to the lysosomes of NG 108-15 cells. Hybrid cells were incubated with 10 nM ^{3}H-DADLE in the presence of 0.1 mM chloroquine (-0-0-) for (a) 5 min, (c) 1 hr, (d) 2 hrs, (e) 4 hrs, and (f) 12 hrs. Percoll gradient fractionation of the homogenates (minus nuclei) was carried out. Then, 0.65 ml fractions were collected and radioactivity in each fraction was determined. In (e) and (f), (-●-●-) represents the Percoll gradient profile of the homogenates from the hybrid cells treated with 10 nM ^{3}H-DADL chronically in the absence of chloroquine. In (b), the cells were treated with 0.1 mM chloroquine for 4 hrs and exposed to ^{3}H-DADL for 5 min at 37°C.

INVOLVEMENT OF CYTOSOLIC FACTORS IN THE INCREASE OF ADENYLATE CYCLASE ACTIVITY

It has been suggested by Nirenberg and his coworkers that the increase in adenylate cyclase activity after chronic opiate treatment was not due to the de novo synthesis of adenylate cyclase molecules, but rather due to the activation of the existing enzymatic molecule. Wilkening and Nirenberg (1980) suggested that serum lipids or linoleic acid were required for the full expression of this increased activity since the culturing of the hybrid cells in delipidized serum reduced the magnitude of the adenylate cyclase response, an effect which was reversed by the addition of linoleic acid. We can demonstrate that selective hydrolysis of the phospholipids with phospholipase C, but not phospholipase A_2, can attenuate the increase of the adenylate cyclase activity during chronic treatment. However, culturing hybrid cells in a serum-free chemically-defined medium did not alter the magnitude of the increased response. Hence, it can be concluded that the acyl side chains of the phospholipids did not play a role in the increase of the adenylate cyclase activity during chronic opiate treatment.

If an increase in membrane fluidity cannot account for the positive regulation of adenylate cyclase activity, then what cellular components could stimulate adenylate cyclase activity during chronic treatment? One such candidate is calmodulin. It has been reported that opiates can acutely decrease the amount of calmodulin bound to the plasma membrane (Nehmed et al. 1982) of the hybrid cells. Since the ability of calmodulin to stimulate adenylate cyclase is well known (Brostrom et al. 1978), it is possible that during chronic treatment, there is a retranslocation of the calmodulin. There is evidence to suggest that the naloxone-induced increase in adenylate cyclase activity following chronic opiate treatment may be calcium dependent. When the experiments with intact cells were carried out in calcium free medium, in the presence of EGTA, it could be demonstrated that the increase in adenylate cyclase is attenuated. Furthermore, addition of La^{+3}, the calcium antagonist, completely abolished the increase in adenylate cyclase activity (figure 6). When membrane fragments are prepared from hybrid cells chronically treated with opiates in the presence of EGTA, a reduction in the magnitude of the increased adenylate cyclase activity is observed. Upon combining the cytosol preparations, there was a potentiation of the increased activity (table 4). Intermixing of membranes isolated from both control cells and opiate treated cells with cytosols from these same two conditions revealed that maximal stimulation of the adenylate cyclase was achieved when the chronic opiate-treated cytosol was added with the membranes isolated from cells treated with opiates. Resolution of the cytosol preparations with a Bio-Gel P6DG desalting column revealed two components which stimulated adenylate cyclase. One component, which is at the void volume of the column, representing a M.W. greater than

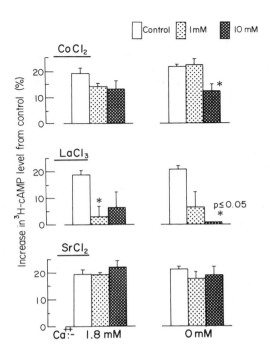

FIGURE 6. 'Effect of La^{+3} and Other Cations on Naloxone-Induced Increase in Adenylate Cyclase Activity.

5,000, is calcium dependent (figure 7). The other component, which has a molecular weight approximately equal to 300, is not calcium dependent. We have determined that a second component which stimulates adenylate cyclase activity is adenosine, since its activity is inhibited by 1) an adenosine antagonist, 2) desensitization of the cells to adenosine and 3) adenosine deaminase. During chronic opiate treatment, there was an apparent increase in the adenosine level within the hybrid cells. Furthermore, the activity of adenosine and the first component, possibly calmodulin, is synergistic in cells chronically treated with an opiate. Hence, a model for the increase of the adenylate cyclase could be formulated to involve these two components. One can postulate that after chronic opiate treatment there is an increase in the efficiency of coupling between stimulatory receptors such as adenosine, and an increase in binding of calmodulin to the adenylate cyclase molecules. Since phospholipase C could attenuate the increase, and phospholipase C could hydrolyze the polar head groups which bind calcium, and since there are also reports of alteration in ganglioside metabolism during chronic opiate treatment (another calcium binding component), the increase in

131

the adenylate cyclase activity could be due to an alteration in the membrane-bound calcium level in the plasma membrane. These events must remain under the control of the opiate receptor, since the increase in adenylate cyclase activity is only observed upon the removal of opiate agonist. This hypothesis is currently under investigation in our laboratory.

TABLE 4. Effect of Cytosolic Factors on Adenylate Cyclase Activities Following Acute and Chronic Etorphine Treatment.

Adenylate Cyclase Activity (pmole/min/mg protein)

Additions to Membrane	Control	% Increase Over Control Membranes	Chronic Etorphine	% Increase Over Control Membranes
None	3.35±0.10		4.88±0.43	+ 45.8
Peak I (control)	6.22±0.76	+ 85.9	8.89±0.76	+ 165.6
Peak II (control)	9.01±1.05	+ 169.5	10.08±0.35	+ 201.0
Peak I + II (control)	11.56±0.85	+ 245.1	16.14±1.04	+ 381.9
Peak I (etorphine)	8.08±0.20	+ 141.2	10.85±0.65	+ 223.9
Peak II (etorphine)	10.47±0.88	+ 212.8	12.74±0.05	+ 280.3
Peak I + II (etorphine)	180.2±1.96	+ 437.9	25.81±1.84	+ 670.7

Following vehicle or chronic etorphine treatment (100 nM, 16 hrs), cells were lysed and separated into membrane (control and etorphine) and cytosol (control and etorphine) preparations. Cytosol was further separated by column chromatography into two fractions (Peak I and Peak II). Adenylate cyclase activity was assayed in the presence of 100 nM etorphine + 400 uM naloxone and contained equal equivalents of cytosol and membrane protein.

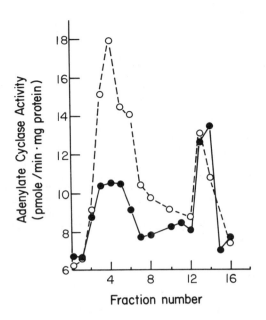

FIGURE 7. Adenylate cyclase activity profiles of cytosol from chronic etorphine-treated cells following gel chromatography on a Bio-Gel P-6DG desalting column (exclusion limit 6,000 daltons). Hybrid cells were treated with 1 uM etorphine for 4 hrs and separated into cytosolic and membrane fractions. Following chromatography, equal portions of cytosol fractions were added back to membrane fragments and adenylate cyclase was assayed in the presence (-0-0-) and absence (-●-●-) of 0.5 mM Ca^{++}.

CONCLUDING REMARKS

From our current studies, it is clear to us that multiple cellular adaptation processes occur during chronic opiate treatment. Thus far, we have identified three: receptor desensitization, receptor down-regulation and the increase in adenylate cyclase activity. This does not mean that these three processes are the only ones. Because of the complexity of the cyclic nucleotide's systems, it is possible that other cellular reactions which involve the cyclic nucleotides, e.g., protein phosphorylation, are also altered during chronic opiate treatment. A possible mechanism for receptor desensitization, i.e., the uncoupling of the receptor from the effector system, could be caused by a phosphorylation or dephosphorylation of the receptor molecules. Other cellular adaptation processes remain to be identified.

If one assumes that receptor desensitization and increase in adenylate cyclase activity after chronic treatment are the biochemical correlates of tolerance development and the dependence behavior (hyperactivity of the system), then from our current data, it could be suggested that these two events are separate cellular adaptation processes. The mechanisms involved are different and it is possible to induce one process without inducing the other. Hence, probably, tolerance and dependence behavior in animals are also two separate processes.

Although the neuroblastoma x glioma NG 108-15 hybrid cells have proven to be an excellent model in studies of the molecular basis of chronic opiate effects, one must realize its limitation. Unfortunately, most of the observations reported with NG 108-15 cells have not been repeated with brain preparations. Conceivably, because the hybrid cells are transformed cells, there might be some unusual expression of chromosomal material. However, one must also realize that the complexity of the cell types in brain might mask some of the effects. For example, not until recently, because of the relatively small inhibition (20%), opiate inhibition of brain striatal adenylate has not been reported. Thus, the failure to observe opiate effects in the brain similar to those in the hybrid cells does not necessarily invalidate the model. On the other hand, interpretation of the results from the model should be restrained, also. If such guidelines are followed, the studies with neuroblastoma x glioma NG 108-15 hybrid cells can provide us with some excellent insights into the molecular basis of chronic opiate action.

REFERENCES

Blume, A.J., Lichtstein, D., and Boone, G. Coupling of opiate receptors to adenylate cyclase: requirement for Na^+ and GTP. Proc Natl Acad Sci USA, 76:5626-5630, 1979.
Brostrom, M.A., Brostrom, C.O., Breckenridge, B.M. and Wolff, D.L. Calcium-dependent regulation of brain adenylate cyclase. Adv Cyclic Nucl Res, 9:85-99, 1978.
Brown, M.S., Anderson, R.G.W., and Goldstein, J.L. Recycling receptors: the round-trip itinerary of migrant membrane proteins. Cell, 32:663-667, 1983.
Chang, K.J., Eckel, R.W., and Blanchard, S.G. Opioid peptides induce reduction of enkephalin receptors in cultured neuroblastoma cells. Nature, 296:446-448, 1982.
Chang, K.J., Miller, R.J., and Cuatrecasas, P. Interaction of enkephalin with opiate receptors in intact cells. Molec Pharmacol, 14:961-970, 1978.
Glaser, T., Hubner, K., and Hamprecht, B. Neuroblastoma x glioma hybrid cells synthesize enkephalin-like opioid peptides. J Neurochem, 39:59-69, 1983.
Hamprecht, B. Structural, electrophysiological, biochemical and pharmacological properties of neuroblastoma x glioma cell hybrids in cell culture. Int Rev Cytol, 49:99-170, 1977.

Law, P.Y., Hom, D.A., and Loh, H.H. Opiate regulation of adenosine 3',5'-monophosphate level in neuroblastoma x glioma NG108-15 hybrid cells - relationship between receptor occupancy and effect. Molec Pharmacol, 23:25-35, 1983.

Law, P.Y., Koehler, J.E., and Loh, H.H. Comparison of opiate inhibition of adenylate cyclase activity in neuroblastoma N 18TG2 and neuroblastoma x NG 108-15 hybrid cell lines. Molec Pharmacol, 21: 483-491, 1982.

Lefkowitz, R.J., Wessels, M.R., and Stadel, J.M. Hormones, receptors and cyclic AMP: their role in target cell refractoriness. Topics in Cellular Regulation, 17:205-230, 1980.

Nehmed, R., Nadler, H., and Simantov, R. Effects of acute and chronic morphine treatment on calmodulin activity of rat brain. Molec Pharmacol, 22:389-394, 1982.

Sharma, S.K., Klee, W.A., and Nirenberg, M. Opiate-dependent modulation of adenylate cyclase. Proc Natl Acad Sci USA, 74: 3365-3369, 1977.

Sharma, S., Nirenberg, M., and Klee, W. Morphine receptor as regulators of adenylate cyclase activity. Proc Natl Acad Sci USA, 72:590-594, 1975.

Wilkening, D., and Nirenberg, M. Lipid requirement for long-lived morphine-dependent activations of adenylate cyclase of neuroblastoma x glioma hybrid cells. J Neurochem, 34:321-326, 1980.

ACKNOWLEDGEMENTS

Supported in part by Grants DA-00564 and DA-01696 from the National Institute on Drug Abuse. H.H.L. is a recipient of a NIDA Research Scientist Career Award, 5-K02-DA-70554.

AUTHORS

Ping-Yee Law, Ph.D., Michael T. Griffin, Ph.D., and Horace H. Loh, Ph.D., Departments of Psychiatry and Pharmacology, School of Medicine, University of California, San Francisco, CA 94143, USA

The Opioid-Induced Desensitization (Tolerance) in Neuroblastoma X Glioma NG 108-15 Hybrid Cells: Results from Receptor Uncoupling

Michael Wüster and Tommaso Costa

The phenomena of tolerance and physical dependence arising from chronic opiate exposure have attracted the interest of numerous investigators for many years, and several concepts for the underlying biochemical processes have been advanced (Collier 1980; Goldstein and Goldstein 1968; Martin 1968; Shuster 1961). The different theories, though diverging with respect to the precise nature of the adaptive mechanisms, are in agreement that the development of both tolerance and dependence is due to the same substrate.

Investigations from this laboratory on the development of opioid tolerance and dependence in isolated tissue preparations rejected the idea of a common mechanism between these two phenomena (see Schulz and Herz, this volume). The isolated mouse vas deferens, offering a system where extremely high degrees of opioid tolerance can be developed, does not show any sign of dependence, as evidenced by the absence of withdrawal signs after discontinuing opioid action, as well as the lack of increased sensitivity towards excitatory compounds under these conditions (Gillan et al. 1979, Schulz et al. 1980). Another classical tissue preparation used to study opioid effects, the isolated guinea pig ileum preparation, exhibits both tolerance and dependence on chronic opioid treatment. It is obvious, however, that a quantitative correlation of both phenomena is missing; indeed, in the mouse vas deferens most of the tolerance development occurs without a concomitant generation of dependence (Schulz et al. 1982, Wüster et al. 1982). Electrophysiological investigations in the central nervous system have revealed that the locus coeruleus slices, obtained from morphine-pretreated animals, display a significant degree of opioid tolerance; again, no signs of dependence are detectable (Andrade et al. 1983). Taken together, there are increasing indications that opioid tolerance and dependence may be generated by distinct adaptive processes; the underlying biochemical mechanisms for these events, however, are still obscure.

These difficulties are due mainly to the extreme complexity of neuronal networks in both the central and peripheral nervous system, which severely limits any investigation into the cellular processes by which opioid receptors exert a control on neuronal activity. It is evident that such studies are best performed on in vitro systems such as cultured cell clones; their availability has facilitated numerous studies on the cellular regulation of the intracellular second messenger system, adenylate cyclase. The classical cell clone for investigations of opioid-receptor interactions is the mouse neuroblastoma x rat glioma hybrid cell line NG 108-15 which has been extensively employed to study the cellular mechanisms of opioid-receptor mediated inhibitory effects (see also W. Klee and H.H. Loh, this volume). Apart from the opioid receptors, there are other inhibitory receptors (adrenergic, cholinergic) that control cAMP-synthesis in these cells (Traber et al. 1975a, Hamprecht 1977). Also, excitatory receptor systems (prostaglandin, adenosine) have been demonstrated in this cell line (Hamprecht 1977). Thus, a single pool of adenylate cyclase is under multireceptor control (Sabol and Nirenberg 1979).

The experiments described here focus on the problem of whether opioid-induced tolerance and dependence result from a common biochemical process within the opioid receptor system. There are a number of questions of particular interest: 1. Is tolerance development towards opioid agonists associated with desensitization towards the other prototype inhibitory compounds acting via different receptor types? The recent concept of receptor functioning supports the existence of a common intermediate for excitatory as well as inhibitory hormone receptors (N-unit, G/F protein), (Rodbell 1980), but their significance for the adaptive processes has not yet been investigated. 2. Is the development of subsensitivity towards opioids necessarily correlated with supersensitivity of adenylate cyclase towards excitatory hormones? Earlier investigations employing this cell clone have suggested that an increase in adenylate cyclase activity as a consequence of chronic opioid receptor activation is the common biochemical mechanism underlying both tolerance and dependence (Sharma et al. 1975; Traber et al. 1975b). 3. What is the significance of the recent investigations that revealed a down-regulation of opioid binding sites in neuroblastoma x glioma hybrid cells as a consequence of prolonged treatment with particular opioid agonists (Chang et al. 1982; Law et al. 1982)? Receptor down-regulation could eventually explain a phenomenon such as drug tolerance but not dependence.

Mouse neuroblastoma x rat glioma hybrid cells NG 108-15 were kindly donated by Dr. B. Hamprecht, Würzburg, FRG, and cultured as described (Hamprecht 1977). Chronic drug treatment was performed over a 24-hr period by the addition of different concentrations of D-Ala[2],D-Leu[5]-enkephalin (DADL), morphine or other opioid agonists to the cell medium. Thereafter, cells were harvested and divided into aliquots to test for the acute effects of DADL and other inhibitory compounds upon the PGE_1-stimulated cAMP-formation. Care was taken to maintain during the acute testing period the drug concentration which was employed for the chronic treatment, in order not to disturb the newly established equilibrium. Details of the methods and materials employed are given elsewhere (Wüster et al. 1983).

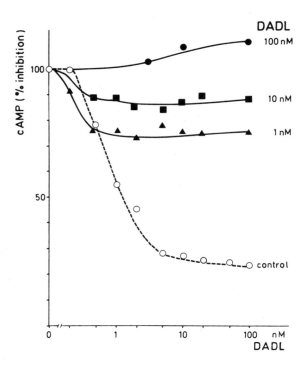

Figure 1. Effect of chronic DADL pretreatment upon the inhibition
of PGE_1-stimulated cAMP accumulation by an acute DADL challenge.
Values are given as percent of the respective cAMP content obtained in the absence of the acute DADL. Each point is the mean
of three experiments performed in duplicate. SEM was generally
less than 10%.

DADL inhibits the PGE_1-stimulated cAMP accumulation in control
cells by 75%. Pretreatment of cells for 24 hr with increasing
doses of DADL resulted in a dose-dependent decrease in the inhibitory effect of a subsequent acute opioid challenge (figure 1). It
was apparent that the pretreatment solely affected the maximal inhibition obtainable: the doses needed for a half-maximal effect
were not significantly different from controls. These findings
are at variance with results obtained in the intact animal and in
isolated tissue preparations such as the guinea pig ileum and the
mouse vas deferens, where drug tolerance is characterized by a
parallel shift of the dose-effect curve to the right. Drug tolerance has been explicitly defined as a state of the organism, where
"an increased dosage will again elicit the typical drug response"
(Goldstein 1974). The findings with the opioid-pretreated hybrid
cells obviously do not fit such a definition; it is appropriate,
therefore, to employ the term "desensitization" rather than "tolerance" for the observed effect. However, the correlation of the
desensitization observed in hybrid cells to the tolerance phenomena in intact nervous tissues is indicated by the fact that

careful analyses of tolerance phenomena have, in fact, revealed
that similar noncompetitive mechanisms also occur in the isolated
guinea pig ileum (Schulz, unpublished) and intact animals (Bläsig
et al. 1979).

Complete desensitization of NG 108-15 cells by DADL occurred with
a treatment of 100 nM DADL for 24 hr. Thus, doses which induce
a maximal inhibitory effect in naive cells also produce a maximal
desensitization after long-term exposure. This close correlation
between the dose necessary to produce maximal acute inhibition
and maximal desensitization was also confirmed using other types
of opioid agonists. Morphine and dynorphin A produced results
qualitatively identical with those of DADL; a concentration of
100 μM morphine and 1 μM dynorphin A induced a maximal inhibition
and a maximal desensitization. These experiments furthermore revealed a complete cross-desensitization between the different
prototypes of opioid ligands, supporting the notion that NG 108-15
cells contain a homogeneous δ-opioid receptor population (Chang
et al. 1978; McLawhon et al. 1981).

Opioid-desensitized cells were also tested for dependence, as revealed by the ability of the opiate antagonist naloxone to precipitate a "withdrawal sign" in the form of elevated cAMP-levels.
However, these "withdrawal signs" were either highly variable or,
in highly desensitized preparations, not apparent. Indeed, a naloxone challenge affected only preparations which had not yet regained their initial (naive) cAMP levels, as the doses of DADL
or morphine were too small to induce a complete desensitization
within 24 hr. Thus, the activity of naloxone was attributed to
the reversal of a still persisting agonistic effect in these
preparations. A minor (< 20%) net overshoot (rebound effect) of
cAMP formation over control data was observed in some of these
experiments.

The specificity of opioid desensitization was investigated using
non-opioid compounds by testing their inhibitory effect on cAMP-
formation. The adrenergic agonist noradrenaline and cholinergic
agonist carbachol retained their potencies, irrespective of the
degree of desensitization which was displayed towards opioids
(figure 2). Thus, the opioid-induced desensitization is "specific"
and does not occur with a change of the inhibitory effects mediated via adrenergic or muscarinic receptors. Accepting that the
different inhibitory receptors control adenylate cyclase activity
through a uniform transducer component (N_i), these findings therefore reveal that the adaptive process is localized neither at the
level of the catalytic unit nor at the N_i-component.

Down-regulation of opioid binding sites within the cell membrane
has been demonstrated to occur after long-term DADL administration
(Chang et al. 1982; Law et al. 1982) and could explain an opioid-
specific desensitization; however, the present data are at variance
with such a hypothesis. In contrast to effects seen with DADL,
chronic morphine treatment does not affect receptor density in
the cells (Chang et al. 1982), yet, the present investigation reveals an identical desensitization process. Furthermore, the DADL-

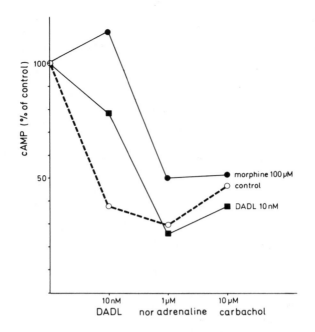

FIGURE 2. Effect of maximal inhibitory concentrations of DADL, noradrenaline and carbachol on the PGE$_1$-stimulated cAMP formation in controls, morphine and DADL-pretreated preparations. For further information see legend to figure 1.

induced changes in opioid receptor density become apparent at concentrations which are 10- to 100-fold higher than those required for desensitization.

In summary, these results draw attention to the functional integrity of the opioid binding protein as the point where the opioid-induced adaptive processes occur. It is concluded, therefore, that the binding sites in these cells are still capable of binding opioid ligands, but have lost their ability to funtion properly in mediating agonistic effects to the subsequent N-units.

The concept that chronic opioid treatment of NG 108-15 hybrid cells results in an uncoupling of the binding sites from N_i-units has gained considerable support from our experiments employing a recently available toxin from Bordetella pertussis (pertussis toxin, islet activating protein, IAP). IAP has been shown to catalyze the ADP-ribosylation of a specific, neuronal membrane protein with the molecular weight of 41,000 daltons and this coincides with an elimination of all inhibitory hormone effects upon adenylate cyclase (Katada and Ui 1981; Hazeki and Ui 1981; Aktories et al. 1983; Hildebrandt et al. 1983). Thus, by analogy with excitatory hormone effects being abolished by cholera toxin, pertussis toxin

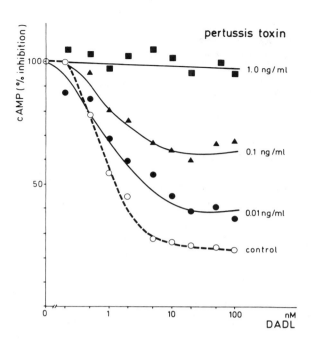

FIGURE 3. Effect of pertussis toxin pretreatment upon the inhibition of PGE_1-stimulated cAMP accumulation by DADL. For further explanation, refer to legend of figure 1.

impaires the signal transmission at inhibitory hormone receptors by permanently affecting the function of N_i (Katada and Ui 1982; Hildebrandt et al. 1983).

Using methods similar to chronic opioid treatment, NG 108-15 hybrid cells were grown in the presence of increasing concentrations of pertussis toxin and tested for the ability of DADL to inhibit PGE-stimulated cAMP formation (figure 3). As was observed with chronic DADL treatment (figure 1), pertussis toxin dose-dependently reduced the maximal inhibitory effect of DADL. With 1 ng x ml[-1] of toxin all opioid effects were completely abolished. Concerning the inhibitory effects of adrenergic and muscarinic agonists on cAMP accumulation, the results are identical with those of DADL (data not shown). The mechanism underlying the pertussis toxin effects may be related to the particular modulations which are exerted in the binding of opioid agonists, but not of antagonists, in neuroblastoma x glioma hybrid cells (Costa et al. 1983).

When comparing the kinetics of pertussis-toxin induced desensitization (figure 3) with those produced by chronic opioid treatment (figure 1), the similarity is striking. In both cases the curves are superimposable: the maximal opioid effects are changed without alterations of half-maximal effective concentrations. This indicates that both treatments are non competitive with respect to the ligand inhibitory effect. This may suggest that- although the phenomena are induced in both cases at different sites and they differ in selectivity- both treatments have a similar consequence: regulatory proteins (N_i) have an impaired ability to interact with the receptor binding sites and therefore fail to receive hormone signals.

CONCLUSIONS

The results presented here may advance our understanding of adaptive processes occurring as a consequence of chronic opioid action. On theoretical grounds, a unitary mechanism underlying both tolerance and dependence has been postulated for many years and there are several studies in support of such a concept. Indeed a significant role for adenylate cyclase in the expression of opiate tolerance and dependence appeared indicated (Sharma et al. 1975). In recent years, however, an increasing number of reports have investigated the relationship of the development of opioid tolerance and dependence in vitro: in several cases data from these studies revealed a pronounced dissociation of the two phenomena (Schulz et al. 1980; Schulz et al. 1982; Wüster et al. 1982; Andrade et al. 1983). Accordingly, the present data on NG 108-15 hybrid cells further support the notion of a development of opioid tolerance (desensitization) separate from the development of dependence.

This hypothesis is strengthened considerably by the cross-tolerance studies, which reveal an unaltered sensitivity of the adenylate cyclase pool of opioid-pretreated cells towards non-opioid inhibitory compounds. An analogous investigation, employing the identical cell clone, has reported similar observations on carbachol-pretreated preparations (Green and Clark 1982). Thus, the earlier concept which assumed a counterregulatory hypertrophy of adenylate cyclase (Sharma et al. 1975) is in need of reevaluation. Evidence now indicates that chronic opioid receptor activation results from an inability of the binding proteins to properly interact with the subsequent N-units, thus failing to transmit its signal to the catalytic units of adenylate cyclase.

In contrast to these in vitro observations, chronic opioid administration into an intact animal or humans clearly induces the development of both tolerance and dependence. Extrapolating the observations derived from model preparations such as the NG 108-15 hybrid cells, it may be speculated that drug tolerance and dependence are initiated by different biochemical mechanisms and are localized at separate neuronal levels. Opioid tolerance in vivo may, indeed, be produced by an uncoupling of the opioid binding sites, analogous to the events in in vitro preparations. Drug dependence, on the other hand, is displayed in intact nervous circuits, and may be, for example, caused by a compensatory hypertrophy of any intra- or extracellularly localized mechanism which is involved in signal transmission within an opioid-affected nervous pathway. A prerequisite for the initiation of such a hypertrophy, however, is a continuing opioid inhibitory effect. Consequently, adaptation towards opioids within the complexity of an intact nervous system may be characterized by the simultaneous uncoupling of particular opioid receptor populations, resulting in the phenomenon of drug tolerance, whereas others remain coupled. Their persisting inhibitory effect generates a hypersensitivity within the inhibited pathway, an event which gives rise to withdrawal symptoms upon cessation of the opioid inhibitory effect.

ACKNOWLEDGEMENTS

We are grateful to Dr. B. Hamprecht, Würzburg, for the neuroblastoma x glioma hybrid clone; to Dr. H. Glossman, Gießen, for the cAMP antibody; and to Drs. K. Aktories, K.H. Jacobs, and G. Schultz, Heidelberg, for the generous supply of pertussis toxin. The assistance of Ms. U. Bäuerle in cell culturing and S. John and U. Reuss in conducting experiments is very much acknowledged. Supported by the Deutsche Forschungsgemeinschaft, Bonn.

REFERENCES

Aktories, K.; Schultz, G.; and Jakobs, K.H. Islet activating protein prevents nicotinic acid-induced GTPase stimulation and GTP but not GTP's-induced adenylate cyclase inhibition in rat adipocytes. Febs Lett, 156:88-92, 1983.

Andrade, R.; van der Maelen, C.P.; and Aghajanian, G.K. Morphine tolerance and dependence in the locus coeruleus: Single cell studies in brain slices. Europ J Pharmacol, 91:161-169, 1983.

Bläsig, J.; Meyer, G.; Höllt, V.; Hengstenberg, J.; Dum, J; and Herz, A. Non-competitive nature of the antagonistic mechanisms responsible for tolerance development to opiate induced analgesia. Neuropharmacology, 18:473-481, 1979.

Collier, H.O.J. Cellular site of opiate dependence. Nature 283: 625-629, 1980.

Chang, K.-J.; Miller, R.J.; and Cuatrecasas, P. Interaction of enkephalin with opiate receptors in intact cultured cells. Mol Pharmacol 14:961-970, 1978.

Chang, K.-J.; Eckel, R.W.; and Blanchard, S.G. Opioid peptides induce reduction of enkephalin receptors in cultured neuroblastoma cells. Nature 296:446-448, 1982.

Costa, T.; Aktories, K.; Schultz, G.; and Wüster, M. Pertussis toxin decreases opiate receptor binding and adenylate cyclase inhibition in a neuroblastoma x glioma hybrid cell line. Life Sci 33:Suppl. 1, 219-222, 1983.

Gillan, M.G.C.; Kosterlitz, H.W.; Robson, L.E.; and Waterfield, A.A. The inhibitory effects of presynaptic alpha-adrenoceptor agonists on contractions of guinea-pig ileum and mouse vas deferens in the morphine-dependent and withdrawn states produced in vitro. Br J Pharmac 66:601-608, 1979.

Goldstein, A., and Goldstein, D.B. Enzyme expansion theory of drug tolerance and physical dependence. Res Publ Assoc Res Nerv Ment Dis 46:265-267, 1968.

Goldstein, A. Drug tolerance and physical dependence. In: Principles of Drug Action, A. Goldstein, L. Aronow and S.M. Kalman, eds. New York: Harper and Row, 1974. pp. 569-621.

Green, D.A., and Clark, R.B. Specific muscarinic-cholinergic desensitization in the neuroblastoma-glioma hybrid NG 108-15. J Neurochem, 39:1125-1131, 1982.

Hamprecht, B. Structural, electrophysiological, biochemical and pharmacological properties of neuroblastoma-glioma cell hybrids in cell culture. Int Rev Cyt 49:99-170, 1977.

Hazeki, O., and Ui, M. Modification by islet-activating protein of receptor-mediated regulation of cyclic AMP accumulation in isolated rat heart cells. J Biol Chem 256:2856-2862, 1981.

Hildebrandt, J.D.; Sekura, R.D.; Codina, J.; Iyengar, R.; Manclark, C.R.; and Birnbaumer, L. Stimulation and inhibition of adenylyl cyclases mediated by distinct regulatory proteins. Nature 302: 706-709, 1983.

Katada, T., and Ui, M. Islet activating protein. J Biol Chem 256: 8310-8317, 1981.

Katada, T., and Ui, M. ADP ribosylation of the specific membrane protein of C6 cells by islet-activating protein associated with modification of adenylate cyclase activity. J Biol Chem 257: 7210-7216, 1982.

Law, P.Y.; Hom, D.S.; and Loh, H.H. Loss of opiate receptor activity in neuroblastoma x glioma NG 108-15 hybrid cells after chronic opiate treatment: A Multiple-step process. Mol Pharmacol 22:1-4, 1982.

Martin, W.R. A homeostatic and redundancy theory of tolerance to and dependence on narcotic analgesics. Res Publ Assoc Res Nerv Ment Dis 46:206-223, 1968.

McLawhon, R.W.; West, Jr., R.E.; Miller, R.J.; and Dawson, G. Distinct high-affinity binding sites for benzomorphan drugs and enkephalin in a neuroblastoma - brain hybrid cell line. Proc Natl Acad Sci 78:4309-4313, 1981.

Rodbell, M. The role of hormone receptors and GTP-regulatory proteins in membrane transduction. Nature 284:17-22, 1980.

Sabol, S.L., and Nirenberg, M. Regulation of adenylate cyclase of neuroblastoma x glioma hybrid cells by α-adrenergic receptors. J Biol Chem 254:1913-1920, 1979.

Schulz, R.; Seidl, E.M.; Wüster, M.; and Herz, A. Opioid dependence and cross-dependence in the isolated guinea-pig ileum. Europ J Pharmacol 84:33-40, 1982.

Schulz, R.; Wüster, M.; Krenss, H.; and Herz, A. Selective development of tolerance without dependence in multiple opiate receptors of mouse vas deferens. Nature 285:242-243, 1980.

Sharma, S.K.; Klee, W.A.; and Nirenberg, M. Dual regulation of adenylate cyclase accounts for narcotic dependence and tolerance. Proc Natl Acad Sci 72:3092-3096, 1975.

Shuster, L. Repression and de-pression of enzyme synthesis as a possible explanation of some aspects of drug action. Nature 189:314-315, 1961.

Traber, J.; Fischer, K.; Buchen, C.; and Hamprecht, B. Muscarinic response to acetylcholine in neuroblastoma x glioma hybrid cells. Nature 255:558-560, 1975a.

Traber, J.; Gullis, R.; and Hamprecht, B. Influence of opiates on the levels of adenosine 3':5'-cyclic monophosphate in neuroblastoma x glioma hybrid cells. Life Sci 16:1863-1868, 1975b.

Wüster, M.; Schulz, R.; and Herz, A. The development of opiate tolerance may dissociate from dependence. Life Sci 31:1695-1698, 1982.

Wüster, M.; Costa, T.; and Gramsch, Ch. Uncoupling of receptors is essential for opiate desensitization (tolerance) in neuroblastoma x glioma hybrid cells NG 108-15. Life Sci 33:Suppl 1, 341-344, 1983.

Dr. Michael Wüster
Dr. Tommaso Costa
Department of Neuropharmacology, Max-Planck-Institut für Psychiatrie, Am Klopferspitz 18 A, 8033 Planegg-Martinsried, FRG.

Opiate Receptor Upregulation and Functional Supersensitivity

R. Suzanne Zukin, Ann Tempel, and Eliot L. Gardner

Opiate narcotic analgesics are well known to produce tolerance and dependence in vivo and desensitization in vitro. The observation of these phenomena originally raised the question as to whether opiate receptor populations undergo up- or down-regulation in response to long-term administration of opiate drugs. Drug- and lesion-induced receptor up-regulation were well documented in other neurotransmitter systems. Snyder and coworkers (Burt et al. 1977; Creese et al. 1977) investigated the influence of denervation and functional dopamine blockade on [^{3}H]haloperidol binding. They found that chronic treatment with the neuroleptic drugs haloperidol or fluphenazine elicits a 25% increase in striatal dopamine receptors. In addition, they showed that 6-hydroxydopamine-induced lesion of the nigrostriatal tract results in enhanced apomorphine-induced rotational behavior which is reflected in increased numbers of [^{3}H]haloperidol binding sites in rat striatum.

Although the evidence for behavioral and biochemical supersensitivity in the CNS was greatest in catecholaminergic pathways, the clinical problems presented by opiate tolerance and dependence made the endogenous opioid system an obvious target for research into molecular mechanisms of neural plasticity. Lesion-induced receptor up-regulation has been found in the enkephalinergic system. Our laboratory studied the influence of 6-hydroxydopamine lesions of the substantia nigra on opiate receptors of specific brain regions (Gardner et al. 1980). In the case of lateral nigral lesions, enkephalin receptor number was found to be significantly increased in the striatum and amygdala on the lesioned side relative to that of the same regions in the intact hemisphere.

Opiate receptor supersensitivity has also been induced by chronic blockade of receptors with specific opiate antagonists. In preliminary studies, Tang and Collins (1978) found that long-term treatment with naloxone resulted in enhanced morphine-induced analgesia. Because naloxone was rapidly metabolized, it

146

was necessary to prepare rats with indwelling venous cannulas. Lahti and Collins (1978) determined that the enhanced analgesia correlated with an increased number of [3H]naloxone binding sites. Almost simultaneously, Schulz et al. (1979) reported that guinea pigs exposed to naloxone for 1-2 weeks by implantation with naloxone pellets showed increased sensitivity to the inhibitory properties of opiates in the isolated ileum preparation. Chronic naloxone treatment also resulted in increased [3H]etorphine binding in the ileum and brainstem of guinea pigs. These studies were preliminary reports and as such did not control for 1) possible changes induced in endogenous opioid peptide levels that might give rise to <u>apparent</u> changes in receptor densities and 2) the effects of acute antagonist administration.

In 1982 our laboratory published the first detailed study of opiate receptor up-regulation (Zukin et al. 1982). A coordinated up-regulation of Mu and Delta opiate receptors was observed following chronic, but not acute, exposure to naltrexone. No change in the density or other properties was observed in the case of the Kappa or Sigma receptors (Tempel et al. 1982). Chronic, but not acute administration of antagonist was shown to elicit the up-regulation phenomenon. Thorough washing and a 37°C preincubation of the brain were shown to be crucial for obtaining accurate results. These procedures facilitate the dissociation of endogenous ligand and of residual naltrexone.

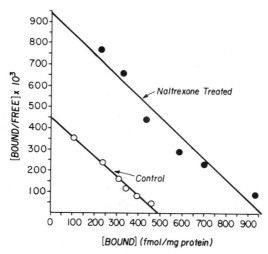

FIGURE 1. Scatchard analysis of 3H-etorphine binding to whole brain homogenates from chronic naltrexone and control-treated rats. Reprinted with permission from [Life Sciences, 31, A. Tempel, R.S. Zukin, and E.L. Gardner, Supersensitivity of brain opiate receptor subtypes after chronic naltrexone treatment] copyright (1982), Pergamon Press, Ltd.

This chapter presents a review of 1) the molecular events associated with opiate receptor up-regulation, 2) the nature of opiate functional supersensitivity, 3) the neuroanatomical patterns of receptor up-regulation as visualized by in vitro autoradiography and 4) the neurochemical correlates of this receptor phenomenon. These studies document both quantitatively and visually an important example of neuronal plasticity. An understanding of the molecular mechanisms underlying this up-regulation phenomenon will hopefully shed light on the mechanisms subserving opiate tolerance and dependence.

DEMONSTRATION OF OPIATE RECEPTOR UP-REGULATION BY IN VITRO BINDING STUDIES

Naltrexone, a long-acting opiate antagonist, has been used in clinical studies of heroin withdrawal. Our laboratory investigated the molecular correlates of chronic naltrexone administration (Zukin et al. 1982; Tempel et al. 1982). In vitro binding studies of [^{3}H]etorphine binding to whole rat brain homogenates were carried out. We observed a 95% increase in opiate receptor number with no change in receptor affinity in brain tissue from naltrexone-treated rats relative to that from control (untreated) animals (figure 1). Half-maximal increase in receptor number occurred at 4 days. Receptor number increased until 8 days, after which it leveled off (figure 2a). Withdrawal from chronic naltrexone treatment resulted in a decrease from elevated receptor levels to nearly control receptor levels in a period of about 6 days, as revealed by [^{3}H]etorphine binding (figure 2b).

In order to determine whether the state of coupling of the receptors undergoes a change, the sensitivity of opiate binding to inhibition by guanyl nucleotides was examined. The newly synthesized or unmasked receptors were shown to be more sensitive to guanyl nucleotide modulation. That finding suggested that up-regulation is accompanied by an increased coupling of the receptors to a guanyl nucleotide binding protein (Zukin et al. 1982).

FUNCTIONAL SUPERSENSITIVITY

The observation of a pronounced up-regulation of opiate receptor sites raised the question as to whether long-term treatment with naltrexone also produced a behavioral supersensitivity to morphine. Chronic naltrexone treatment was seen to result in enhanced morphine-induced analgesia as determined by the flinch-jump paradigm for measuring pain threshold (figure 3). Morphine produced an increased pain threshold in a dose-dependent manner as measured by this paradigm. After chronic naltrexone treatment, a leftward shift in the dose-response curve for morphine was observed. This finding suggested that a behavioral supersensitivity develops following long-term administration of naltrexone. Following removal of the naltrexone pellets, morphine supersensitivity decreased monotonically to pre-naltrexone

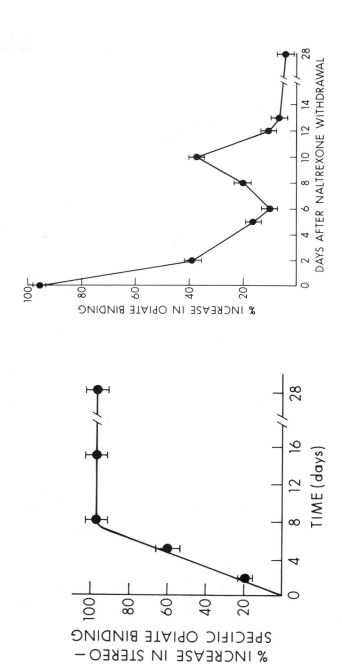

FIGURE 2. Time-course of the a) increase in brain opiate receptors following implantation of naltrexone minipumps and b) decrease in brain opiate receptor number following withdrawal from chronic naltrexone treatment.

149

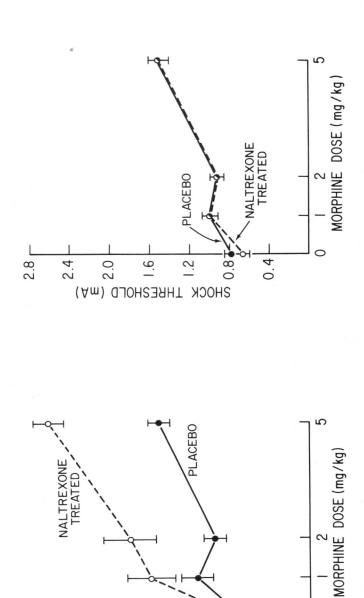

FIGURE 3. Morphine-induced analgesia as a function of morphine dose in animals treated chronically with naltrexone (8 days). Thresholds were determined a) 24 hours or b) 6 days after removal of the naltrexone. Male Sprague-Dawley rats were used in the flinch-jump paradigm. Reprinted with permission from [Journal of Pharm. Exp. Ther., in press, A. Tempel, E.L. Gardner, and R.S. Zukin] copyright (1984), The American Society for Pharmacology and Experimental Therapeutics.

treatment levels within 6 days. These behavioral data suggested a functional significance for the naltrexone-induced opiate receptor up-regulation, as the time course is well correlated with that for the disappearance of opiate receptor up-regulation following withdrawal from chronic naltrexone. These results serve to confirm those of Tang and Collins (1978) and are consistent with the functional supersensitivity observed in the dopaminergic system (Burt et al. 1977; Creese et al. 1977).

VISUALIZATION OF OPIATE RECEPTOR UP-REGULATION BY LIGHT MICROSCOPY AUTORADIOGRAPHY

Preliminary studies, in which the effects of chronic naltrexone blockade on opiate receptors were examined in dissected brain regions, revealed a heterogeneous distribution of receptor density changes. In order to visualize neuroanatomical patterns of brain opiate receptor up-regulation, light microscopy autoradiography was carried out on thaw-mounted frozen brain sections from chronic naltrexone-treated and control rats (Tempel et al. 1984). Figure 4 shows autoradiograms of coronal sections through the telencephalic region. In the striatum discrete patches of densely-labeled Mu opiate receptors were observed, surrounded by areas of diffusely organized receptors. Dense labeling was also observed along the subcallosal streak. This topographical organization of receptors is similar to that previously reported for the striatum (Atweh and Kuhar 1977). In the case of brain exposed to chronic naltrexone (figure 4b), receptor density in the striatal patches was markedly increased relative to that of control brain (figure 4a), whereas the diffusely labeled receptors of surrounding areas remained essentially unchanged. Additional structures shown in these autoradiograms which exhibited pronounced receptor density changes were the dopamine-rich nucleus accumbens and lateral septal nuclei (figure 4). In the neocortex dense labeling by [^{3}H]dihydromorphine (DHM) along molecular layers was observed as had been previously reported (figure 4a) (Goodman and Snyder 1982). Whereas layers I and III showed significant increases in receptor density after chronic naltrexone treatment (figure 4b), layers II, IV, V, and VI remained unchanged.

Nuclei of the thalamus exhibited high densities of [^{3}H]dihydromorphine (DHM) binding (figure 5). Long-term naltrexone administration (figure 5b) resulted in an increase in binding to the posterior thalamic nucleus (PO), but produced no significant change in binding to the lateral or medial ventroposterior thalamic nuclei (VPL or VPM) relative to control brains (figure 5a). In the region of the hippocampus (figure 5) very dense labeling of Mu receptors was seen to overlie the molecular layers; diffuse labeling was observed in the surrounding areas. Autoradiography (figure 5b) revealed antagonist-induced increases in opiate receptor density closely opposed to the pyramidal cells within the molecular layers of the hippocampus (e.g. mossy fiber tract and CA$_3$ area) but not in the dentate gyrus; surrounding areas were not affected. This pattern is

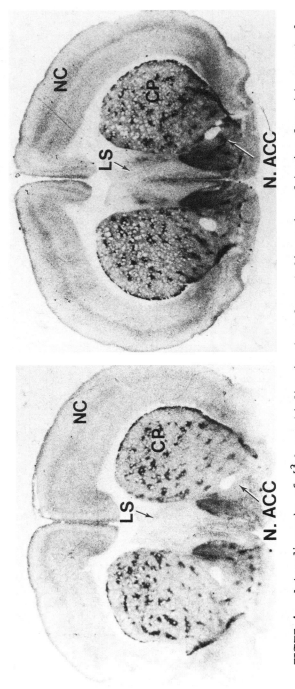

FIGURE 4. Autoradiographs of [³H] DHM binding in the telencephalic region of brains from (a) a control animal and (b) from a chronic naltrexone-treated animal. Note the specific regions of high grain density relative to control brain in the lateral septum and nucleus accumbens. Opiate receptor patches of the striatum showed significant increases in optical density while surrounding areas of the striatal patches did not show changes in density. Abbreviations are: N. ACC = nucleus accumbens; LS = lateral septum; CP = caudate putamen; NC = neocortex.

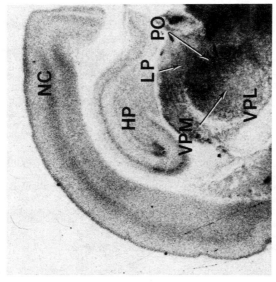

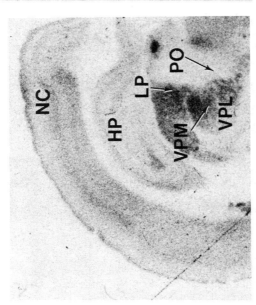

FIGURE 5. Autoradiographs of [³H] DHM binding to brain sections from (a) control and (b) chronic naltrexone-treated animals. Large increases in density were observed in the posterior thalamic nuclei of naltrexone-treated brain (b) relative to control brain (a). Note the high grain density in the molecular layers of the hippocampus of naltrexone-treated brain (b) relative to control brain (a). Abbreviations: LP = lateral posterior thalamic nucleus; PO = posterior thalamic nucleus; VPL and VPM = lateral and medial ventroposterior thalamic nucleus; NC = neocortex; HP = hippocampus.

similar to that observed for the striatum, in that only densely organized Mu receptors were observed to undergo up-regulation.

Table 1 summarizes the quantification of opiate receptor density changes following chronic naltrexone treatment throughout the brain. Largest increases were observed in Layer I of the neocortex, the nucleus accumbens, the amygdala, the ventral tegmental area, the ventromedial hypothalamus, and the substantia nigra compacta. Moderate increases were observed in Layer III of the neocortex, the striatum, the lateral septum, the posterior thalamic nucleus and the superior colliculus. No significant changes in density were found in areas surrounding the striatal patches, the medial septum, the ventral thalamic nuclei and the substantia nigra reticulata. Opiate receptor binding to the rat brainstem at the level of the locus coeruleus revealed dense labeling in the parabrachial nuclei and the locus coeruleus as previously reported (Herkenham and Pert 1982; 1980). Chronic naltrexone treatment produced significant increases in density in the parabrachial nuclei (+39%), but no significant change in the locus coeruleus, which contains almost exclusively norepinephrine cell bodies (table 1). These results document in a visual manner neuroanatomical patterns of opiate receptor up-regulation.

NEUROCHEMICAL CORRELATES OF OPIATE RECEPTOR UP-REGULATION

In order to examine correlate patterns of peptide regulation, methionine-enkephalin content in brain regions of naltrexone-treated and control animals was measured by radioimmunoassay. The distribution of methionine-enkephalin throughout the brain following long-term exposure to naltrexone is summarized in table 2. Two dopamine-rich structures, the striatum and nucleus accumbens, showed significant increases in methionine-enkephalin content after chronic naltrexone treatment (+94% and +40%, respectively; t-test, p<.05). Moderate increases were detected in the periaqueductal gray and hypothalamic areas. Neocortex did not show a significant change in methionine-enkephalin levels after chronic naltrexone treatment.

Changes in the levels of other opioid peptides have also been reported. Ragavan et al. (1983) found dramatic decreases in β-endorphin levels in rat brain following long-term administration (36 days) of naltrexone (4 mg/kg). Preliminary findings showed greatest decreases in the hypothalamus and amygdala with no significant change in the periaqueductal gray.

Thus, we have shown that specific brain regions vary markedly with respect to peptide and receptor density changes. Two possible mechanisms to account for this finding are 1) that the drug does not have uniform effects throughout the brain or 2) that the receptors or endogenous peptides themselves may be associated with specific functional pathways. In support of the latter possibility, several functionally defined pathways were found to show particularly large increases in opiate receptor

TABLE 1. Optical Density Measurements of Opiate Receptors in
Chronic Naltrexone vs. Control Treated Rat Brain

Brain sections were labeled in vitro with 5 nM [^{3}H]DHM, and
exposed to tritium-sensitive film for 12 weeks. Optical density
readings were taken from at least three sections from each
structure per rat and averaged. Averages across rats are
expressed as average ± deviation.

Region	Control Brain (n=2)	Naltrexone Treated Brain (n=2)	% Change	
Neocortex				
Layer I	.11 ± .04	.22 ± .02	+100%	
Layer II	.17 ± .03	.27 ± .01	+59%	
Subcallosal streak	.36 ± .06	.31 ± .04	----	(-14%)
Striatum				
Patches	.38 ± .11	.55 ± .02	+45%	
Other areas	.22 ± .03	.26 ± .04	+18%	
Nucleus Accumbens	.29 ± .06	.55 ± .02	+90%	
Septum				
Lateral	.16 ± .03	.29 ± .01	+81%	
Medial	.28 ± .01	.26 ± .01	----	(-7%)
Amygdala	.23 ± .01	.51 ± .03	+122%	
Habenular Nuclei				
Lateral	.18 ± .01	.16 ± .01	----	(-11%)
Medial	.28 ± .02	.53 ± .01	+89%	
Thalamus				
Post. Thal. Nuc.	.33 ± .02	.57 ± .03	+73%	
Dorsal Thal. Nuc.	.46 ± .04	.61 ± .02	+33%	
Ventral Thal. Nuc.	.14 ± .01	.13 ± .02	----	(-7%)
Hippocampus				
Molecular layer	.34 ± .03	.51 ± .02	+50%	
Other areas	.19 ± .03	.23 ± .02	+21%	
Hypothalamus				
Ventromedial	.12 ± .02	.45 ± .02	+275%	
Central Gray	.20 ± .01	.42 ± .04	+110%	
Superficial Gray Layer				
of Superior Colliculus	.27 ± .01	.50 ± .02	+85%	
Substantia Nigra				
Compacta	.10 ± .02	.30 ± .04	+200%	
Reticulata	.21 ± .02	.21 ± .03	----	
Ventral Tegmental Area	.12 ± .01	.45 ± .02	+275%	
Locus Coeruleus	.24 ± .03	.21 ± 0.0	----	(-13%)
Parabrachial Nucleus	.39 ± .03	.54 ± .04	+39%	

density after chronic naltrexone treatment. One example is the limbic system, consisting of the nucleus accumbens, the lateral septal nucleus, various nuclei of the hypothalamus, and the amygdala. These areas are known to contain dopamine as a neurotransmitter. There is, to date, considerable evidence supporting the notion of dopaminergic-enkephalinergic anatomical and functional interactions (Gardner et al. 1980; Zukin and Zukin 1981; Goodman et al. 1980; Biggio et al. 1978). Several laboratories have reported that opiates and opioid peptides inhibit dopamine release from rat striatal slices in vitro (Pollard et al. 1977; Schwartz et al. 1978; Celsen and Kaschinsky 1974) a finding which suggests a possible modulatory effect on dopamine-mediated behaviors. A second important system which exhibits pronounced up-regulation is the periaqueductal gray matter, thought to play a role in nociception and analgesia (Loh et al. 1976; Sabramanian et al. 1977). A third system includes several of the major structures which receive input from afferent sensory pathways. These areas include the superficial layers of the superior colliculus, the molecular layers of the hippocampus, layers I and III of neocortex and the parabrachial nuclei. All of these structures are particularly rich in opiate receptors relative to other areas (Atweh and Kuhar 1977). These findings are congruent with suggestions that opiates may function as neuromodulators in the CNS. When the system is challenged, as by chronic opiate antagonist treatment, specific enkephalinergic pathways (i.e., limbic, pain, sensory pathways) respond by synthesizing or unmasking new receptors. It is also possible that enkephalin levels increase first and that the receptor changes are of a compensatory nature.

Other examples of drug- and lesion-induced opiate receptor up-regulation have also been reported. Recently, Simantov and Amir (1983) showed that lesions of the hypothalamic arcuate nucleus of the mouse, produced by neonatal application of monosodium glutamate (MSG) (Hong et al. 1981; Krieger et al. 1979; and Romagnano et al. 1982), increased the binding of [^{3}H] dihydromorphine to membranes prepared from the midbrain. These MSG-treated mice also exhibited an enhanced response to morphine and naltrexone regarding thermal pain sensitivity. The same lesion in neonatal rats produced an increase only in the number of Delta receptors in the thalamus (as measured by [^{3}H]DADLE), with no changes in mu receptors (Young et al. 1982). The apparent discrepancy in these two studies may be due to an interspecies difference. Bardo and coworkers found that rat pups (ages 1-21 days) treated chronically with naltrexone exhibited an increased number of opiate binding sites, but did not demonstrate a functional supersensitivity to morphine (Bardo et al. 1982). These studies underline the importance of monitoring neurochemical correlates of chronic drug or food additive administration.

In contrast to the case of opiate receptor up-regulation, opiate receptor down-regulation has been difficult to document.

Several groups have reported that chronic administration of narcotic agonists in vivo does not produce any change in either receptor number or affinity (Holaday et al. 1982; Hitzemann et al. 1974; Klee and Streaty 1974; Pert et al. 1973; Simon and Hiller 1978; Perry et al. 1982; Bardo et al. 1982). More recently, Holaday and coworkers reported 17-20% increase in opiate receptor density following chronic morphine treatment. Using a different approach, Davis and coworkers (1979) showed that the development of tolerance to morphine is accompanied by a reduction of opiate binding as measured by [^{3}H]naloxone, [^{3}H] etorphine and [^{3}H] morphine binding in the brain-stem slice preparation. Homogenization was carried out after ligand incubation in this preparation, a procedure which may be important for maintaining membrane-receptor integrity. More recently, down-regulation has been observed in neurotumor cell lines following long-term exposure to enkephalin (Chang et al. 1982; Hazum et al. 1981; Blanchard et al. 1983) but not to alkaloid agonists (Chang et al. 1982). Possible interpretations of the latter findings are 1) opioid peptides and opioid narcotic agonists bind differently to the same receptor or 2) only a subpopulation of opioid receptors can be so modulated. These findings are discussed in more detail in another chapter in this monograph by Law et al.

The question arises as to the molecular mechanisms underlying opiate receptor up-regulation and functional supersensitivity. One possible hypothesis is that active opiate receptors in the absence of drug treatment exist in a dynamic equilibrium with a nearly equal concentration of inactive, "silent" receptors. Long-term exposure of the system to opiate antagonist leads to the activation or unmasking of the "silent" receptors, giving rise to an apparent up-regulation. Long-term exposure of the system to opiate agonists or opioid peptides might lead to coupling of the receptors to cyclase, followed by internalization. As active receptors disappear, these would be replaced by the conversion of "silent" receptors to active ones. In the case in which activation paralleled internalization, no apparent change in receptor density would be observed. Only in the case in which internalization exceeded reactivation (i.e. opioid peptides) would apparent down-regulation occur. It is possible to test aspects of this hypothesis by binding studies involving an in vitro system. Explant cultures of spinal cord with attached dorsal root ganglia provide a valuable in vitro system for studies of such mechanisms. Those experiments are discussed in another chapter in this monograph by Crain.

The overall significance of these studies lies in their ability to shed light on the mechanisms subserving the phenomena of opiate supersensitivity and tolerance and neuronal plasticity in general. There are potential clinical ramifications for naltrexone-induced supersensitivity. For example, naltrexone is in use as a treatment for opiate dependence (Resnick et al. 1974; O'Brien et al. 1978). After cessation of naltrexone therapy in humans, a resulting supersensitivity could be reflected in

TABLE 2. Regional Distribution of Met-Enkephalin After
          Long-Term Exposure to Naltrexone

Methionine-enkephalin content was measured by radioimmunoassay.
Values are reported as means of 4 determinations from 4 individual
sets (1 naltrexone brain, 1 control brain) of rats.

	Naltrexone-Treated	Control	%
	(ng/mg Protein) (n=4)	(ng/mg Protein) (n=4)	Change
Neocortex	10.0 ± 0.6	11.8 ± 1.5	-15%
Hypothalamus	9.5 ± 0.1	7.3 ± 0.8	+30%
Periaqueductal Gray	9.6 ± 0.3	7.6 ± 0.7	+26%
Nucleus Accumbens	11.6 ± 0.5	8.3 ± 0.8	*+40%
Striatum	18.4 ± 2.1	9.5 ± 1.0	*+94%

*Asterisks indicate statistically significant differences (t-test,
$p < .05$).

increased susceptibility to a dosage of heroin which would have
been well tolerated initially, and thus lead to an unintentional
overdose. A potential use of naltrexone-induced supersensitivity might be to enhance the analgesic effects of opiates prior
to surgery. The studies of the effects of long-term agonist
treatment on opiate receptors are important to our understanding
of the molecular basis of opiate tolerance and of receptor down-
regulation in general. Together these studies should contribute
significantly to our understanding of how the brain works in
regard to the regulation of enkephalinergic transmission and
receptors for the opioid peptides. Ultimately, studies with the
purified opiate receptor subtypes should enable a precise determination of the molecular mechanisms underlying brain receptor
regulation.

REFERENCES

Atweh, S.F., and Kuhar, M.J. Autoradiographic localization of
     opiate receptors in rat brain. Brain Res, 129:1-12, 1977.
Bardo, M.T., Bhatnagar, R.K., and Gebhart, G.F. Differential
     effects of chronic morphine and naloxone on opiate
     receptors, monoamines and morphine-induced behaviors in
     preweanling rats. Dev Brain Res, 4:139-147, 1982.
Biggio, G., Casu, M., Corda, M.G., Dibello, C., and Gessa,
     G.L. Stimulation of dopamine synthesis in caudate nucleus
     by intrastriatal enkephalins and antagonism by naloxone.
     Science, 200:552-554, 1978.

Blanchard, S.G., Chang, K.-J, and Cuatrecasas, P. Characterization of the association of tritiated enkephalin with neuroblastoma cells under conditions optimal for receptor down regulation. J Biol Chem, 258: 1092-1097, 1983.

Burt, D., Creese, I., and Snyder, S. Antischizophrenic drugs: chronic treatment elevates dopamine receptor binding in brain. Science, 196:326-327, 1977.

Celsen, B., and Kaschinsky, K. Effects of morphine on kinetics of ^{14}C-dopamine in rat striatal slices. Naunyn-Schmiedeberg's Arch Pharmacol, 284:159-165, 1974.

Chang, K.-J., Eckel, R.W., and Blanchard, S.G. Opioid peptides induce reduction of enkephalin receptors in cultured neuroblastoma cells. Nature (London), 296:446-448, 1982.

Creese, I., Burt, D., and Snyder, S. Dopamine receptor binding enhancement accompanies lesion-induced behavioral supersensitivity. Science, 197:596-598, 1977.

Davis, N.E., Akera, T., and Brody, T.M. Reduction of opiate binding to brainstem slices associated with the development of tolerance to morphine in rats. J Pharm Exper Ther, 211 (1): 112-119, 1979.

Gardner, E.L., Zukin, R.S., and Makman, M. Modulation of opiate receptor binding in striatum and amygdala by selective mesencephalic lesions. Brain Research, 194:232-239, 1980.

Goodman, R.R., and Snyder, S.H. Opiate receptors localized by autoradiography to deep layers of cerebral cortex: Relation to sedative effects. Proc Natl Acad Sci USA, 79:5703-5707, 1982.

Goodman, R.R., Snyder, S.H., Kuhar, M.J., and Young III, W.S. Differentiation of delta and mu opiate receptor localizations by light microscopic autoradiography. Proc Natl Acad Sci USA, 77: 6239-6243, 1980.

Hazum, E., Chang, K.-J., and Cuatrecasas, P. Receptor redistribution induced by hormones and neurotransmitters: Possible relationship to biological functions. Neuropeptides, 1:217-230, 1981.

Herkenham, M., and Pert, C.B. A general autoradiographic method which preserves tissue quality. J Neuroscience, 2:1129-1149, 1982.

Herkenham, M., and Pert, C.B. In vitro autoradiography of opiate receptors in rat brain suggests loci of "opiatergic" pathways. Proc Natl Acad Sci USA, 77:5532-5536, 1980.

Hitzemann, R., Hitzemann, B., and Loh, H. Binding of [^{3}H] naloxone in the mouse brain: Effect of ions and tolerance development. Life Sci, 14: 2393-2404, 1974.

Holaday, J.W., Hitzemann, R.J., Curell, J., Tortella, F.C., and Belenky, G.L. Repeated electroconvulsive shock or chronic morphine treatment increases the number of [^{3}H] D-Ala^2, D-Leu^5-enkephalin binding sites in rat brain membranes. Life Sci, 31: 2359-2362, 1982.

Hong, J.-S., Lowe, C., Squibb, R.E., and Lamartiniere, C.A. Monosodium glutamate exposure in the neonate alters hypothalamic and pituitary neuropeptide levels in the adult. Regulat Pep, 2: 347-352, 1981.

Klee, W.A., and Streaty, R.A. Narcotic receptor sites in morphine-dependent rats. Nature, 248:61-63, 1974.

Krieger, D.T., Liotta, A.S., Nicholsen, G., and Kizer, J.S. Brain ACTH and endorphin reduced in rats with monosodium glutamate-induced arcuate nuclear lesions. Nature (London), 278:562-563, 1979.

Lahti, R., and Collins, R. Chronic naloxone results in prolonged increases in opiate binding sites in brain. Eur J Pharmacol, 51:185-186, 1978.

Loh, H.H., Brase, D.A., Sampath-Khanna, S., Mar, J.B., and Way, E.L. β-Endorphin in vitro inhibition of striatal dopamine release. Nature (London), 264:567-568, 1976.

O'Brien, C., Greenstein, R., Ternes, J., and Woody, G. Treatment approaches: Opiate antagonists. Ann NY Acad Sci, 311:232-242, 1978.

Perry, D.C., Rosenbaum, J.S., and Sadee, W. In vitro binding of [^{3}H] etorphine in morphine-dependent rats. Life Sci, 31:1405-1408, 1982.

Pert, C.B., Pasternak, G.W., and Snyder, S.H. Opiate agonists and antagonists discriminated by receptor binding in brain. Science, 182: 1359-1361, 1973.

Pollard, H., Llorens-Cortes, C., and Schwartz, J.C. Enkephalin receptors in dopaminergic neurons in rat striatum. Nature (London), 268:745-747, 1977.

Ragavan, V.V., Wardlaw, S.L., Kreek, M.J., and Frantz, A.G. Effect of chronic naltrexone and methadone administration on brain β-endorphin in the rat. Neuroendocrinology, 37:266-268, 1983.

Resnick, R., Volavka, J., Freedman, A.M., and Thomas, M. Studies of EN-1639A (naltrexone): A new narcotic antagonist. Am J Psychiatry, 131:646, 1974.

Romagnano, M.A., Chapel, T.L., Pilcher, W.H., and Joseph, S.A. The distribution of enkephalin in the mediobasal hypothalamus of the mouse brain: Effects of neonatal administration of MSG. Brain Research, 236:497-504, 1982.

Sabramanian, N., Mitznegg, P., Sprugel, W., Domschke, W., Domschke, S., Wunsch, E., and Demling, L. Influence of enkephalin on K$^+$-evoked efflux of putative neurotransmitters in rat brain. Naunyn-Schmiedeberg's Arch Pharmacol, 299:163-165, 1977.

Schulz, R., Wuster, M., and Herz, A. Supersensitivity to opioids following chronic blockade of endorphin activity by naloxone. Naunyn Schmiedeberg's Arch Pharmacol, 306:93-96, 1979.

Schwartz, J.J., Pollard, H., Llorens, C., Malfroy, B., Gross, C., Pradelles, P.L., and Dray, F. In: Costa, E. and Trabucci, M., eds., The Endorphins. N.Y.: 1978. Raven Press, pp. 245-264.

Simantov, R., and Amir, S. Regulation of opiate receptors in mouse brain: Arcuate nuclear lesion induces receptor up-regulation and supersensitivity to opiates. Brain Res., 262:168-171, 1983.

Simon, E.J., and Hiller, J.M. In vitro studies on opiate receptors and their ligands. Fed Proc, 37:141-146, 1978.

Tang, A., and Collins, R. Enhanced analgesic effects of morphine after chronic administration of naloxone in the rat. Europ J Pharmacol, 47: 473-474, 1978.

Tempel, A., Zukin, R.S., and Gardner, E.L. Supersensitivity of brain opiate receptor subtypes after chronic naltrexone treatment. Life Sci, 31: 1401-1404, 1982.

Young, E., Olney, J., and Akil, H. Increase in delta, but not mu receptors in MSG-treated rats. Life Sci, 31(12&13): 1343-1346, 1982.

Zukin, R.S., Sugarman, J.R., Fitz-Syage, M.L., Gardner, E.L., Zukin, S.R., and Gintzler, A.R. Naltrexone-induced opiate receptor supersensitivity. Brain Research, 245:285-292, 1982.

Zukin, R.S., and Zukin, S.R. MiniReview: Multiple opiate receptors: Emerging concepts. Life Sci, 29:2681-2690, 1981.

ACKNOWLEDGMENT

This research was supported by National Science Foundation Grant BNS 83-08634, National Institute on Drug Abuse Grants DA 00069 and DA 01843 (awarded to R.S. Zukin), by National Institute of Child Health and Human Development Training Grant HD 07154, and by a generous private donation in support of neurobiological research from Mr. H.I. Corkin.

AUTHORS

R. Suzanne Zukin, Ph.D.; Ann Tempel, Ph.D.; and Eliot L. Gardner, Ph.D.

Departments of Biochemistry (R.S.Z. and A.T.), Neuroscience (R.S.Z. and E.L.G.) and Psychiatry (E.L.G.)
Albert Einstein College of Medicine
1300 Morris Park Avenue
Bronx, New York 10461

The Role of Dynorphin in Narcotic Tolerance Mechanisms

Nancy M. Lee

A central unsolved problem in the study of opiate drugs is the mechanism of the development of tolerance and physical dependence. Although there are many ways to prevent these phenomena from occurring or to alter the rate at which they develop, there is no known way of reversing tolerant and dependent states once they have been established, except through the slow and painful process of withdrawal. A promising new alternative approach to this problem, however, has recently been offered by the discovery of a variety of endogenous opioid peptides in the brain. Many of these peptides are not analgesic, yet they seem to play a modulatory role; that is, they may affect the analgesic potencies of other substances. This conclusion is supported by studies of both the enkephalins and dynorphin, which have been shown under certain conditions to enhance or inhibit the analgesic effect of morphine and of the endogenous peptide B-endorphin (Vaught and Takemori 1979; Friedman et al. 1981). These observations suggest that pain regulation may be a reflection not of a single opiate, but of the interaction of several.

In the development of tolerance and dependence to opiates, dynorphin seems to be particularly important because it has been shown to alter their analgesic potency differently in chronically-treated and naive animals. While dynorphin inhibits morphine analgesia in the latter, it potentiates it in tolerant animals. Thus both analgesia and tolerance may result from disruption of a balance or equilibrium normally existing among the three established endogenous opioid systems, represented, for example, by dynorphin, B-endorphin and enkephalin. In this article, we will discuss the evidence for this idea in some detail, as well as its implications.

PHARMACOLOGICAL PROPERTIES OF DYNORPHIN

Dynorphin is a 17 amino acid peptide first isolated from pituitary glands by Goldstein and his colleagues (Goldstein et al. 1979). In in vitro bioassays such as the guinea pig ileum and the mouse vas deferens, dynorphin and one of its fragments, dynorphin-(1-13), proved to have greater potency than most other opiates. It also displaced tritiated opiate ligands, including dihydromorphine (DHM), D-ala^2-D-leu^5-enkephalin (DADLE) and naloxone from brain tissue in in vitro binding assays.

In the ileum, dynorphin exhibits properties similar to the prototypic k-agonist, ethylketocyclazocine (EKC). This conclusion was established on the basis of naloxone sensitivity and on cross-tolerance studies between dynorphin and EKC in the guinea pig ileum myenteric plexus preparation (Huidobro-Toro et al. 1981). In further support, other investigators (Oka et al. 1981; Rezvani et al. 1983) demonstrated that in the rabbit vas deferens, which appears to be a specific bioassay system for k-like opiates, dynorphin, but not B-endorphin nor the enkephalins, mimics the actions of EKC. Finally, Goldstein and his group reported that dynorphin also behaves like a k-ligand in the protection of brain opiate receptors from alkylation (Chavkin et al. 1982). That is, if opiate receptors are preincubated with dynorphin and the alkylating agent B-chlornaltrexamine, the EKC binding sites are protected from alkylation but those of μ or δ ligands, are not protected. Thus, all these in vitro studies provide strong evidence for the notion that dynorphin is a k-ligand.

Additional studies in our laboratory in the intact animal, however, revealed that dynorphin does not behave in the classic manner of prototypic k agonists. For example, dynorphin displayed no analgesic activity in mice (Friedman et al. 1981). While this lack of effect was originally ascribed to rapid degradation of dynorphin in the brain, we were able to show that dynorphin exhibited other pharmacological effects, indicating it should have remained intact long enough to produce analgesia. Of particular interest, dynorphin was found to reduce the analgesic response to both morphine and B-endorphin, but not to the synthetic enkephalins, D-ala^2-D-leu^5-enkephalin and FK-33824 (Sandoz).

For striking contrast, a subsequent study in our laboratory revealed that dynorphin had the opposite effect in tolerant animals; it potentiated the analgesic effect of both morphine and B-endorphin (Tulunay et al. 1981). In the same study, dynorphin also suppressed abrupt morphine withdrawal signs. Dynorphin has also been demonstrated to be effective in preventing withdrawal signs in both opiate-dependent monkeys and humans. In monkeys, this peptide suppressed withdrawal signs in a dose-dependent manner, being effective at doses as low as 0.06 mg/kg (Aceto et al. 1982). In humans, 0.06 mg/kg of dynorphin(1-13) suppressed withdrawal signs and symptoms of heroin addicts. Only 3 out of 12 subjects reported mild side effects such as warmness or dizziness (Wen and Ho 1982). Similar results have been obtained with dynorphin in the morphine-tolerant guinea pig ileum; the effect of morphine was restored and the naloxone-induced contraction of the tolerant-dependent ilea was suppressed (Rezvani and Way 1983).

More recently, we have investigated the effects of chronic infusion of dynorphin on tolerance and dependence development. Infu-

163

sion of doses as high as 3.1 nmole dynorphin/hr for 72 hrs by itself resulted in no development of dependence, as measured by naloxone-induced escape jumping. Dynorphin also modulates the action of morphine on body temperature and respiration rate. Unlike morphine, which produces pronounced hypothermia 30-60 minutes after administration, dynorphin has a slight hyperthermic effect. When combined with morphine, however, it potentiates the latter's hypothermic action. Dynorphin-(1-13) alone has no effect on the respiratory rate; however, it enhances the inhibitory effect of morphine on this parameter in naive mice, while antagonizing it in morphine-tolerant animals (Woo et al. 1983), just the opposite of its modulating effect with respect to analgesia. Another peptide closely related to dynorphin, α-neo-endorphin, was shown to have similar modulatory effects in naive mice, but not in tolerant animals.

The effects of dynorphin, in summary, can be conveniently understood in terms of a "set point" model. For example, in considering analgesia, when dynorphin is administered with morphine, dynorphin tends to maintain the animals' sensitivity to the latter at a more or less fixed level. In the naive animal, it raises the ED_{50} for morphine from about 5 to 15-20 mg/kg, while in the tolerant animal, it lowers the ED_{50} from about 60 mg/kg to the range of 10-15 mg/kg. Thus, in the presence of dynorphin, both naive and tolerant animals display approximately equal sensitivity to morphine; in the absence of dynorphin, this sensitivity is less than that exhibited by naive animals, but more than that observed in tolerant animals. In essence, the effects of tolerance have been partially nullified, with the animals' response to morphine largely restored.

In the case of hypothermia and respiratory depression, a similar model operates, but with opposite consequences. However, the effect of dynorphin in tolerant animals is again to counteract the acute responses to morphine; thus, dynorphin apparently acts to maintain these physiological parameters at a level close to that found in untreated animals. The overall effect of dynorphin in the morphine-tolerant animal is, in every respect, a stabilizing one on morphine action, attenuating the withdrawal signs, potentiating analgesia and reducing its side effects.

DYNORPHIN BINDING SITES

An important approach to understanding dynorphin's role in the brain would be to determine the nature of its receptors and their relationship to receptors for other opioid ligands. This, of course, would enable us to decide whether or not it is actually a k-agonist in this system and, if not, decide what is its relationship to other endogenous opioids. Tritiated dynorphin is not yet commercially available, but we have studied the interaction of the unlabelled peptide with the binding of other tritiated opioids in vitro. Somewhat surprisingly, we have found evidence of dynorphin interaction with each of the three distinct types of binding sites now believed to exist in brain - μ, δ and

164

k (Garzon et al. 1982). These interactions are complex, with concentration-displacement curves suggesting that dynorphin does not interact witn any of these sites in a simple competitive manner, but seemingly non-competitively (Garzon et al. 1984). These results thus contrast with those carried out in the guinea pig ileum, where dynorphin seems to behave as a k agonist (Huidobro-Toro et al. 1981), and suggest that dynorphin may not be a typical k ligand like EKC.

The most important and unexpected result of these studies, however, is that a long-lasting inhibition of binding by dynorphin was revealed. When mice were pretreated icv with $1 - 20 \mu g$ of this peptide, binding of ^{3}H-DHM or ^{3}H-DADLE to tissue fractions prepared from the brains of these animals was significantly reduced. The maximum reduction was observed 30 min to 3 hrs after injection, with recovery not taking place until 6-12 hrs after injection. The B_{max}, but not the affinity, was reduced for both ligands; the high affinity site was most affected in each case. A similar inhibition resulted from addition of dynorphin to tissue in vitro, although in this case complete recovery occurred within 90 minutes.

These results are very provocative, since earlier studies have shown that dynorphin is rapidly metabolized in brain. We actually confirmed this fact in these studies, showing by means uf the mouse vas deferens assay that over 95% of the peptide had disappeared from the incubation media within 20-45 minutes. It is unlikely that dynorphin's inhibitory effect is achieved through the small amount of dynorphin not metabolized, since this would make the peptide several orders of magnitude more potent than any other opioid known. It is also unlikely that a metabolite of dynorphin is responsible for the effect, since fragments of less than 11 amino acids had no effect on opiate binding. We have thus tentatively concluded that dynorphin remains bound to its receptor for a long period of time to exert protracted effects. We believe it may be the endogenous inhibitor of opiate binding that several investigators have described (Simantov et al. 1976).

THE ROLE OF DYNORPHIN IN TOLERANCE

The data discussed above indicate not only that dynorphin can modulate the activity of other opioids, but that the nature of this modulation depends on the state of the animal. In naive animals, dynorphin inhibits the analgesic action of morphine and B-endorphin, yet it potentiates it in animals chronically morphinized. Similar effects are observed with respect to other opiate agonists, including meperidine, methadone, D-ala[2]-D-leu[5]-enkephalin, FK33824, and ethylketocyclazocine (manuscript in preparation). At the same time, dynorphin potentiates the "side effects" of these agonists, such as respiratory depression, in naive animals, but inhibits them in chronically morphinized animals.

Since dynorphin, as well as B-endorphin, is endogenous, these findings suggest a fresh way of viewing analgesia and its regulation. The analgesic state is not simply the outcome of the

interaction of a single type of ligand with its specific receptors, but rather results from a complex interaction among several
ligands: B-endorphin, dynorphin and perhaps leu- and met-enkephalin as well. It is reasonable to speculate that in the normal
brain these substances exist in a state of dynamic balance; the
effects of morphine, both acute and chronic, are then seen as
upsetting this balance. This would explain why dynorphin, though
not itself analgesic, can suppress withdrawal signs and symptoms;
its administration restores an altered balance between endogenous
dynorphin and other peptides during tolerance. This operational
hypothesis can be subjected to experimental testing.

How exactly is this balance manifested? The most attractive, yet
unproven, possibility is that dynorphin and the other opiates
actually interact with a common receptor possessing multiple
binding sites. We have previously cited considerable evidence
indicating that morphine, B-endorphin and the enkephalins bind to
different sites on a common receptor complex (Lee and Smith
1980). One interpretation of the data presented in this paper is
that dynorphin also interacts with this receptor; alternatively,
it may interact with its own site, affecting B-endorphin binding
allosterically.

If this is true, of course, these peptides should coexist in certain areas of the brain; they definitely show marked differences
in their brain distribution (Weber et al. 1982). However, there
may be certain areas where the distribution and/or projections of
dynorphin and B-endorphin, at least, do coincide, e.g., the PAG
and hypothalamus; it is significant that pain transmission is
known to be mediated through both these areas. Alternatively,
these peptides may be in different, but interacting, regions of
the brain. Mapping studies should eventually settle this question.

In summary, dynorphin in the brain seems to regulate several
activities affected by opiates that may be a key factor in tolerance development. The latter results not from a perturbation
of one particular opiate in the brain, but from an imbalance among
several. A dramatic change in sensitivity to external opiates
may thus occur without any changes in receptors. Pharmacological,
electrophysiological and biochemical studies of the interactions
of these peptides should reveal more about these imbalances and
the way they underlie analgesia and tolerance.

REFERENCES

Aceto, M.D., Dewey, W.L., Chang, J.K., and Lee, N.M. Dynorphin-1-
13: effects in nontolerant and morphine-dependent rhesus monkeys. Europ J Pharmacol, 83:139-142, 1982.
Chavkin, C., James, I.F., and Goldstein, A. Dynorphin is a specific endogenous ligand of the k opiate receptor. Science, 215:
13-415, 1982.
Friedman, H.J., Jen, M.F., Chang, J.K., Lee, N.M. and Loh, H.H.
Dynorphin: a possible modulatory peptide on morphine or B-endorphin analgesia in mouse. Europ J Pharmacol, 69: 351-360, 1981.

Garzon, J.G., Jen, M.F., Sanchez-Blazquez, P., and Lee, N.M. Dynorphin-1-13: a long-lasting inhibition of opiate receptor binding in vitro. Life Sci, 31:1789-1792, 1982.

Garzon, J., Sanchez-Blazquez, P., Gerhart, J., Loh, H.H. and Lee, N.M. Dynorphin-1-13: interaction with other ligand bindings in vitro. Brain Res., in press, 1984.

Goldstein, A., Tachibana, S, Lowney, L.I., Hunkapiller, M., and Hood, L. Dynorphin-1-13, an extraordinary potent opioid peptide. Proc Natl Acad Sci USA, 76:6666-6670, 1979.

Huidobro-Toro, J.P., Yoshimura, K., Lee, N.M., Loh, H.H., and Way, E.L. Dynorphin interaction at the k-opiate site. Europ J Pharmacol, 72:265-266, 1981.

Lee, N.M., and Smith, A.P. A protein-lipid model of the opiate receptor. Life Sci, 26:1459-1464, 1980.

Oka, T., Negishi, K., Suda, M., Matsumiya, T., Inazu, T., and Ueki, M. Rabbit vas deferens: a specific bioassay for opioid k-receptor agonists. Europ J Pharmacol, 73:235-236, 1981.

Rezvani, A., Höllt, V., and Way, E.L. k receptor activities of the three opioid peptide families. Life Sci, 33:271-274, 1983.

Rezvani, A., and Way, E.L. Dynorphin-1-13 restores the potency of morphine on the tolerant guinea pig ileum. Europ J Pharmacol, in press, 1984.

Simantov, R., Snowman, A.M., and Snyder, S.H. Temperature and ionic influences on opiate receptor binding. Mol Pharmacol, 12:977-986, 1976.

Tulunay, F.C., Jen, M.F., Chang, J.K., Loh, H.H., and Lee, N.M. Possible regulatory role of dynorphin on morphine and B-endorphin induced analgesia. J Pharmacol Exp Ther, 219:296-298, 1981.

Vaught, J.L., and Takemori, A.E. Differential effects of leucine and methionine enkephalin on morphine-induced analgesia, acute tolerance and dependence. J Pharmacol Exp Ther, 208:86-90, 1979.

Weber, E., Roth, K.A., and Barchas, J.D. Immunohistochemical distribution of ∝ -neo-endorphin/dynorphin neuronal systems in rat brain. Evidence for colocalization, Natl Acad Sci USA, 79:3062-3066, 1982.

Wen, H.L., and Ho, W.K.K. Suppression of withdrawal symptoms by dynorphin in heroin addicts. Europ J Pharmacol, 83:134-142, 1982.

Woo, S.K., Tulunay, F.C., Loh, H.H., and Lee, N.M. Effect of dynorphin-1-13 and related peptides on respiratory rate and morphine-induced respiratory rate depression. Europ J Pharmacol, 96:117-122, 1983.

ACKNOWLEDGEMENT

Supported by Grants DA-02643 and KO2-DA-00020 from the National Institute on Drug Abuse.

AUTHOR

Nancy M. Lee, Ph.D.
Department of Pharmacology
& Langley Porter Psychiatric Institute
University of California
San Francisco, CA 94143

Post-Translational Processing of Neuropeptide Precursors

Richard E. Mains and Betty A. Eipper

Neuropeptides, and in fact a very large number of small peptides, are synthesized as portions of larger precursor proteins which are themselves inactive; this review will frequently use the ACTH/endorphin system as an example (figure 1; Mains et al. 1983).

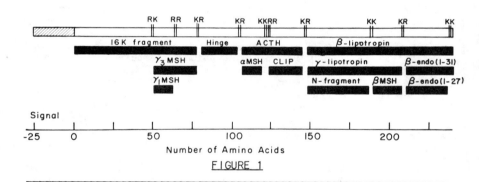

FIGURE 1

Rapid DNA sequencing techniques have been instrumental in the recent dramatic explosion of information about the structure of such precursors, but there is still a great deal to be learned about the enzymatic processing steps that must occur between the synthesis of precursors and synthesis of their bioactive peptide products. As it is now possible to proceed rapidly from the amino acid sequence of a purified peptide to the nucleotide sequence and hence the entire amino acid sequence of its precursor, we are now in the position of knowing the sequences of a large number of precursors but not which product peptides are actually made or even which product peptides are physiologically important. Based on the limited number of examples that have been adequately studied, it is clear that discrete cleavages in these precursors result in the creation of a whole family of peptide products; all of the progeny peptides are secreted along with the particular bioactive peptide that was originally thought to be the focus of interest. Thus it is important to determine the structures of all of the product peptides (i.e. secretory products). One important example of this rule was the old clinical observation that peptides related to β-lipotropin are secreted along with ACTH under a variety of circumstances. This was a key observation in the discovery that the molecule already known to be the precursor to ACTH (pro-ACTH) also contained the structure of β-lipotropin and thus the potent opiate peptide β-endorphin (hence, the name pro-ACTH/endorphin) (Eipper and Mains 1980).

Although a set of general principles for peptide hormone processing has been developed over the past years, they really only define a set of likely products; the actual product peptides produced must be determined for each tissue where those peptides occur. For example, in the pro-ACTH/endorphin system a pair of basic amino acids (Arg-Lys) precedes the γMSH sequence in the precursor (figure 2); instead of producing peptides with γMSH

Residue number	48 49 50 51 52 53
16K fragment	-Pro-Arg-Lys-Tyr-Val-Met-
γMSH, as predicted by removal of pairs of basic residues	Tyr-Val-Met-
Actual product	Lys-Tyr-Val-Met-

FIGURE 2. Sequences of 16K Fragment and Progeny

---

at their amino terminus, bovine and rat intermediate pituitary cells produce peptides with Lys_o-γMSH at their amino terminus (Esch et al. 1981). The Lys_o-γMSH shows far greater binding affinity for adrenal cortical cells (the presumed target in vivo) than γMSH (Pedersen and Brownie 1983).

Neuropeptides and peptide hormones display quite an array of important co- and post-translational modifications. Since the precursors are bigger than their product peptides, proteolytic processing is clearly a very important modification during biosynthesis. For simplicity, these proteolytic modifications can be grouped into three categories: removal of the signal peptide from the precursor during or immediately after synthesis of the precursor and its deposition into the lumen of the rough endoplasmic reticulum; endoproteolytic steps which break the precursor into the peptide regions which approximately comprise the final product peptides; and exoproteolytic events which trim the carboxyl and/or amino terminal ends of the peptides into the forms found in the mature product. It is not yet clear how distinct the endo- and exoproteolytic steps will be for any peptide family. It is not even clear whether a few proteases will function in the biosynthesis of many different peptides or whether a large number of proteases with narrow specificity will be involved. It is clear that expression of the proinsulin gene in monkey kidney cells results in secretion of proinsulin into the medium without production of insulin and C-peptide (Laub et al. 1983); thus the biosynthetic processing proteases of peptide hormone biosynthesis are not normally expressed in all cells.

In order to discern the number of proteolytic steps that were actually used in the cell to produce a product peptide from its precursor, one must identify intermediates in the biosynthetic pathway. However, many other co- and post-translational covalent modifications are easily detectable in the smaller products, and in several instances these alterations are very important in determining the bioactivity of the peptide products. This list includes glycosylation (both asparagine-linked and serine/threonine-linked), α-N-acetylation, phosphorylation, sulfation, and α-amidation. Neuropeptides are thought to function as neurotransmitters or neuromodulators; synthesis of precursor and the subsequent co- and post-translational modifications represent the biosynthetic pathway for these molecules (Snyder 1984). In order to understand the functioning and malfunctioning of these peptidergic systems, we have to understand the physiological and pharmacological factors that can regulate each step. Studying these steps can be thought of as analogous to studying the role and regulation of tyrosine hydroxylase, aromatic amino acid decarboxylase, dopamine β-hydroxylase and phenylethanolamine N-methyltransferase in catecholamine biosynthesis.

Another important point about bioactive peptides is that any given peptide and its siblings can occur in more than one tissue in major amounts. In addition, the final peptide products found in the different tissues can differ structurally in very important ways. For example (figure 3), ACTH(1-39) is the peptide which directs the adrenal cortex to synthesize and release glucocorticoids into the blood; ACTH(1-39) is a major product pep-

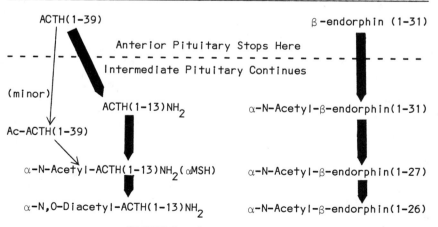

FIGURE 3. Biosynthetic Pathways

tide of pro-ACTH/endorphin in the anterior pituitary. Alpha-melanotropin [αMSH; α-N-acetyl-ACTH(1-13)NH$_2$] stimulates skin darkening in lower vertebrates and may also have behavioral actions in higher vertebrates; αMSH is a major product peptide from pro-ACTH/endorphin in the intermediate pituitary, and molecules similar to αMSH also occur in the brain. Since it is now clear that in several species there is only one pro-ACTH/endorphin gene, the differences in the product peptides in the different tissues must be due to differences in enzymatic processing of the primary gene product.

FOCUS ON ENZYMES

This review will discuss two enzymatic activities which are apparently important in the post-translational processing of pro-ACTH/endorphin. Both enzymes are involved in late biosynthetic events which determine the final structure and bioactivity of the product peptides, after initial processing steps are done. Each of the enzymatic activities is primarily localized in secretory granules.

The first activity to be discussed will be the secretory granule-associated α-N-acetyltransferase activity found in rat and beef intermediate pituitary but not in rat anterior pituitary. Current data argue that the same enzyme puts α-N-acetyl groups onto both ACTH(1-13)NH$_2$ [to produce αMSH or α-melanotropin] and β-endorphin(1-31) [to produce α-N-acetyl-β-endorphin(1-31)] (figure 3, previous page).

The second enzymatic activity to be examined will be a peptidyl-glycine α-amidation activity. Many neuropeptides terminate in a carboxyl-terminal α-amide and data accumulated to date suggest that α-amidated peptides are derived from precursor peptides that have an additional glycyl residue at the carboxyl terminus. This enzymatic activity cleaves within the original COOH-terminal glycyl residue to liberate glyoxylate and leave a product peptide bearing a COOH-terminal α-amide group. Some similarities of this enzyme activity to other known enzymes, most notably dopamine β-hydroxylase, will be discussed.

α-N-ACETYLTRANSFERASE

The enzymatic activity utilizing acetyl coenzyme A (AcCoA) to mediate the α-N-acetylation of ACTH(1-13)NH$_2$ and β-endorphin(1-31) has been examined by Woodford and Dixon (1979), Glembotski (1982b) and O'Donohue and coworkers (O'Donohue and Dorsa 1982). The thorough subcellular fractionation work of Glembotski (1981; 1982a,b) made clear two important points. First, only about 10-30% of the acetylating activity in intermediate pituitary was found in a secretory granule fraction with the rest of the activity associated with other cellular organelles or cytoplasm. The secretory granule-associated activity is the only acetylating activity of physiological relevance to the α-N-acetylation of αMSH, since previous work (Glembotski 1982a) demonstrated that the α-N-acetylation of ACTH(1-13)NH$_2$ and β-endorphin(1-31) in intact cells occurs exclusively in secretory granules. In addition, it was expected that other acetyltransferases would be detected in the cell, mediating the acetylation of histones and the α-N-acetylation of many nascent polypeptide chains (Simpson 1978; Belikoff et al. 1980; Traugh and Sharp 1977; Pestana and Pitot 1975). These latter acetyltransferase activities would not be expected to be tissue specific.

Second, a secretory granule-associated α-N-acetyltransferase activity was only found in the intermediate pituitary and not in the anterior pituitary (Glembotski 1982b). Thus the observed tissue specificity of α-N-acetylation could be explained by tissue specific expression of an enzyme. Alternate explanations for the observed tissue specificity of α-N-acetylation would be that anterior pituitary granules possessed the appropriate α-N-acetyltransferase enzyme, but did not express this enzymatic activity in vivo. One way to achieve this result would have been for the anterior pituitary cells to fail to provide the secretory granule lumen with AcCoA; however, given adequate AcCoA in a test tube, anterior pituitary secretory granule extracts still do not have demonstrable α-N-acetyltransferase activity. Thus, the current data argue that the tissue specificity of α-N-acetylation is achieved by the inclusion (or not) of α-N-acetyltransferase enzyme in secretory granules. Mixing experiments will be necessary, however, to show that anterior pituitary secretory granules do not contain inhibitors of α-N-acetylation.

The enzymatic activity studied by Glembotski (1982b) is probably the physiologically relevant acetyltransferase activity for several reasons. The peptide substrates acetylated by the enzyme activity in a test tube--ACTH(1-13)NH$_2$, ACTH(1-39), β-endorphin(1-31), β-endorphin(1-27)--are also α-N-acetylated in intermediate pituitary secretory granules, while several other possible substrates--CLIP [ACTH(18-39); corticotropin-like intermediate lobe peptide], histones, 16K fragment (the NH$_2$-terminal glycoprotein region of the pro-ACTH/endorphin precursor; figure 1)--are not utilized (table 1, next page). The ^{3}H-labeled peptide products created by incubation of ACTH(1-13)NH$_2$ or β-endorphin(1-31) with secretory granule extracts are correctly α-N-acetylated, rather than N-acetylated on the ε-NH$_2$ groups of lysine residues as expected for a histone acetyltransferase (Simpson 1978). Finally, the amount of enzyme activity detected is reasonable for the rate and extent of α-N-acetylation of peptides that actually occurs in intermediate pituitary secretory granules; it takes roughly twelve hours to α-N-acetylate the peptides during biosynthesis in the intact tissue, and the secretory granule enzyme activity would also take about a half day to α-N-acetylate the relevant peptides in the granules.

Glembotski (1983) has also shown that the α-N-acetylation seen in intact intermediate pituitary cells is effectively irreversible. In pulse-chase experiments using [^{35}S]methionine and [^{3}H]acetate double labeling, there was no decrease in the acetate:methionine

172

TABLE 1. α-N-Acetyl Transferase

Substrates:	ACTH(1-13)NH$_2$	
	ACTH(1-39)	
	β-endorphin(1-27)	
	β-endorphin(1-31)	
Not substrates:	ACTH(1-8)	
	β-endorphin(1-16)	
	Histones	
	CLIP	

Inhibitors of acetylation of BOTH
ACTH(1-13)NH$_2$ and β-endorphin(1-31):   ACTH(1-8)
β-endorphin(1-16)
αMSH
Acetyl-β-endorphin(1-31)

---

ratio in αMSH, diacetyl-αMSH or β-endorphin-sized peptides during incubations for up to 48 hours in nonradioactive medium. Both the α-N-acetyl modifications of αMSH and acetylated β-endorphin and the O-acetylation of diacetyl-αMSH were thus found to be quite stable, at least while the peptides were still inside the secretory granules. These double label experiments also suggest that the same pool of ^{3}H-acetyl CoA is used to α-N-acetylate ACTH(1-13)NH$_2$ and β-endorphin and to O-acetylate αMSH, since the ^{3}H/^{35}S ratios for αMSH, α,N-O-diacetyl- αMSH and acetylated β-endorphins were found to occur in a 1:2:1 relationship.

A full understanding of the enzymatic mechanism of the α-N-acetyltransferase from intermediate pituitary should be very interesting. Current data of Glembotski (1982b; unpublished) strongly suggest that the same enzyme α-N-acetylates both ACTH- and β-endorphin-related peptides. As expected, the α-N-acetylation of β-endorphin(1-31) is inhibited by product peptides such as α-N-acetyl-β-endorphin(1-31); interestingly, αMSH also inhibits the acetylation of β-endorphin(1-31). Likewise, α-N-acetylated endorphins inhibit the acetylation of ACTH(1-13)NH$_2$. Substantially shortened peptides, such as ACTH(1-8) and β-endorphin(1-16) [also known as α-endorphin], are not detectably α-N-acetylated under the same reaction conditions used for ACTH(1-13)NH$_2$ and β-endorphin(1-31). Importantly, ACTH(1-8) and β-endorphin(1-16) each inhibit the α-N-acetylation of the longer ACTH- and endorphin-related peptides. The very similar patterns of inhibition of α-N-acetyltransferase activity by acetylated product peptides and by shortened nonacetylated peptides are most economically explained by the existence of one enzyme performing the α-N-acetylation of both ACTH- and β-endorphin-related peptides. The requirements of the binding and catalytic sites of this enzyme will be very interesting and probably quite complex.

When rat intermediate and anterior pituitary cells are placed in tissue culture, they are deprived of many of the influences they receive in the animal. Anterior pituitary cells no longer receive occasional bursts of corticotropin releasing factor in the hypothalamic portal blood system, and the varying levels of feedback from circulating glucocorticoids are also lost in tissue culture. Intermediate pituitary cells lose the several kinds of direct innervation they receive in vivo. It might be expected that the loss of some of these inputs, which are believed to control secretory rates in vivo, would result in the loss of some of the tissue-specific differences seen in the intact animal. However, the anterior pituitary corticotropes do not detectably begin to α-N-acetylate ACTH or β-endorphin in culture, nor do intermediate pituitary cells cease to α-N-acetylate β-endorphin or ACTH. This result is in striking contrast to the rapid loss of α-amidation seen when intermediate pituitary cells are placed in culture (see below).

PEPTIDYL-GLYCINE α-AMIDATION ACTIVITY

Dozens of bioactive peptides have COOH-terminal α-amide groups which are essential for the expression of full biological potency (reviewed in Mains et al. 1983; Eipper et al. 1983a,b). Using the small synthetic peptide substrate originally designed by Bradbury et al. (1982), we have found peptidyl-glycine α-amidating activity in secretory granules from anterior, intermediate, and neural lobes of the rat and beef pituitary as well as from AtT-20 mouse corticotropic tumor cells and rat hypothalamus (Eipper et al. 1983b,c; Glembotski et al. 1984; Mains et al. 1984; Emeson 1984) (figure 4). In this assay the conversion of D-Tyr-Val-Gly into D-Tyr-Val-NH$_2$ is monitored; substrate and product are easily separated by ion exchange chromatography and the D-Tyr residue provides a site for radioiodination as well as protecting against proteolytic degradation.

[^{125}I]-D-Tyr-Val-Gly + goodies $\longrightarrow$
(passes through)

$\qquad$ [^{125}I] -D-Tyr-Val-NH$_2$ + glyoxylate
$\qquad$ (binds; elutes)

Resin: SP-Sephadex
Bind/Wash: 10 mM NaPi, pH 5.0
Elute: 0.5 M NaCl, 10 mM NaPi, pH 5.0

FIGURE 4. α-Amidation Assay

For all these cases, optimal enzyme activity requires the presence of copper ions, reduced ascorbic acid, and molecular oxygen. Enzyme activity is: 1) greatly decreased by removal of copper ions with micromolar amounts of diethyldithiocarbamate, and rejuvenated by replacement of copper (no other metal ion tested will substitute for copper); 2) stimulated by addition of ascorbate better than by addition of any other redox cofactors tested, and largely abolished by pretreatment with ascorbate oxidase; and 3) substantially diminished by replacement of much of the dissolved oxygen in the reaction tube with nitrogen or argon. The enzymatic activity is operationally soluble, in that simple repeated freezing and thawing releases the enzyme from secretory granules (summarized in table 2).

TABLE 2. Properties of α-Amidation Activity

1. Similar enzymatic activity in different tissues:
    rat anterior, intermediate, neural pituitary
    bovine anterior, intermediate, neural pituitary
    rat hypothalamus
    rat serum
    mouse corticotropic tumor cells
    human plasma and cerebrospinal fluid

2. Secretory granule associated

3. Requires molecular oxygen

4. Stimulated by copper

5. Enhanced by ascorbate

6. Inhibited by endogenous inhibitors

7. Soluble

8. Secreted along with peptides

9. Broad specificity for many peptides with a carboxyl terminal glycine residue

In striking contrast to the α-N-acetyltransferase, peptidyl-glycine α-amidation activity is found in a wide variety of tissues and in particular is found in all three lobes of the rat and beef pituitary. In most cases, the α-amidating activity cannot be detected directly in crude tissue extracts made in hypotonic buffers, due to the presence of high amounts of endogenous inhibitory activity. The effect of the endogenous inhibitory activity is greatly diminished when the α-amidation activity is assayed using a secretory granule fraction, although some inhibitory activity is still detectable even in secretory granule preparations. Endogenous inhibitory activity is largely overcome by addition of appropriate amounts of copper ions.

Its requirement for copper, ascorbate, and oxygen, plus the

175

presence of endogenous inhibitors which can be neutralized with addition of optimal levels of copper, make the peptidyl-glycine α-amidating activity very similar to the well-known enzyme, dopamine β-hydroxylase (Rush and Geffen 1980).

The peptidyl-glycine α-amidating activity studied by our group and by Bradbury and Smyth (1983) exhibits a very different pattern of specificity for peptide substrates from that seen for the α-N-acetyltransferase (above). The α-amidating activity will produce a peptide ending in -X-NH$_2$ from a substrate with the structure -X-Gly; although there are quantitative differences, neutral amino acids such as Phe, Val, and Gly function effectively as the residue (X) to be amidated. Based on ability to inhibit α-amidation of D-Tyr-Val-Gly, peptides where X is Trp can also interact with the enzyme. In addition, the peptide to be amidated need not be very long (unlike the case for α-N-acetylation); the synthetic tripeptide D-Tyr-Val-Gly gives Michaelis constants indistinguishable from the K$_1$ values for longer and presumed natural substrates such as α-N-acetyl-ACTH(1-14) and γ$_2$MSH.

The original work of Bradbury et al. (1982) showed that porcine pituitary granules contained an enzymatic activity which utilized D-Tyr-Val-Gly as peptide substrate and produced D-Tyr-Val-NH$_2$ and glyoxylate (HCOCOOH) as products. The reaction scheme suggested by Bradbury et al. (1982) is:

D-Tyr-Val-NH-CH$_2$-COOH + oxidized cofactor + H$_2$O $\rightleftharpoons$

D-Tyr-Val-NH$_2$ + HCOCOOH + reduced cofactor

This scheme does not incorporate the subsequent findings of the need for copper, reduced ascorbate and oxygen, although copper could presumably function as the cofactor. One argument against this scheme is the observation that oxidized cofactors (NADP, NAD, FAD, FMN, ascorbate oxidase-treated ascorbic acid) do not stimulate the reaction when relatively clean secretory granules are used as the enzyme source; in addition, the requirement for molecular oxygen would not be explained (Eipper et al. 1983b,c; Glembotski et al. 1984; Mains et al. 1984; Emeson 1984).

A second possible reaction scheme that takes into account the dependence of the reaction on molecular oxygen resembles that of the amine oxidases:

D-Tyr-Val-NH-CH$_2$-COOH + O$_2$ + H$_2$O $\rightleftharpoons$

D-Tyr-Val-NH$_2$ + HCOCOOH + H$_2$O$_2$

Since several of the amine oxidases characterized as diamine oxidases utilize copper to perform their reactions, the above scheme deserves serious consideration (Gorkin 1983; Kapeller-Adler 1970). It does utilize molecular oxygen, but does not explain why reduced cofactors such as ascorbate (and, less well, biopterin) stimulate the reaction. Addition of a range of monoamine oxidase inhibitors (pargyline, tranylcypromine, iproniazid phosphate, D-amphetamine) did not inhibit the α-amidation activity when the inhibitors were used at concentrations of 1-2 mM. Addition of semicarbazide, generally considered to be a relatively good diamine oxidase inhibitor, had an inhibitory effect only at high levels (slight inhibition at 2.5 mM; no inhibition at 0.5 mM). Addition of millimolar levels of inhibitors such as cyanide and azide does inhibit the enzyme but lower levels are ineffective.

The reaction scheme presently considered most plausible is that of a monooxygenase:

$$D-Tyr-Val-NH-CH_2-COOH + 2(ascorbate) + O_2 \rightleftharpoons$$

$$D-Tyr-Val-NH_2 + 2(semidehydroascorbate) + HCOCOOH + H_2O$$

A variant of the above scheme would involve only one ascorbate molecule being fully oxidized to dehydroascorbate. This scheme draws on our data and that of Bradbury et al. (1982) plus the current data on the very similar reaction performed by dopamine β-hydroxylase (Skotland and Ljones 1980; Diliberto and Allen 1981), in which semidehydroascorbate (ascorbate free radical) is now believed to be the immediate reaction product (instead of dehydroascorbate). Several important aspects of this model must be confirmed experimentally before it is accepted, however. Peptide substrate-dependent ascorbate consumption will need to be measured and compared to the simultaneous production of α-amidated product peptides. Quantitation of glyoxylate production will be crucial, as well as the demonstration that the predicted amount of oxygen is consumed without production of H_2O_2. Final confirmation that this is a monooxygenase reaction would require use of $^{18}O_2$ and detection of ^{18}O in the glyoxylate by mass spectrometry (Kaufman et al. 1962).

The fact that the peptidyl-glycine α-amidating activity is readily released from secretory granules by simple freezing and thawing suggested that the activity might be secreted along with peptide hormones. When AtT-20 mouse corticotropic tumor cells are stimulated to release ACTH- and β-endorphin-related peptides, α-amidating activity is also secreted. Both peptides and α-amidating activity are released coordinately in response to several secretagogues which can increase the secretory rate up to 20-fold for brief periods: corticotropin releasing factor, isoproterenol, $BaCl_2$, and cyclic AMP (table 3, next page). The stimulated release of peptides and of α-amidating activity is blocked by addition of $CoCl_2$ to the medium, consistent with previous demonstrations that an inward flux of calcium ions is required for the release of the soluble contents of the secretory granules by exocytosis (Mains and Eipper 1981, Surprenant 1982, Adler et al. 1983). In each case cited above, the ratio of α-amidating activity (measured at 0.5 μM D-Tyr-Val-Gly substrate) to hormone in the stimulated secretion is the same as that ratio in the secretory granules, again suggesting that release occurs by exocytosis of all of the soluble contents of granules (table 3). These co-release data also further strengthen the claim that the

TABLE 3. Ratio of α-Amidation Activity to ACTH/ β-endorphin Content

	Enzyme/Hormone
AtT-20 Cells	0.15
Granules	0.15
Medium	0.15
Bovine Intermediate Pituitary Granules	0.02
Rat Anterior Pituitary Granules	14
Rat or human plasma	6000

Units: Enzyme pmol/ml/h
Hormone pmol/ml (nM)

α-amidating activity being studied is localized in secretory granules rather than in a minor contaminating organelle with similar sedimentation properties to secretory granules.

Since corticotropic tumor cells release α-amidating activity along with the peptides derived from pro-ACTH/endorphin, it was considered possible that α-amidating activity could be detected in plasma and/or cerebrospinal fluid (CSF). Indeed, when human plasma and CSF are assayed, α-amidating activity is easily demonstrated; the plasma and CSF activities are dependent on copper ions, ascorbate, and molecular oxygen (Wand et al. 1984). The correct product (D-Tyr-Val-NH$_2$) is produced, as demonstrated by high performance liquid chromatography, and the plasma and CSF activities have several other properties consistent with their being similar to the pituitary activity.

However, there is far more α-amidating activity in human and rat plasma than can reasonably be expected to have come from anterior pituitary corticotropes (table 3). This has led to an examination of α-amidation activity in other tissues in the rat, with the interesting finding that the submaxillary glands contain sufficient α-amidating activity to be major candidates to have secreted a significant amount of the α-amidating activity found in plasma. The hypothalamus and cerebral cortex certainly contain enough α-amidating activity to provide the enzyme activity found in CSF. The cerebellum has very low levels of α-amidating activity (using crude extracts at a wide variety of copper levels), consistent with the very low levels of bioactive peptides usually reported for the cerebellum.

Cellular Studies of Peptide α-Amidation

Rat intermediate pituitary cells maintain or increase their content of pro-ACTH/endorphin-derived peptides for at least 2 weeks in tissue culture (Eipper et al. 1983a). The cultured intermediate pituitary cells continue to carry out a large number of co- and post-translational modifications in culture; some of the modifications are of the tissue-specific type [e.g., α-N-acetylation and cleavage of ACTH(1-39) into amino and carboxyl terminal pieces] and some are not (e.g., phosphorylation and glycosylation of the COOH-terminal region of ACTH and many of the proteolytic cleavages). However, rat intermediate pituitary cells in tissue culture specifically lose the ability to α-amidate αMSH; the loss of peptide α-amidation occurs with a half-life of about 15-18 hours (Eipper et al. 1983a; Glembotski et al. 1983). Instead of producing various acetylated forms of ACTH(1-13)NH$_2$, the cells produce the correspo...ding set of non-, mono-, and diacetylated ACTH(1-14). The COOH-terminal sequence of ACTH(1-14) is -Lys^{11}-Pro^{12}-Val^{13}-Gly^{14}, while αMSH terminates -Lys^{11}-Pro^{12}-Val^{13}-NH$_2$; normally, <2% of the αMSH-related peptides in rat or beef intermediate pituitary terminate in -Val-Gly rather than in -Val-NH$_2$. Given the above discussion of the intricate properties of the α-amidation enzyme, it was important to examine whether any of these properties of the α-amidation enzyme could be associated with the loss of the ability of the rat intermediate pituitary cells to α-amidate peptides in tissue culture.

The tissue culture media in our previous work, as in nearly all work with primary cells and cell lines in the literature, contained no added ascorbic acid and very low levels of copper ions ($\leq$.0055 μM). Although a large proportion of the copper in serum is bound to other molecules and is unavailable to tissues (total serum copper is about 16 μM; Riordan 1983; Sarkar 1981; Danks 1980), it seemed reasonable to explore the effect of additional copper on α-amidation by the cells in culture. Serum levels of ascorbate are about 50 μM and it is all in the reduced form (Hornig 1975; Basu and Schorah 1982; Kabrt et al. 1981). Ascorbate is synthesized primarily in the liver of mammals such as rats that can synthesize their own ascorbate, and it seemed likely that exogenous ascorbate would be needed by the pituitary cells.

The simple inclusion of 2 or 20 μM CuSO$_4$ in the serum-free tissue culture medium had no effect on the rapid loss of the ability to α-amidate peptides (Eipper et al. 1983d). When ascorbic acid was included in the culture medium along with copper, a significant recovery of the ability to α-amidate newly synthesized peptides was always seen (table 4, next page). Experiments varying the time of addition of ascorbate indicated that ascorbic acid added only for the incubation with radiolabeled amino acid, (during which time the ability to α-amidate newly synthesized peptides was being tested) was just as effective as ascorbic acid added for the entire time in culture (even when added fresh every few hours). A rough dose-response curve for the response of α-amidation to the dose of ascorbate was also seen, with the bulk of the recovery from the loss of amidation occurring between 0 and 200 μM ascorbate, but with significant increases in α-amidation seen up to 1.0 mM ascorbic acid. The full ability to α-amidate peptides was never regained in these experiments, although the fraction of the newly synthesized αMSH-related molecules which were correctly α-amidated increased up to four-fold in the presence of 2 μM CuSO$_4$ and 1 mM ascorbate.

TABLE 4. Reversal of Loss of α-Amidation in Tissue
Culture by Addition of Reduced Ascorbic Acid

		Percent Amidated αMSH
Experiment 1:	control	12
	0.2 mM ascorbate	37
	0.5 mM ascorbate	41
	1.0 mM ascorbate	45
Experiment 2:	control	15
	0.05 mM ascorbate	30
	2.0 mM ascorbate	42

Rat intermediate pituitary cells were incubated for a day in complete serum-free medium plus 2.0 μM $CuSO_4$ and the indicated concentration of ascorbate. At the end of the pre-incubation, cells were incubated in the same medium plus $[^3H]$tryptophan for 3 hours; RP-HPLC analyses of the tryptic peptides of the labeled αMSH-sized molecules separated peptides derived from ACTH(1-13)NH_2- and ACTH(1-14)-related molecules.

Possible Consequences of Inappropriate Copper and Ascorbate Levels in Vivo

Ascorbate is made in the liver of most mammals including rats, but primates and guinea pigs must rely on the diet for their ascorbate. The pituitary has a higher concentration of ascorbic acid than any other tissue in the body (Hornig 1975; Kabrt et al. 1981), although ascorbate is also very high in the central nervous system, most notably in the hypothalamus (Milby et al. 1981; Schreiber et al. 1979). Copper is an essential trace element in the diet, and modern human diets are frequently low or only marginally adequate in copper (Danks 1980; Sarkar 1981; Riordan 1983). Two human genetic disorders, Wilson's and Menkes' diseases, involve altered copper metabolism; the mottled series of mutant mice are considered to be a good model for Menkes' disease (Riordan 1983; Danks 1980; Hunt 1980). Copper levels can be low in patients undergoing disulfiram (Antabuse) therapy for chronic alcoholism, or in people on high zinc or high ascorbate diets (Danks 1980; Riordan 1983; Schreiber et al. 1979).

Experimental animals (rats, guinea pigs, mice, mottled mutant mice) have been examined for the effects of altered ascorbate and/or copper metabolism on dopamine β-hydroxylase levels and on catecholamine production, and interesting but somewhat conflicting observations have appeared in the literature. Since the α-amidating activity has many striking similarities to dopamine β-hydroxylase, consideration of the catecholamine literature is particularly relevant to the study of α-amidation of peptides. Since dopamine β-hydroxylase is not the rate-limiting step in vivo for norepinephrine biosynthesis, a fairly major drop in the expression of dopamine β-hydroxylase activity in intact tissue would be needed in order to produce a decrease in norepinephrine levels (Rush and Geffen 1980).

Copper deficiency due to dietary insufficiency or to a genetic defect preventing an adequate supply of copper from reaching the adrenals and the nervous system results in a marked decrease in the norepinephrine content of the adrenals and the brain (Hunt 1980; Sourkes 1980; Danks 1980). A clear prediction from this result is that copper deficiency (for dietary, genetic, or drug therapeutic reasons) might also result in a marked decrease in the levels of many crucial bioactive α-amidated peptides. The response of dopamine β-hydroxylase levels to copper deficiency, when the dopamine β-hydroxylase is tested in tissue extracts, is less clear; some workers find enzyme levels to be decreased (Holtzman 1976; Danks 1980; Sourkes 1980), while others report an increase in enzyme activity (Hunt 1980; Prohaska and Smith 1982). Some of the differences in results for the effect of copper deficiency on dopamine β-hydroxylase levels may reflect whether assay conditions were optimized for copper levels (Hunt 1980). At least for brief periods of time, purified dopamine β-hydroxylase is fully stable with all of its copper removed by chelation, and activity is fully restored by the return of copper to the enzyme (Skotland et al. 1980).

Ascorbate deficiency in guinea pigs results in a drop in brain norepinephrine levels within 2 to 3 weeks in most (Hoehn and Kanfer 1980; Saner et al. 1975; Deana et al. 1975) but not all studies (Green et al. 1979). An elevated ascorbate diet in the rat does not alter cerebral norepinephrine levels (Behrens and Madere 1980). Since the rate of ascorbate reduction of enzyme-bound copper on dopamine β-hydroxylase is not the rate-limiting step of dopamine β-hydroxylation (Skotland et al. 1980), it is actually quite striking that a drop in norepinephrine levels is detected so rapidly in most studies. The clear implication from these studies is that ascorbate deficiency in vivo will manifest itself as a drop in the levels of key α-amidated peptides; already there are good data from the tissue culture studies that ascorbic acid supplies directly affect the cellular expression of peptide α-amidation activity (table 4, previous page).

CONCLUSIONS

The study of the co- and post-translational biosynthetic processing events leading to the production of bioactive peptides is a fast-growing field with many potential ramifications in studies of human health and disease. The interaction of various drugs of abuse with bioactive peptides, both at their plasma membrane receptors and during biosynthesis, is only beginning to be examined.

REFERENCES

Adler, M., Wong, B.S., Sabol, S.L., Busis, N., Jackson, M.B., and
    Weight, F.F. Proc Natl Acad Sci (USA), 80:2086-2090, 1983.
Basu, T.K., and Schorah, C.J. Vitamin C in Health and Disease.
    Westport, CT: AVI Publishing Co., 1982
Behrens, W.A., and Madere, R. J Nutr, 110:720-724, 1980.
Belikoff, E., Wong, L.J., and Alberts, B.M. J Biol Chem,
    255:11448-11453, 1980.
Bradbury, A.F., and Smyth, D.G. Biochem Biophys Res Commun,
    112:372-377, 1983.
Bradbury, A.F., Finnie, M.D.A., and Smyth, D.G. Nature (Lond.),
    298:686-688, 1982.
Danks, D.M. CIBA Found Symp, 79:209-221, 1980.
Deana, R., Bharaj, B.S., Verjee, Z.H., and Galzigna, L. Int J
    Vitam Nutr Res, 45:175-182, 1975.
Diliberto, E.J., and Allen, P.L. J Biol Chem, 256:3385-3393,
    1981.
Eipper, B.A., Glembotski, C.C., and Mains, R.E. J Biol Chem,
    258:7292-7298, 1983a.
Eipper, B.A., Glembotski, C.C. and Mains, R.E. Peptides, 4:
    921-928, 1983c.
Eipper, B.A., and Mains, R.E. Endocrine Rev, 1:1-27, 1980.
Eipper, B.A., Mains, R.E., and Glembotski, C.C. Proc Natl Acad
    Sci (USA), 80:5144-5148, 1983b.
Eipper, B.A., Mains, R.E., and Glembotski, C.C. Ferring Symp, in
    press, 1983d.
Emeson, R.B. J. Neurosci, 4: in press, 1984.
Esch, F.S., Shibasaki, T., Bohlen, P., Wehrenberg, W.B., and Ling,
    N.C. In: Rich, D.H., and Gross, E., eds. Peptides. Rockford,
    IL: Pierce Chemical Co., 1981.
Glembotski, C.C., Eipper, B.A., and Mains, R.E. J Biol Chem,
    259:6385-6392, 1984.
Glembotski, C.C., Eipper, B.A., and Mains, R.E. J Biol Chem,
    258:7299-7304, 1983.
Glembotski, C.C. J Biol Chem, 257:10493-10500, 1982a.
Glembotski, C.C. J Biol Chem, 257:10501-10509, 1982b.
Glembotski, C.C. J Biol Chem, 256:7433-7439, 1981.
Gorkin, V.Z. Amine Oxidases in Clinical Research, New York,
    Pergamon Press, 1983.
Green, M.D., Bell, W., Kraut, C., and Omaye, S. Experientia,
    35:515, 1979.
Hoehn, S.K., and Kanfer, J.N. J Nutr, 110:2085-2094, 1980.
Holtzman, N.A. Fed Proc, 35:2276-2280, 1976.
Hornig, D. Ann NY Acad Sci, 258:103-111, 1975.
Hunt, D.M. CIBA Found Symp, 79:247-260, 1980.
Kabrt, J., Pribyl, T., Ocenaskova, J., Dobrovolna, E., and Klein, O.
    Cas Lek Cesk, 120:211-214, 1981.
Kapeller-Adler, R. Amine Oxidases and Methods for Their Study.
    New York: Wiley, 1970.
Kaufman, S., Bridgers, W.F., Eisenberg, F., and Friedman, S.
    Biochem Biophys Res Commun, 9:497-502, 1962.
Laub, O., Rall, L., Bell, G.I., and Rutler, W.J. J Biol Chem,
    258:6037-6042, 1983.
Mains, R.E., Eipper, B.A., Glembotski, C.C., and Dores, R.M.

Trends Neuroscience, 6:229-235, 1983.

Mains, R.E., and Eipper, B.A. J Cell Biol, 89:21-28, 1981.

Mains, R.E., Glembotski, C.C., and Eipper, B.A. Endocrinology, 114:1522-1530, 1984.

Milby, K.H., Mefford, I.N., Chey, W., and Adams, R.N. Brain Res Bull, 7:237-242, 1981.

O'Donohue, T.L., and Dorsa, D.M. Peptides, 3:353-395, 1982.

Pedersen, R.C., and Brownie, A.C. Endocrinology, 112:1279-1287, 1983.

Pestana, A., and Pitot, H.C. Biochemistry 14:1397-1403, 1975.

Prohaska, J.R., and Smith, T.L. J Nutr, 112:1706-1717, 1982.

Riordan, J.R., In: Sarkar, B., ed., Biological Aspects of Metals and Metal-Related Diseases. New York, Raven Press, 1983. pp. 159-170.

Rush, R.A., and Geffen, L.B. CRC Crit Rev Clin Lab Sci, 12:241-277, 1980.

Saner, A., Weiser, H., Hornig, D., DaPrada, M. and Pletscher, A. J Pharm Pharmacol, 27:896-902, 1975.

Sarkar, B. Metal Ions in Biological Systems, 12:233-281, 1981.

Schreiber, V., Pribyl, T., and Jahodova, J. Endocrinologia Experimentalis, 13:131-138, 1979.

Simpson, R.T., Cell, 13:691-699, 1978.

Skotland, T., and Ljones, T. Biochim Biophys Acta, 630:30-35, 1980.

Skotland, T., Petersson, L., Backstrom, D., Ljones, T., Flatmark, T. and Ehrenberg, A. Eur J Biochem, 103:5-11, 1980.

Snyder, S.H. Science, 224:22-31, 1984.

Sourkes, T.L. CIBA Found Symp, 79:143-154, 1980.

Surprenant, A.M. J Cell Biol, 95:559-566, 1982.

Traugh, J., and Sharp, S.B. J Biol Chem, 252:3738-3744, 1977.

Wand, G., Baylin, S., Ney, R. and Eipper, E. 7th International Congress of Endocrinology, Quebec, Canada, Abstract, 1984.

Woodford, T.A., and Dixon, J.E. J Biol Chem, 254:4993-4999, 1979.

ACKNOWLEDGMENTS

This work was supported by National Institutes of Health grants AM-32948 and AM-39249 and by the McKnight Foundation and the Upjohn Company.

AUTHORS

Richard E. Mains, Ph.D.
Dept. of Neuroscience
The Johns Hopkins University School of Medicine
725 N. Wolfe Street
Baltimore, MD 21205

Betty A. Eipper, Ph.D.
Dept. of Neuroscience
The Johns Hopkins University School of Medicine
725 N. Wolfe Street
Baltimore, MD 21205

Opiate-Mediated Control of Luteinizing Hormone in the Male: Role in the Development of Narcotic Tolerance and Physical Dependence

Theodore J. Cicero

In this review, the possible involvement of opiate-induced perturbations in endocrine status in the development of narcotic tolerance and physical dependence will be discussed. Although the opiates affect a wide range of neuroendocrine axes, the discussion will be limited to their effects on the endocrine secretions of the hypothalamic-pituitary-gonadal axis in the male rat, since this system has been by far the most extensively examined. The review has been divided into three sections: the impact of opiates on the function of the hypothalamic-pituitary-gonadal axis; the plasticity and physiological significance of endogenous opioid-mediated control of LHRH; and, finally, the preliminary data implicating opiate-induced alterations in hormonal status in the development of tolerance to and physical dependence on the narcotics.

DIRECT EFFECTS OF THE OPIATES ON THE HYPOTHALAMIC-PITUITARY-GONADAL AXIS

It has been clearly established that serum testosterone levels are markedly depressed following acute or chronic narcotic administration in the male of every species (e.g., Cicero 1980; Cicero et al. 1976, 1977, 1979; Cicero and Badger 1977; Mendelson et al. 1979; Mirin et al. 1976). There are four mechanisms that could account for this: first, narcotics could enhance the metabolism of testosterone by the liver; second, they could block the biosynthesis of the steroid at the level of the testes; third, they could suppress the synthesis and/or release of LH from the pituitary and, thereby, inhibit LH-dependent testicular steroidogenesis; or, finally, they could inhibit the release of LHRH from the hypothalamus.

Liver or other target organs. There are no reports in the literature that either acute or chronic narcotic administration enhances the catabolism of testosterone. Furthermore, it has been shown (Cicero et al. 1976, 1977a) that narcotics do not affect the fate of testosterone in its target organs.

Testes. It has been conclusively demonstrated that narcotics do not depress serum testosterone levels by a direct effect on the testes. The relevant information can be summarized as follows: first, narcotics are totally ineffective in lowering serum testosterone levels when narcotic-induced reductions in LH are prevented by administration of LH (Cicero et al. 1976; Cicero et al. 1977 a,b); second, narcotics do not interfere with the basal or stimulated production of testosterone in the testes (Cicero et al. 1977a); and, finally, it has been shown (Cicero et al. 1977a,b; Cicero 1980) that the narcotics do not interfere with the uptake or binding of LH in the testes.

Hypothalamic-pituitary-LH axis. A large number of studies have demonstrated that narcotics exert their primary effect on the hypothalamic-pituitary-gonadal axis by depressing the elaboration of LH by the hypothalamic-pituitary-axis, which leads to a secondary depression in LH-dependent testicular steroidogenesis (Cicero et al. 1977a, 1977b; Bruni et al. 1979; Blank et al. 1979; Kalra 1982; Mendelson et al. 1979; Mirin et al. 1976; Ieiri et al. 1980).

The locus of action of the narcotics within the hypothalamic-pituitary-LH axis appears to be at the hypothalamus. The evidence supporting this conclusion is as follows. First, morphine blocks the postcastration-induced increase in serum LH in the male rat, and this effect can be completely overcome by the administration of LHRH (Cicero et al. 1977b). Second, it has been shown that even very large doses of morphine do not reduce the elevations in serum LH produced by LHRH in the rat (Cicero 1980; Cicero et al. 1977b). Third, it has been demonstrated that the narcotics do not inhibit the basal or LHRH-stimulated synthesis and secretion of LH from anterior pituitaries incubated in vitro (Cicero et al. 1977b). Finally, it has been shown that both exogenous and endogenous opiates inhibit the release of LHRH from the hypothalamus under in vitro conditions (Rotsztejn et al. 1978a,b).

PARTICIPATION OF ENDOGENOUS OPIOIDS IN THE FUNCTION OF THE HYPOTHALAMIC-PITUITARY-LH AXIS

The findings described above indicate quite clearly that opiate alkaloid drugs are potent inhibitors of activity within the hypothalamic-pituitary-gonadal axis in the male and that they exert their effects exclusively by inhibiting the release of LHRH from the hypothalamus. As will be more fully discussed below, it is clear that these drugs affect the release of LHRH via specific opiate receptors in the hypothalamus which are as yet unidentified. Since it is quite obvious that these receptors would not exist simply to bind synthetic opioid compounds, it has been hypothesized that endogenous opioids exist which normally play a role in the physiological regulation of LHRH release.

This hypothesis has been impressively supported by the following data: first, several endogenously occurring opioid peptides significantly inhibit the secretion of serum LH (Blank et al.

1979; Bruni et al. 1977; Meites et al. 1979); second, within minutes after the subcutaneous injection of naloxone precipitous increases in serum LH levels occur in the male and female of every species (e.g., Blank et al. 1979; Mendelson et al. 1979; Mirin et al. 1976; Cicero et al. 1979; 1980b; Ieiri et al. 1980; Sylvester et al. 1980; Meites et al. 1979; Wilkes and Yen 1981); third, under in vitro conditions it has been shown that opiate agonists and antagonists increase and decrease, respectively, the efflux of LHRH from the hypothalamus (Rotsztejn et al. 1978a,b; Wilkes and Yen 1981); and, finally, the negative feedback control of the hypothalamic-pituitary-LH axis exerted by testosterone (Cicero et al. 1979) and estrogens (Ieiri et al. 1980; Sylvester et al. 1980; Van Vugt et al. 1982) in the male and female, respectively, can be blocked by the administration of naloxone.

The foregoing results have led to the hypothesis that opioid-containing neuronal elements represent an intermediate link between the effects of steroids on the hypothalamus and their ultimate inhibition of the release of LHRH (Cicero 1980; Meites et al.1979; Van Vugt et al. 1982). If this hypothesis is correct, then it would follow that endogenous opioids, or narcotic drugs with an affinity for the relevant opiate receptors, would mimic the effects of gonadal steroids on the hypothalamic-pituitary-LH axis. To assess this possibility, we have examined whether morphine, as a prototypic opioid agonist, had androgen-like effects in the castrated male rat (Cicero et al. 1980a). We found that morphine was just as effective as testosterone in preventing the initial castration-induced increase in serum LH levels and the reduction in the hypothalamic content of LHRH in the male rat that occurs 7 to 10 days following orchiectomy (Cicero et al. 1980a). Although it is now widely accepted that endogenous opioid systems are in some way involved in regulating LHRH release from the hypothalamus, many questions remain unanswered: (a) Which of the many endogenously occurring opioids is the principal one involved? (b) Which opiate receptor subtype mediates the effects of endogenous and exogenous opiates on the hypothalamic-pituitary-LH axis? (c) Are these systems integral and physiologically relevant components of this axis?

PHYSIOLOGICAL SIGNIFICANCE AND PLASTICITY OF ENDOGENOUS OPIOID-MEDIATED CONTROL OF LHRH.

As discussed above, a major problem encountered in assessing the characteristics of opioid-mediated control of LHRH is the absence of any information regarding the identity of the endogenous opioid involved. This has precluded many crucial experiments, such as increasing or decreasing the activity of the peptide to assess the precise nature of the interaction between the relevant opioid systems and LHRH release mechanisms-a traditional strategy used to assess the role of neurotransmitters/neuro-modulators. As an indirect means of examining this issue, we have developed a different strategy in our laboratory over the last 2 years (Cicero et al. 1983a,b,c). Specifically, we have used exogenous and endogenous opioid agonists and antagonists, with presumed affinity

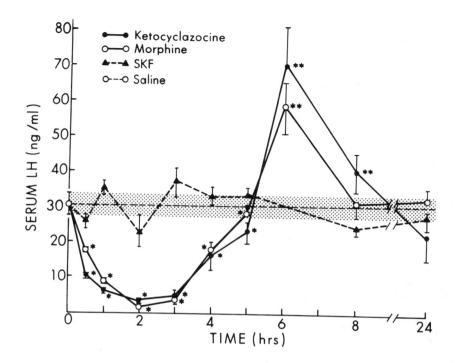

FIGURE 1. The effects of morphine, ketocyclazocine and SKF-10,047 on serum LH levels in normal rats (N=12 to 18). T.J. Cicero, D.P. Owens, P.F. Schmoeker, E.R. Meyer. Opiate-Induced Enhancement of Naloxone's Effects on Serum Luteinizing Hormone Levels in the Male Rat: Specificity for mu Agonists. The Journal of Pharmacology and Experimental Therapeutics, 226:770-775, 1983. © 1983, Williams and Wilkins. Reprinted by permission.

for specific opiate receptor subtypes in brain, to selectively enhance or block opiate receptors and then assessed the response to subsequently administered opiate agonists and antagonists. Our rationale was that, since endogenous opioids must interact with a receptor to exert their effects, an alteration in the responsiveness of these receptors would have the same effect as enhancing or depressing the actions of the peptide, accomplished by more traditional means (e.g., destruction of the pathways). Thus, our strategy been two-fold: first, to determine whether one or more receptors appear to mediate the effects of endogenous and exogenous opioids on the release of LHRH; and, second, to determine whether these receptors are influenced by the prior administration of opioid agonists and antagonists.

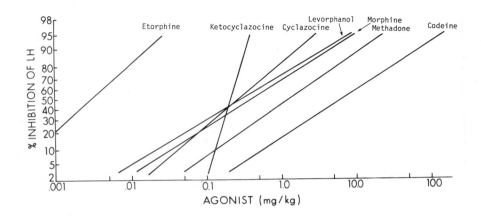

FIGURE 2. Percent inhibition of serum LH levels produced by a wide range of opiates. Each dose-response curve is the best-fit line and represents at least 5 doses of each drug with an N of 18 to 40. The slopes of the lines were virtually identical except for ketocyclazocine (p<.01) and cyclazocine (p<.05) which were significantly more steep than the others. Data for SKF have not been included since it had no effect on serum LH levels. T.J. Cicero, D.P. Owens, P.F. Schmoeker, E.R. Meyer. Opiate-Induced Enhancement of Naloxone's Effects on Serum Luteinizing Hormone Levels in the Male Rat: Specificity for mu Agonists. The Journal of Pharmacology and Experimental Therapeutics, 226:770-775, 1983. ©1983, Williams and Wilkins. Reprinted by permission.

Effects of mu, kappa and sigma opiate agonists on serum LH levels. The time-course for the effects of morphine, ketocyclazocine and SKF on serum LH levels are shown in figure 1. As can be seen, following an injection of 5 mg/kg morphine oketocyclazocine, serum LH levels declined sharply in a time-dependent fashion, reaching peak levels of depression 1 to 3 hours after the injection; thereafter, LH levels gradually returned to control levels. Six to 8 hours after the injection, serum LH levels "rebounded" significantly above control levels and then returned to normal values 8 to 24 hours later. In contrast to the effects of morphine and ketocyclazocine, 15 mg/kg SKF had no

TABLE 1

ED_{50}s and potencies of various opiate agonists in depressing serum LH levels

Agonist	ED_{50}s	(95% confidence limits	Potency (morphine=1
Morphine	0.41	(0.37-0.43)	1
Etorphine	0.0012	(0.0009-0-0.0016)	341.6
Ketocyclazocine	0.21	(0.19-0.24)	1.95
Cyclazocine	0.27	(0.23-0.30)	1.52
Levorphanol	0.29	(0.25-0.36)	1.41
Methadone	1.30	(1.19-1.38)	0.32
Codeine	6.0	(5.81-6.20)	0.07

T.J. Cicero, D.P. Owens, P.F. Schmoeker, E.R. Meyer, Opiate-Induced Enhancement of Naloxone's Effects on Serum Luteinizing Hormone Levels in the Male Rat: Specificity for mu Agonists. The Journal of Pharmacology and Experimental Therapeutics, 226:770-775, 1983. © 1983, Williams and Wilkins. Reprinted by permission.

TABLE 2

Naloxone antagonism of opiate-induced inhibitions of serum LH levels

Agonist	K_e (nM)	pA_2
Morphine	1.41 (±0.23)	7.86 (±0.07)
Levorphanol	1.44 (±0.05)	7.87 (±0.02)
Methadone	1.49 (±0.06)	7.82 (±0.01)
Ketocyclazocine	11.99 (±1.13)	6.92 (±0.05)
Cyclazocine	13.27 (±0.89)	6.87 (±0.50)

pA_2 and K_e values were determined as described elsewhere (Tallarida et al 1981).

T.J. Cicero, D.P. Owens, P.F. Schmoeker, Meyer, E.R., Opiate-Induced Enhancement of Naloxone's Effects on Serum Luteinizing Hormone Levels in the Male Rat: Specificity for mu Agonists. The Journal of Pharmacology and Experimental Therapeutics, 226:770-775, 1983. © 1983, Williams and Wilkens. Reprinted by permission.

significant effect on serum LH at any post-injection time interval examined .

On the basis of the preceding studies, a 2-hour time interval was selected to construct LH dose-response curves for a wide range of opiate agonists. Figure 2 depicts the best-fit lines, plotted on log-probit paper; all opiates tested depressed serum LH levels in a dose-dependent fashion, with the exception of SKF which had no

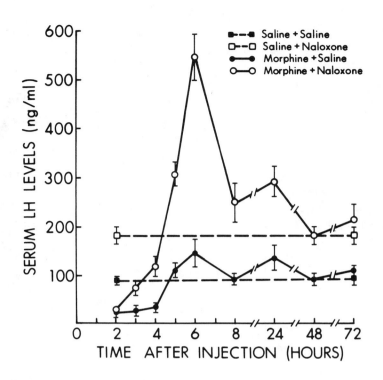

FIGURE 3. Serum LH levels in animals injected with morphine (10 mg/kg) or saline and then injected with saline or naloxone (0.5 mg/kg) at the intervals shown. Values for saline + saline and saline + naloxone groups have been pooled. T.J. Cicero, D.P. Owens, P.F. Schmoeker, Meyer, E.R. Morphine-Induced Supersensitivity to Naloxone's Effects on Luteinizing hormone Secretion in the Male Rat. The Journal of Pharmacology and Experimental Therapeutics, 225:35-41, 1983. ©1983, William and Wilkins. Reprinted by permission.

appreciable effect at any dose examined. The ED_{50}s and the potencies of these compounds, relative to morphine, are shown in table 1.

Naloxone blockade of opiate-induced depressions in serum LH levels. The efficacy of naloxone in competitively inhibiting the LH-depressing effects of several representative opiates is shown in table 2. As can be seen, naloxone effectively reversed the effects of both putative mu and kappa agonists, but was nearly 10 times more potent in antagonizing the effects of mu agonists than it was for kappa compounds. In addition, it is also apparent that two distinct binding sites appear to mediate the effects of these agonists.

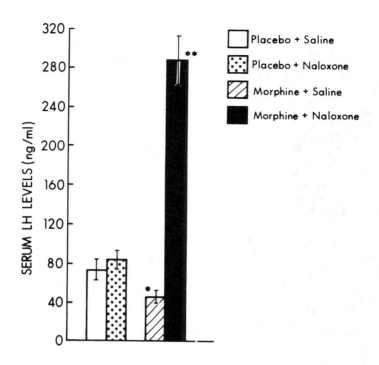

FIGURE 4. The effects of naloxone (0.025 mg/kg) or saline on
serum LH levels in rats (N=20) implanted with morphine or placebo
pellets 48 hours earlier. *Significantly (p<.01) lower than
placebo-saline groups; **Significantly (p<.001) higher than all
other groups. T.J. Cicero, D.P. Owens, P.F. Schmoeker, Meyer,
E.R. Morphine-Induced Supersensitivity to Naloxone's Effects on
Luteinizing Hormone Secretion in the Male Rat. The Journal of
Pharmacology and Experimental Therapeutics, 225:35-41, 1983.
©1983, Williams and Wilkins. Reprinted by permission.

Influence of acute morphine administration on naloxone-induced
increases in serum LH levels. The effects of a single morphine or
saline injection on the increase in serum LH levels produced by
naloxone at various intervals after the initial injection are
shown in figure 3. As can be seen, in animals receiving saline or
naloxone as the second injection, serum LH levels were substantially depressed in morphine-pretreated rats when compared to
saline-pretreated animals from 2 to 4 hours after the initial
injections. Thereafter, LH levels returned to normal levels in
control values 6 to 24 hours after the injection. With respect to
the effects of naloxone on serum LH levels in morphine and saline
pretreated rats, 2-3 hours after the morphine injection, naloxone-
induced increases in serum LH were suppressed, when compared to
saline-injected controls. By 4 hours post-morphine injection,

TABLE 3
Naloxone dose-response curves in controls and in animals injected acutely with morphine or implanted with morphine pellets.

	ED_{50}(95% confidence limits)
Saline - Placebo	0.23 (0.18-0.25)
Acute Morphine	0.124 (0.116-0.131)
Morphine Pellet	0.0053 (0.0048-0.0056)

normal LH responses to naloxone returned. However, 5-24 hours after morphine, the increases in serum LH levels produced by naloxone were markedly exaggerated in morphine pretreated animals when compared to controls, with the peak degree of enhanced sensitivity occurring at 6 hours.

Naloxone-induced increases in serum LH levels in morphine pellet implanted animals. The effects of saline or naloxone on serum LH levels in male rats implanted with a single morphine or placebo pellet 48 hrs earlier are shown in figure 4. Serum LH levels were significantly depressed in morphine-implanted animals when compared to placebo controls. Moreover, at this dose of naloxone (0.025 mg/kg) there was no statistically significant stimulation of serum LH levels in placebo-implanted male rats. In marked contrast to these results, naloxone was extremely effective in elevating serum LH levels in morphine-implanted animals, producing increases nearly 8 times greater than those found in controls.

Magnitude of the shift in the naloxone dose response curve after acute and chronic morphine administration. The naloxone dose-response curves generated in rats pretreated with saline/placebo, a morphine injection or one morphine pellet implantation are shown in figure 5. Both acute and chronic morphine administration markedly shifted the naloxone dose-response curve significantly to the left when compared to controls. However, this shift was much more striking in chronically treated animals when compared to controls or those animals receiving acute morphine pretreatment. the ED_{50}s in the respective groups are shown in table 3.

Opiate-induced enhancement of naloxone's effects on serum LH levels. To assess whether the opiate-induced enhancement of naloxone's effects was specific to morphine or represented a more general property of the opiates, we assessed whether the wide range of opiates utilized in the preceding studies (see figure 2) produced an enhanced response to naloxone. The results of these experiments are shown in figure 6. As can be seen, serum LH levels in opiate-injected animals, receiving saline as the second injection 6 hours later, were somewhat elevated with respect to saline-pretreated animals (shaded area in this figure). When naloxone was given as the second injection, a markedly enhanced response was observed in those animals pretreated with mu agonists, relative to saline-pretreated controls; the order of potency was etorphine >levorphanol >morphine >methadone >codeine.

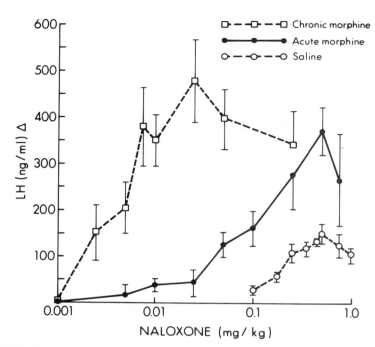

FIGURE 5. Naloxone dose-response curves in animals (N=17 to 57) injected with saline or morphine (10 mg/kg) 6 hours earlier or implanted with morphine or placebo pellets 48 hr earlier. T.J. Cicero, D.P. Owens, P.F. Schmoeker, Meyer, E.R. Morphine-induced Supersensitivity to Naloxone's Effects on Luteinizing Hormone Secretion in the Male Rat. The Journal of Pharmacology and Experimental Therapeutics, 225:35-41, 1983. © 1983, Williams and Wilkins. Reprinted by permission.

In contrast to these results neither ketocyclazocine, cyclazocine nor SKF produced any facilitation of naloxone's effects.

Effects of FK 33-824 on naloxone-induced increases in serum LH levels. To determine whether FK 33-824, as a metabolically stable analog of the endogenously occurring methionine enkephalin (Roemer et al. 1977), produced an enhanced sensitivity to naloxone's effects on serum LH levels, rats were injected with saline or FK 33-824 at a dose (0.05 mg/kg) selected to produce modest decreases in serum LH levels (Cicero et al. 1983c). At intervals, thereafter, the animals in each group received a second injection of either saline or naloxone (0.25 mg/kg). The results of this study are shown in figure 7. Serum LH levels were modestly reduced in FK 33-824-saline injected animals, when compared to controls at intervals up to 2 hours after the initial injection: thereafter the two groups were indistinguishable. When naloxone was given as

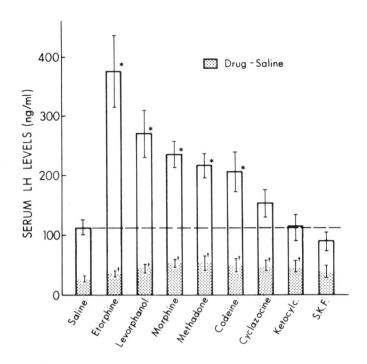

FIGURE 6. Serum LH levels in animals (N=20-28) injected with saline or opiate followed 6 hours later by saline (see shaded area within bar) or 0.25 mg/kg naloxone (open bars). The doses of each opiate were selected to provide an initial 60-80% inhibition of serum LH 2 hours after its adminitration, and were as follows: etorphine .005 mg/kg, levorphanol 0.5 mg/kg, morphine 2.5 mg/kg, methadone 2.5 mg/kg, codeine 7.5 mg/kg, cyclazocine 0.5 mg/kg, ketocyclazocine 0.5 mg/kg, and SKF 5 mg/kg. *Significantly (p<.01) greater than saline-naloxone injected animals; †Significantly (p<.05) greater than saline-saline injected animals. T.J. Cicero, D.P. Owens, P.F. Schmoeker, E.R. Meyer. Opiate-Induced Enhancement of Naloxone's Effects on Serum luteinizing Hormone Levels in the Male Rat: Specificity for mu Agonist. The Journal of Pharmacology and Experimental Therapeutics, 226:770-775, 1983. © 1983, Williams and Wilkins. Reprinted by permission.

the second injection to saline-pretreated rats, serum LH levels were significantly elevated above values obtained in saline-saline treated animals, but the increase was quite small at the very low dose of the narcotic antagonist employed. In the case of FK 33-824, the inhibitory effects of the peptide on serum LH levels were initially (<2 hours) overcome by naloxone. However, at 4 to 6

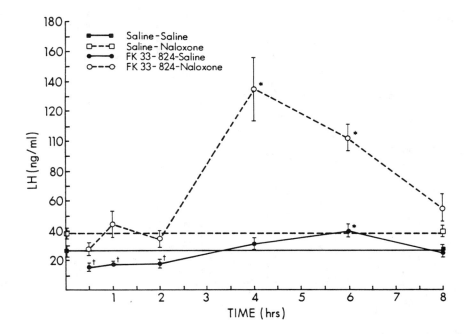

FIGURE 7. Serum LH levels in animals (N=10 to 15) injected with saline or FK 33-824 (0.05 mg/kg) followed by saline or naloxone (0.25 mg/kg) at the intervals shown. Values for the saline-saline and saline-naloxone groups were pooled (shown as continuous solid or dashed lines). * Significantly (p<.01) higher than respective control; † Significantly (p<.05) lower than control. T.J. Cicero, D.P. Owens, K.S. Newman, P.F. Schmoeker, Meyer, E.R. Exogenous and Endogenous Opioid-induced Enhancements of Naloxone's Effects on Serum Luteinizing Hormone Levels in the Male Rat. European Journal of Pharmacology, in press. © 1984, Elsevier Biomedical Press.

hours after the FK 33-824 injection, naloxone was substantially more effective in increasing serum LH levels than it was in saline-pretreated animals. By 8 hours after the injection of FK 33-824 essentially normal responses to naloxone had returned.

Naloxone-precipitated withdrawal behavior following acute and chronic morphine pretreatment. Naloxone-precipitated withdrawal signs in rats implanted with morphine or placebo pellets 48 hours earlier are shown in figure 8. Naloxone (0.5 mg/kg) produced a vigorous withdrawal response in morphine-implanted rats. No other group of animals, notably morphine-implanted rats injected with 0.005 mg/kg naloxone, displayed any opiate withdrawal behavior.

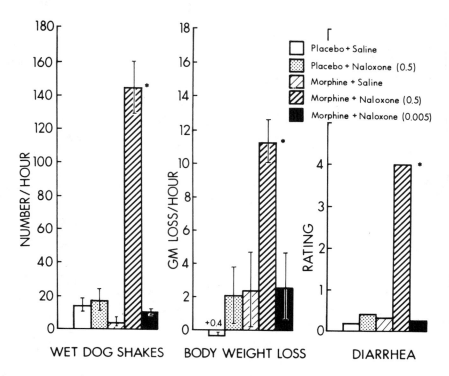

FIGURE 8. Naloxone-precipitated incidence of wet-dog shakes (number/hour), body weight loss (gm/hour) and diarrhea (for rating scale see Cicero and Meyer, 1973) in animals implanted with morphine or placebo pellets 48 hours earlier. T.J. Cicero, D.P. Owens, P.F. Schmoeker, E.R. Meyer. Opiate-Induced Enhancement of Naloxone's Effects on Serum Luteinizing Hormone Levels in the Male Rat: Specificity for mu Agonists. The Journal of Pharmacology and Experimental Therapeutics, 226:770-775, 1983. © 1983, Williams and Wilkins. Reprinted by permission.

Mechanisms involved in opiate-induced enhancement of naloxone's effects on serum LH levels. In a series of studies we have explored a number of mechanisms which could be involved in the development of opiate-induced enhancement of naloxone's effects. The experiments (Cicero et al. 1983a,b,c) can be summarized as follows: first, morphine pretreatment did not influence the uptake of naloxone into brain; second, changes in the sensitivity of the pituitary to LHRH do not seem to be involved in this phenomenon, since LHRH dose-response curves were identical in saline- and morphine-pretreated animals; and, finally, we have been unable to demonstrate any gross changes in the affinity or density of mu, delta or kappa binding sites in whole brain or the hypothalamus of morphine-pretreated rats when compared to controls.

DISCUSSION

The results of these studies demonstrate that either acute or chronic morphine pretreatment markedly sensitizes male rats to the subsequent effects of naloxone on serum LH levels. This phenomenon appears to represent a true example of "supersensitivity", since the following criteria were met: a parallel shift to the left in the dose-response curve, and an enhanced effect of naloxone on serum LH levels at the same brain concentration of the antagonist. Although both acute and chronic morphine administration produced an enhanced sensitivity to naloxone, relative to controls, there were substantial differences between the two treatment regimens. For example, although acute and chronic morphine administration produced an exaggerated LH response to naloxone of approximately the same magnitude, the peak effect was elicited by much lower doses of naloxone in morphine-implanted rats than it was in morphine-injected animals. In addition, at comparable doses, naloxone-induced increases in serum LH levels were up to 20 times greater in chronically morphinized animals than they were in those rats receiving a single injection of morphine. Finally, although a single injection of 10 mg/kg morphine significantly lowered the dose of naloxone producing the half-maximal increase in serum LH levels, relative to controls, the naloxone ED_{50} morphine-pelleted animals was several orders of magnitude less than that found in controls or in acutely morphinized animals.

Our studies also revealed that an enhancement of naloxone's effects on serum LH levels is not a common feature of all drugs which depress activity within the hypothalamic-pituitary axis since neither non-opiate (ethanol and Nembutal) nor certain opiate compounds (cyclazocine and ketocyclazocine) produced this effect, despite a profound initial depression in serum LH levels (Cicero et al. 1983a,b,c). Moreover, we found that this phenomenon is not a general feature of all opiates, but rather is restricted to only those agents with an established affinity for mu binding sites in the brain. We were unable to demonstrate a facilitation of naloxone's effects by the administration of ketocyclazocine, cyclazocine or SKF, representative kappa and sigma agonists (figure 6).

Our observations indicate that at least two receptors appear to be involved in suppressing LH release. In this regard, it is somewhat puzzling that an enhancement of naloxone's effects develops only as a function of mu receptor occupancy, particularly since ketocyclazocine and cylazocine were more potent in depressing LH levels than the mu agonists assessed, with the exception of etorphine. However, it should be noted that functionally important changes in the activity of the hypothalamic-pituitary-LH axis, such as those produced by castration and/or excess steroid administration, have previously been shown to attenuate the effects of mu agonists and antagonists on LH secretion (Cicero et al. 1982; Owens and Cicero 1981) and to alter the density (B_{max}) of mu binding sites in whole rat brain (Hahn and Fishman 1979).

If one makes the assumption that functionally important changes in the activity of the hypothalamic-pituitary axis would be reflected in changes in all components of the axis, including endogenous opioid-containing neuronal systems, then the selective alterations in mu receptor function observed in these and other studies could indicate that they play a significant role in regulating the release of LHRH.

Our data also indicate that a metabolically stable analog of methionine enkephalin (FK 33-824) produced an enhanced response to naloxone analogous to, and perhaps greater than, that generated by opiate alkaloid agonists. These data indicate that an enhancement of naloxone's effects on serum LH levels is not a unique event associated with the administration of drugs, but can be generated by endogenously occurring compounds. Moreover, since it has been suggested in a number of recent reports (Cox and Baizman 1982; Naber et al. 1981; Reid et al. 1982) that endogenous opioids, like most neurotransmitters/neuro-modulators, are released in a pulsatile manner, it seems probable that the changes in the sensitivity of those opiate receptors involved in LHRH release observed under our experimental conditions may occur under in vivo conditions.

Based upon our results, it seems certain that the development of an opiate-induced enhancement of naloxone's effects on serum LH levels is due primarily to fundamental alterations in the hypothalamus, rather than the pituitary. The nature of the changes occurring in the hypothalamus are not clear, but we have shown that the uptake, metabolism and regional distribution of naloxone are not affected by prior opiate administration (Cicero et al. 1983a) and, hence, it is unlikely that there is an increase in the availability of the antagonist at its active binding sites. Rather, the data are consistent with the interpretation that the nature of the ligand-receptor interaction has been altered in some way. However, we have been unable to demonstrate any change in the K_d or B_{max} of $[^3H]$-naltrexone binding to its receptors in whole brain or hypothalamus, nor have we been able to discern differences in the relative proportion of mu and delta binding sites following morphine administration (Cicero et al. 1983a,b,c). It would be premature, however, to dismiss the possibility that such changes may occur under in vivo conditions since it is possible that morphine pretreatment produces subtle changes in opiate receptors in the intact membrane in highly discrete areas of brain which could be obscured by the in vitro analysis of receptor properties using whole brain or gross regional analysis.

The factors leading to the development of supersensitivity to naloxone's effects on serum LH levels are not understood, but on the basis of our studies, the following conclusions can be drawn. First, only those opiates with an affinity for mu binding sites in brain produce an enhancement of naloxone's effects on serum LH levels; opiates which bind selectively to kappa or sigma binding sites are devoid of such activity (Cicero et al. 1983c)

Second, it appears that occupancy of mu receptors alone is insufficient to promote the development of supersensitivity to naloxone's effects, but that an initial depression in serum LH levels, followed by a rebound to supranormal levels is an absolute requirement (Cicero et al. 1983c). However, it should be noted that a depression of LH per se cannot be the sole determining factor, since many opiate and non-opiate compounds which depress LH do not lead to the development of supersensitivity (Cicero et al. 1983c).

The present results add to the growing evidence supporting the hypothesis that endogenous opioid-containing neuronal systems play an integral role in regulating LHRH release in the male and female. Our results not only reinforce these conclusions but indicate that these systems are markedly sensitive to transient phases of depression and excitation.

As a potentially important offshoot of the work described in this paper, it appears that naloxone-induced increases in serum LH levels can serve as an extremely useful index of opiate dependence. A sensitive and reliable index of the extent and severity of opiate dependence should satisfy at least three criteria: first, that naloxone produces increases in serum LH levels in morphine pretreated rats which are greater than those found in controls; second, that the naloxone dose-response curve, and corresponding ED_{50} should shift in parallel to the left; and, third, that the enhanced sensitivity to naloxone-induced increases in serum LH levels should correlate with the development of other behavioral and physiological indices of opiate withdrawal. From the data presented above, it seems clear that the naloxone-precipitated increase in serum LH levels in the morphine-exposed male rat satisfies each of these criteria. Although acute naloxone-precipitated withdrawal has been reported by a number of investigators following morphine administration (Aceto et al. 1977; Cox et al. 1968; Kosersky et al. 1974; Meyer and Sparber 1977; Smits 1975; Wiley and Downs 1979), the increase in the incidence of withdrawal signs has been generally unremarkable-making quantifiable assessments difficult at best. In contrast, we found in the present studies that a single morphine injection produced an extremely exaggerated LH response to naloxone which was readily quantifiable and highly reproducible. In addition, we found that with chronic morphine exposure, naloxone-induced increases in serum LH paralleled the development of other signs of withdrawal and that the shift in the sensitivity to naloxone was many times greater than that observed for these other signs.

CONSEQUENCES OF OPIATE-INDUCED ALTERATIONS IN HORMONES SECRETED BY THE HYPOTHALAMIC-PITUITARY-GONADAL AXIS

Because of the pervasive influence of hormones in the biochemistry and function of every organ in the body, it seems reasonable to postulate that acute or persistent drug-induced alterations in any of these hormones could play a significant role in the effects of these drugs, particularly in those adaptive changes occurring

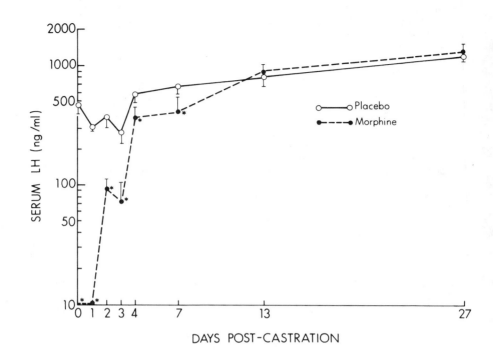

FIGURE 9. The effects of a single morphine or placebo pellet implant on serum LH levels in male rats (N=10) that had been castrated from 0 to 27 days earlier. * Significantly (p<.001) lower when compared to placebo-implanted animals. T.J. Cicero, E.R. Meyer, P.F. Schmoeker. Development of Tolerance to the Effects of Morphine on Luteinizing Hormone Secretion as a Function of Castration in the Male Rat. The Journal of Pharmacology and Experimental Therapeutics, 223:784-789, 1982. © 1982, Williams and Wilkins. Reprinted by permission.

during the development of tolerance and physical dependence. We have recently accumulated a good deal of evidence which supports this hypothesis.

Functional tolerance. In earlier work (Cicero et al. 1980a), we found that tolerance appeared to develop to the effects of morphine on LH secretion as a function of castration. For example, in male rats castrated for 3 days, morphine was a potent suppressor of serum LH levels, but was virtually without effect in animals that had been castrated for 2 weeks. In these studies, however, morphine was administered by pellet implantation so that it was not possible to ascertain the magnitude of the shift in sensitivity to morphine. Because our earlier observations could have considerable significance with respect to the plasticity of

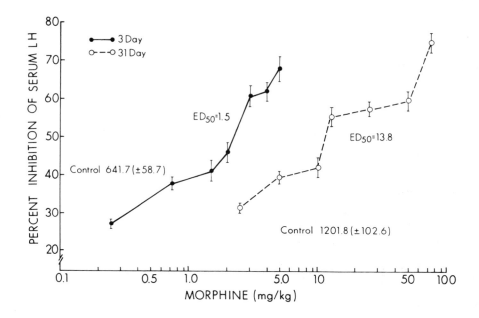

FIGURE 10. The percent inhibition of serum LH levels produced by various doses of morphine (mg/kg) 30 min after its administration to male rats (N=8 to 10) castrated 3 or 31 days earlier. T.J. Cicero, E.R. Meyer, Schmoeker, P.F. Development of Tolerance to the Effects of Morphine on Luteinizing Hormone Secretion as a Function of Castration in the Male Rat. The Journal of Pharmacology and Experimental Therapeutics, 223:784-789, 1982. © 1982, Williams and Wilkins. Reprinted by permission.

the endogenous opioid system controlling the hypothalamic-pituitary axis and the possible involvement of hormones in the development of tolerance to and physical dependence on the opiates, the difference in the sensitivity of castrated male rats to an opiate agonist (morphine), antagonist (naloxone) and testosterone has been further characterized in several recent studies.

Differences in the response of castrated male rats to morphine. To examine the time course for the change in the response to morphine in the castrated animal, groups of rats were implanted with a single morphine or placebo pellet at intervals after castration and were killed 24 hr later. The results are shown in figure 9. When morphine pellets were implanted at the same time or 1 day after castration, the post-castration-induced increases

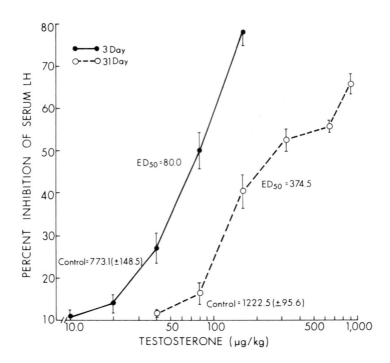

FIGURE 11. The percent inhibition of serum LH levels produced by
testosterone in rats (N=8) castrated 3 or 31 days earlier. T.J.
Cicero, E.R. Meyer, Schmoeker, P.F. Development of Tolerance to
the Effects of Morphine on Luteinizing Hormone Secretion as a
Function of Castration in the Male Rat. The Journal of
Pharmacology and Experimental Therapeutics, 223:784-789, 1982. ©
1982 Williams and Wilkins. Reprinted by permission.

in serum LH levels were nondetectable in morphine-treated rats.
morphine was administered 2 to 3 days after castration, it was
slightly less potent, but, even so, markedly (>80%) depressed
serum LH levels. Thereafter, morphine became progressively less
effective in reducing serum LH levels such that if it was
administered at 13 or 27 days after castration, it did not
significantly reduce serum LH levels.

Magnitude of the shift in sensitivity to morphine in castrates.
The foregoing studies revealed the time course of the change in
the sensitivity of LH secretion to morphine, but gave no
indication of the magnitude of the effect because only pellets
were employed. To determine the extent to which castrated rats
were resistant to the LH-reducing properties of morphine, acute
dose-response curves were determined in rats castrated 3 or 31
days earlier. The results are shown in figure 10. Morphine

produced a 50% inhibition in serum LH levels at a dose of approximately 1.5 mg/kg in animals castrated 3 days earlier, which is comparable to that previously found in normal rats or those castrated for similar periods (Cicero et al. 1979, 1980a,b). In contrast to these results, long-term castration (31 days) produced a parallel shift to the right in the morphine dose-response curve and the ED_{50} was markedly reduced.

Magnitude of the shift in sensitivity to testosterone in castrates. The dose-response curves for testosterone-induced decreases in serum LH levels in animals castrated 3 or 31 days earlier are shown in figure 11. Testosterone more effectively suppressed LH levels in animals castrated 3 days earlier than it did in 31-day castrates.

Uptake of morphine into the brains of long-term castrated animals. To rule out the possibility that the diminished response to morphine observed in long-term castrates was due to an enhanced metabolism of morphine and/or an altered uptake of the drug into the brain, the amount of morphine found in the brains of 31-day castrates was compared with that found in sham-operated animals 30 min after its injection. There was no significant difference in the amount of morphine present in brain 30 min after its administration in 31-day castrates relative to sham-operated controls (data not shown).

Effects of castration on the antinociceptive activity of morphine. In an effort to determine whether the apparent tolerance to the effects of morphine on LH secretion was generalizable to all effects of morphine on the central nervous system, the antinociceptive activity of morphine was assessed in 31-day castrates and sham-operated controls. Castrated rats did not differ significantly from sham-operated controls.

DISCUSSION

The results of these studies indicate that castration renders male rats less responsive to the effects of morphine on LH secretion. The decrease in sensitivity to morphine appears to satisfy the two pharmacological criteria for tolerance: a parallel shift in the dose-response curve to the right, and a reduced effect of the drug at the same brain concentration. Our results further suggest that the tolerance observed in the present studies is not generalizable to other effects of morphine on the brain because the doses of morphine required to produce inhibitions of serum LH levels in long-term castrates by 60% or more (50-75 mg/kg) produced a significant number of deaths (30-40%) which is comparable to that observed in normal animals (Cicero and Meyer 1973). Moreover, we also found that the antinociceptive activity of morphine was not reduced in long-term castrated animals when compared with sham-operated controls. Thus, our results indicate that the development of tolerance to the effects of morphine in the castrated male rat appears to be restricted to LH secretion. The castration-induced development of tolerance to the effects of morphine on LH secretion was accompanied by a change in the responsivity of the hypothalamic-pituitary axis to testosterone; however, it should be noted that the shifts in the morphine and testosterone dose-response curves were not equivalent in our studies since the ED_{50} for morphine increased nearly 10-fold in long-term castrates, relative to short-term castrates, whereas only a 4- to 5-fold increase was found in the case of testosterone. Furthermore, in terms of the absolute decrease in serum LH levels, at specific doses of testosterone and morphine, long-term castrates appeared to be slightly more resistant to testosterone than they did to morphine. Nevertheless, it seems clear that long-term castration produces decreases in the sensitivity of the hypothalamic-pituitary axis to both morphine and testosterone. These data, while correlational in nature, support the previously suggested hypothesis that opioid-containing neuronal elements tonically inhibit LHRH release and may represent a bridge between the actions of steroids on the hypothalamus and their ultimate inhibition of LHRH release.

The mechanisms underlying the development of tolerance to the effects of morphine on LH secretion in castrated male rats are not clear. Two prominent possibilities exist, however; first, castration could produce testosterone-reversible changes in the affinity (K_d) or density (B_{max}) of the relevant opiate receptors involved in LHRH/LH release; and, second, castration could elevate the levels of endogenous opioids in certain areas of brain. With respect to the first of these possibilities, Hahn and Fishman (1979) found marked increases in the B_{max} of [^{3}H]-naltrexone binding sites in whole brains of male rats castrated for 3 or more weeks; testosterone readily overcame these effects. Although these data support the hypothesis that castration-induced changes in opioid receptors could be involved in the development of tolerance to the effects of morphine on LH secretion that we have observed in the present studies, we (Cicero et al. 1983d) and several other groups (Bhanot and Wilkinson 1983; Diez and Roberts 1982; Wilkinson et al. 1981) have been unable to replicate their observations. It is not clear what accounts for this difference in results, but on balance it appears that castration does not influence opiate receptor populations in brain.

The possibility that castration may produce testosterone-reversible elevations in endogenous opioid levels in critical regions of brain has not been systematically examined, but it has been reported that a number of endocrine manipulations significantly alter opioid levels in brain, pituitary and a number of target organs (Mueller 1980; Dupont et al. 1982; Hong et al. 1982). If castration does in fact increase opioid levels in the hypothalamus or other regions of brain, this mechanism could be significantly involved in the effects we have observed. Specifically, prolonged elevations in endogenous opioids could lead to a desensitization of opioid receptors such that the effects of subsequently administered exogenous or endogenous opioids are attenuated, much as is seen in the opiate-dependent animal. If this occurs, then one would expect, as we found, that the morphine dose-response curve with respect to increases in LH would be shifted in parallel to the right. This explanation is a parsimoniuous one and explains all of our data quite well, but it should be reiterated that castration-induced changes in endogenous opioid levels, synthesis and/or release in rat brain have yet to be demonstrated.

The preceding results could have considerable significance with respect to the plasticity of the endogenous opioid system regulating the secretion of LH. In previous work, we have shown that tolerance develops to the effects of naloxone on the secretion of LH after acute or chronic administration (Owens and Cicero 1981) and that morphine tolerance markedly sensitizes male rats to the effects of naloxone. These observations, coupled with the present results, suggest that there is a great deal of plasticity in the opioid-regulated control of LHRH release. It seems probable that these changes could have considerable physiological significance and further studies directed at this issue appear warranted.

In addition, our results suggest that the hormonal status of the animal greatly influences the development of tolerance and possibly physical dependence to the opiates. Since these compounds exert potent effects on most neuroendocrine systems, it seems probable that many of these changes may be intimately involved in both the acute and chronic effects of this class of compounds. Moreover, because most psychoactive compounds influence neuroendocrine status, it may well be that the cross-tolerance and interactions between these compounds may share a common biochemical mechanism (i.e. perturbations in endocrine status).

REFERENCES

Aceto, M.D., Flora, R.E. and Harris, L.S. The effects of naloxone and nalorphine during the development of morphine dependence in rhesus monkeys. Pharmacology, 15:1-19, 1977.
Bhanot, R., and Wilkinson, M. Opiate binding to brain slices and antagonists of hypothalamic [^{3}H]naloxone binding sites. Int J Develop Neurosci, 1983, in press.
Blank, M.S., Panerai, A.E., and Friesen, H.G., Opioid peptides modulate luteinizing hormone secretion during sexual maturation. Science, 203:1129-1131, 1979.
Bruni, F.F, Van Vugt, D., Marshall, S., and Meites, J. Effects of naloxone, morphine and methionine- enkephalin on serum prolactin, luteinizing hormone, follicle-stimulating hormone, thyroid-stimulating hormone, and growth hormone. Life Sci, 21:461, 1977.
Cicero, T.J., and Meyer, E.R., Morphine pellet implantation in rats: Quantitative assessment of tolerance and dependence. J Pharmacol Exp Ther, 184:404-408, 1973.

Cicero, T.J., Meyer, E.R., Bell, R.D., and Koch, G.A., Effects of morphine and methadone on serum testosterone and luteinizing hormone levels and on the secondary sex organs of the male rat. Endocrinology, 98:367-372, 1976.

Cicero, T.J. and Badger, T.M., A comparative analysis of the effects of narcotics, alcohol and the barbiturates on the hypothalamic-pituitary-gonadal axis. Adv Exp Med Biol, 85B:95-116, 1977. (WE HAVE NO REPRINTS)

Cicero, T.J., Bell, R.D., Meyer, E.R. and Schweitzer, J., Narcotics and the hypothalamic-pituitary-gonadal axis: Acute effects on luteinizing hormone, testosterone and androgen-dependent systems. J Pharmacol Exp Ther, 201:76-83, 1977a.

Cicero, T. J., Badger, T.M., Wilcox, C.E., Bell, R.D., and Meyer, E.R., Morphine decreases luteinizing hormone by an action on the hypothalamic-pituitary axis. J Pharmacol Exp Ther, 203:548-555, 1977b.

Cicero, T.J., Schainker, B.A., and Meyer, E.R. Endogenous opioids participate in the regulation of the hypothalamic-pituitary-luteinizing hormone axis and testosterone's negative feedback control of luteinizing hormone. Endocrinology, 104:1286-1291, 1979.

Cicero, T.J., Effects of exogenous and endogenous opiates on the hypothalamic-pituitary-gonadal axis in the male. Fed Proc, 39:2551-2554, 1980.

Cicero, T. J., Meyer, E.R., Gabriel, S.M., Bell, R.D., and Wilcox, C.E., Morphine exerts testosterone-like effects in the hypothalamus of the castrated male rat. Brain Res, 202:151-164, 1980a.

Cicero, T.J., Wilcox, C.E., Bell, R.D., and Meyer, E.R., Naloxone-induced increases in serum luteinizing hormone in the male: Mechanisms of action. J Pharmacol Exp Ther, 212:573-578, 1980b.

Cicero, T.J., Meyer, E.R., and Schmoeker, P.F., Development of tolerance to the effects of morphine on luteinizing hormone secretion as a function of castration in the male rat. J Pharmacol Exp Ther, 223:784-789, 1982.

Cicero, T.J., Owens, D.P., Schmoeker, P.F., and Meyer, E.R., Morphine-induced supersensitivity to naloxone's effects on luteinizing hormone secretion in the male rat. J Pharmacol Exp Ther, 225:35-41, 1983a.

Cicero, T.J., Owens, D.P., Schmoeker, P.F. and Meyer, E.R., Opiate-induced enhancement of naloxone's effects on serum luteinizing hormone levels in the male rat: Specificity for mu agonists. J Pharmacol Exp Ther, 226:770-775, ; 1983b.

Cicero, T.J., Owens, D.P., Newman, K.S., Schmoeker, P.F. and Meyer, E.R., Exogenous and endogenous opioid-induced enhancements of naloxone's effects on serum luteinizing hormone levels in the male rat. Eur J Pharmacol, in press, 1983c.

Cicero, T.J., Newman, K.S., and Meyer, E.R. Testosterone does not influence opiate binding sites in the whole rat brain. Life Sci, 33:1231-1239, 1983d.

Cox, B.M., Ginsberg, M., and Osmond, O.H. Acute tolerance to narcotic analgesic drugs in rats. Br J Pharmacol Chemother, 33:245-256, 1968.

Cox, B.M. and Baizman, E.R. Physiological functions of endorphins. In: Malick, J.B. and Bell, R.M.S. ed. Endorphins: Chemistry, Physiology, Pharmacology and Clinical Relevance, Marcel Dekker, Inc., 1982, p. 141.

Diez, J.A. and Roberts, D.L. Evidence contradicting the notion that gonadal hormones regulate brain opiate receptors. Biochem Biophys Res Commun, 108:1313-1319, 1982.

Dupont, A., Merand, Y., Rouleau, D., Cusan, L., Lemay, A., Vaudry, H., Jegan, S., Lepin, J., and Barden, N. In: Shah, N.S. and Donald, A.G. eds. Endorphins and Opiate Agonists in Pychiatry Research: Clinical Implications, New York: Plenum Press, 1982, p. 99.

Hahn, E.J. and Fishman, J., Changes in rat brain opiate receptor content upon castration and testosterone replacement. Biochem Biophys Res Commun, 90:819-823, 1979.

Hong, J-S, Yoshikawa, K., Huvson, P.M., and Uphouse, L.L. Regulation of pituitary and brain enkephalin systems by estrogen. Life Sci, 31:2181-2184, 1982.

Ieiri, T., Chen, H.T., Campbell, G.A., and Meites, J. Effects of naloxone and morphine on the proestrous surge of prolactin and gonadotropins in the rat. Endocrinology, 106:1568-1570, 1980.

Kalra, S.P. In K. W. McKerns, and V. Pantic eds. Hormonally-Active Brain Peptides: Structure and Function, New York: Plenum Press, 1982 p.141.

Kosersky, D.S., Harris, R.A., and Harris, L.S. Naloxone-precipitated jumping activity in mice following the acute administration of morphine. Eur J Pharmacol, 26:122-124, 1974.

Meites, J., Bruni, J.F., and Van Vugt, D. In Collu, R., Ducharmie, O.R., and Rochefort, G.G. eds. Central Nervous System Effects of Hypothalamic Hormones and Other Peptides, New York:Raven Press: 1979 pp.261-268.

Mendelson, J.H., Ellingboe, J., Kuehnle, J.C., and Mello, N.K. Effects of naltrexone on mood and neuroendocrine function in normal adult males. Psychoneuroendocrinology 3:231-236, 1979.

Meyer, D.R., and Sparber, S.B. Evidence of possible opiate dependence during the behavioral depressant action of a single dose of morphine. Life Sci, 21:1087-1094, 1977.

Mirin, S.M., Mendelson, J.H., Ellingboe, J., and Meyer, R.E. Acute effects of heroin and naltrexone on testosterone and gonadotropin secretion: a pilot study. Psychoneuroendocrinology 1:359-369, 1976.

Mueller, G.P. Attentuated pituitary beta-endorphin release in estrogen-treated rats. Proc Soc Exp Biol Med, 165:75, 1980.

Naber, D., Cohen, R.N., Pickar, D., Kalin, N.H., Davis, G., Pert, C.B., and Bunney, W.E. Episodic secretion of opioid activity in human plasma and monkey CSF: evidence for diurnal rhythm. Life Sci, 28:931-935, 1981.

Owens, D.P. and Cicero, T.J. Development of acute tolerance to the effects of naloxone on the hypothalamic-pituitary-luteinizing hormone axis in the male rat. J Pharmacol Exp Ther, 216:135-141, 1981.

Reid, L.D., Konecka, A.M., Przewlocki, R., Millan, M.J., and Herz. A. Endogenous opioids, circadian rhythm, nutrient deprivation, eating and drinking. Life Sci, 31:1829-1832, 1982.

Roemer, D., Buescher, H.H., Hill, R.C., Pless, J., Bauer, W., Cardincaiux, F., Closse, A., Hauser, D., and Hughenin, R. A synthetic enkephalin analogue with prolonged parenteral and oral analgesic activity. Nature, 268:547, 1977.

Rotsztejn, W., Drouva, S.V., Patton, E., and Kordon, C. Effect of morphine on the basal and the dopamine-induced release of LH-RH from mediobasal hypothalamic fragments in vitro. Eur J Pharmacol, 50:285-289, 1978a.

Rotsztejn, W.H., Drouva, S.V., Patton, E., and Kordon, C. Met-enkephalin inhibits in vitro dopamine-induced LH-RH release from mediobasal hypothalamus of male rats. Nature, (Lond), 274:281-283, 1978b.

Smits, S.E. Quantitation of physical dependence in mice by naloxone-precipitated jumping after a single dose of morphine. Res Comm Chem Path Pharmacol, 10:651-661, 1975.

Sylvester, P.W., Chen, H.T., and Meites, J. Effects of morphine and naloxone on phasic release of luteinizing hormone and follicle stimulating hormone. Proc Soc Exp Biol Med, 164:207, 1980.

Tallarida, R.J., Cowen, A., and Adler, M.W. pA_2 and receptor differentiation: A statistical analysis of competitive antagonism. Life Sci, 28:2355-2360, 1981.

Van Vugt, D.A., Sylvester, P.W., Aylsworth, C.F., and Meites, J. Counteraction of gonadal steroid inhibition of luteinizing hormone release by naloxone. Endocrinology, 34:274-280, 1982.

Wiley, J.N., and Downs, D.A. Naloxone-precipitated jumping in mice pretreated with acute injections of opioids. Life Sci, 25:797-802, 1979.

Wilkes, M.M., and Yen. S.S.C. Augmentation by naloxone of efflux of LRF from superfused medial basal hypothalamus. Life Sci, 28:2355-2360, 1981.

Wilkinson, M., Herdon, H., and Wilson, C.A. Gonadal steroid modification of adrenergic and opiate receptor binding in the central nervous system. In Fuxe, K., Gustafsson, J.A., and Wetterby, L. eds. Steroid Regulation of the Brain, Pergamon Press: New York, 1981, pp. 253-263.

ACKNOWLEDGEMENTS

The author's research reported in this review was supported in part by grants DA-00259 from the National Institute on Drug Abuse and AA-03539 from the National Institute on Alcohol Abuse and Alcoholism. The author also is a recipient of Research Scientist award DA-00095 from the National Institute on Drug Abuse.

AUTHOR

Theodore J. Cicero, Ph.D.
Washington University School of Medicine
Department of Psychiatry
4940 Audubon Avenue
St. Louis, Missouri 63110

Modulation of Opioid Physical Dependence During the Hibernation Cycle

Alexander L. Beckman, Carmen Llados-Eckman,
Steven K. Salzman, and Toni L. Stanton

INTRODUCTION

One early cornerstone of the conventional wisdom
regarding opioid physical dependence is that it is an
inevitable consequence of the prolonged administration
of opioid agonists in the mammalian CNS. Although there
may be some species exceptions (see Dewey, this volume)
to this concept, each of the model systems that have
been most extensively studied commonly displays a
uniform profile of dependence liability to a given
opioid compound throughout its natural range of
function. However, experiments in the mammalian
hibernator suggest that, rather than being an invariant
feature of the response of the nervous system to the
presence of opioids, physical dependence is a CNS
state-dependent phenomenon whose presence is qualitatively and quantitatively determined by a requisite set
of variable characteristics of the CNS. Within one
domain of activity (the euthermic, or nonhibernating,
state in which the functional characteristics of the
CNS are like those of other more commonly studied
mammalian systems), prolonged morphine administration
produces robust signs of physical dependence.
Moreover, seasonal changes in the functional characteristics of the euthermic CNS, as inferred by changes in
naturally occurring behavioral and physiological
variables, are associated with changes in the display
of morphine physical dependence. In contrast, a shift
in the operating mode of the CNS to the state that
produces and maintains hibernation, which is globally
characterized by a radical alteration of CNS activity
and, consequently, of the physiological and behavioral
systems it controls, is associated with the failure of
prolonged morphine administration to produce physical
dependence.

This observation is interesting for reasons that go
beyond the sheer novelty of identifying a mammalian
system that displays a naturally occurring state-

dependent resistance to the development of morphine physical dependence. We may now pose questions regarding the cellular responses that mediate the modulating actions of opioids on physiological and behavioral neural control systems, and how they compare to the opioid-induced changes in neuronal function that produce physical dependence and tolerance in those systems.

This paper will establish a perspective for studying opioid actions in the euthermic/hibernating model. We will first review the characteristics of morphine physical dependence in hibernators (<u>Citellus</u> <u>lateralis</u>, the golden-mantled ground squirrel) and then examine some of the salient characteristics of the CNS during the state of hibernation. Finally, we will consider the potential of CNS mechanisms associated with the hibernating state to modulate morphine physical dependence. These will be discussed in relation to data obtained from species that do not hibernate that are concerned with morphine-induced changes in CNS neurotransmitter dynamics and on neurotransmitter/neuromodulator-induced reduction of morphine physical dependence and tolerance.

CHARACTERISTICS OF MORPHINE PHYSICAL DEPENDENCE DURING THE NONHIBERNATING AND THE HIBERNATING STATES

We have described physical dependence on morphine in the euthermic ground squirrel according to the commonly used technique of administering morphine sulfate subcutaneously via two 75-mg pellets inserted in the interscapular region. In parallel with the development of physical dependence during the 72-hour morphine exposure period, we observed a biphasic effect on behavioral activity (Beckman et al. 1981, 1982a, 1982b) in which the initial phase was usually excitatory. The increased locomotor activity usually resulted in the destruction of the normally well-maintained cotton nest, which the animals did not rebuild for the duration of the morphine exposure. Following the excitatory phase, the animals became quiet, generally remaining in a supine position. Those animals whose nests were not flattened during the period of increased activity generally remained outside their nest for the balance of the behaviorally depressed phase of the development of physical dependence on morphine. Seventy-two hours after inserting the pellets, abstinence was precipitated by a subcutaneous injection of naloxone hydrochloride (1 mg/kg). In this manner, we established that the euthermic ground squirrel develops strong physical dependence on morphine, as evidenced by a pronounced display of a substantial number of autonomic and behavioral responses. These included most of the signs that have been observed in many other species, plus some signs that are novel to the ground squirrel and which resemble behaviors in the natural repertoire of this animal. This constellation of signs, recorded in the 30-min period following naloxone injection, included exploratory behavior, nesting behavior, grooming, vocalization, body and/or head shakes, mouth gaping (giving the appearance of yawning), chewing, milky dacryorrhea, digging, dyspnea, eyetwitch, flattened posture, ptosis, and a forward-extended, fanned tail.

Seasonal Variations in Morphine Physical Dependence

Seasonal variations in the display of the abstinence syndrome were apparent in the majority of the 14 abstinence signs. Figure 1 presents an example of this variation for the 6 signs that were quantified. It is apparent that among these 6 signs, those most intensely displayed in a given animal were vocalizations and shakes. Statistical analysis of the differences in the mean number of occurrences of each sign showed that significant differences were present in the seasonal display of nesting, vocalizations, shakes, and mouth gaping (Beckman et al. 1982a). Nesting responses were significantly greater in the fall than in the summer. Vocalizations were significantly reduced in the fall compared with the winter and spring. Shakes were significantly elevated in the fall compared to spring and summer. In the fall, the occurrence of mouth gaping was significantly greater than in any other season. Exploratory behavior was more prominently displayed in the summer and fall than in the winter and spring, although these differences did not reach statistical significance.

Another way of measuring physical dependence, that of determining the percentage of the morphine-exposed population exhibiting particular abstinence signs, also demonstrated seasonal differences. This measure showed that in 4 of the 6 quantified signs (exploring, nesting, vocalizations, and mouth gaping), differences of 22 - 35% were apparent in the percentage of animals displaying the signs across the four seasons. For example, exploratory behavior was displayed by the fewest animals during the winter, with an increasing percentage of the population displaying the sign through the spring and the fall. Nesting and mouth gaping were most commonly displayed in the fall, with a steadily decreasing incidence through winter, spring and summer. An increasing percentage of the population displayed vocalizations in winter and spring compared to the relatively small percentage observed in summer and fall. Five of the 8 signs that were tabulated as being present or absent in each animal following naloxone administration (as opposed to being quantified on a per occurrence basis) showed progressive seasonal differences. For example, chewing occurred in the highest percentage of the population in the fall and declined progressively in winter, spring, and summer. The incidence of milky dacryorrhea was lowest in the winter and rose rapidly thereafter in the spring, reaching a peak in the summer before declining in the fall. The occurrence of dyspnea in the population rose steadily from winter through fall. The display of eyetwitch was lowest in the spring and increased progressively in summer and fall before declining in

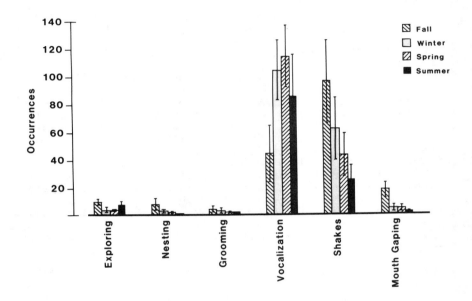

FIGURE 1. Seasonal changes in the number of occurrences of quantified naloxone-precipitated abstinence signs in morphine-dependent animals. Values are mean ± SEM. (Reprinted with permission, from Beckman et al. 1982a, Copyright 1982,, Pergamon Press, Ltd.)

winter. The sign of a forward, fanned tail was least common in the summer and increased rapidly in the fall to reach a peak occurrence in the spring. In contrast to these progressive changes, abrupt changes occurred in two signs, ptosis and flat posture. Ptosis alternated between a high incidence in the summer and fall and low values in winter and spring. A substantially higher percentage of the population displayed flat posture in the fall compared to the other three seasons. No seasonal differences in the population display of digging were apparent.

The seasonal differences in the display of various abstinence signs must be a reflection of regional differences in the development of morphine physical dependence in the CNS. That is, although it is clear that physical dependence is manifest throughout the year, subtle changes in the action of morphine upon particular behavioral or autonomic control systems occur as a consequence of natural changes in the nervous system. These changes, in effect, alter the potency of morphine with respect to the production of physical dependence.

Although there is currently no information available comparing functional properties of the CNS throughout the year in euthermic *C. lateralis*, reports of seasonal changes in physiological and behavioral responses of this species clearly point to underlying changes in CNS mechanisms. These include differences in sleep cycles (Walker et al. 1977), food consumption and body weight (Pengelley and Fisher 1963; Mrosovsky 1975), reproductive behavior (Heller and Poulson 1970) and, of course, hibernation (Mrosovsky 1978). We have suggested (Beckman et al. 1982a) that such changes might conceivably involve the level of excitability or activity of neural networks that controls these variables. That is, slowly increasing levels of excitability in particular networks would be expected to eventually reach the threshold for the presentation of seasonally observed responses. This concept is in agreement with other observations (Muchlinski et al. 1983) in which the regional brain concentration of neuropeptides (bombesin, neurotensin, somatostatin, and cholecystokinin varied during the period of the year in which *C. lateralis* undergoes a rapid increase in body weight.

Thus, we might interpret our results to suggest that the development of morphine physical dependence is contingent upon morphine acting on neuronal populations that exhibit a requisite level of intrinsic activity. Differences in the level of endogenous activity within these networks would therefore modulate the intensity of physical dependence, as shown by differences in the intensity of individual abstinence signs. This concept

213

is supported by reports that discrete regions in the CNS display unique patterns of neural responses to morphine (Dafny et al. 1979) and that the influence of morphine on striatal dopamine (DA) release varies according to the frequency of nigrostriatal spike activity (Moleman and Bruinvels 1979). Other evidence of a relationship between neuronal activity and response to morphine may be found in an autoradiographic study of 2-deoxyglucose (2-DG) uptake in rats (Wooten et al. 1982). Brain regions generally displaying higher baseline levels of 2-DG incorporation responded to chronic administration of morphine with a significant reduction of 2-DG uptake whereas those with lower baseline values showed significant increases (Wooten et al. 1982).

The observation of seasonal differences in the abstinence syndrome raises an important question regarding the process underlying the development of physical dependence: are the associated variables primarily those of changes in the binding characteristics of opioids, or is the variability contained in the sequence of events that the agonist-receptor complex initiates? Our hypothesis concerning the relationship between morphine dependence and the basal level of activity in target neural networks contains an assumption that the basic dynamics of morphine's cellular action do not change on a seasonal basis in C. lateralis. However, data from an invertebrate species, a marine mollusc, suggest that seasonal variation in the binding of morphine may also be a contributing factor (Stefano et al. 1980). The seasonal differences in enkephalin binding that were observed in the marine mollusc were associated with differences in the ability of d-ala,met-enkephalinamide (DALA) and met-enkephalin to alter dopamine parameters in the pedal ganglia of this animal. The possibility that a similar mechanism operates in the ground squirrel will be considered in a subsequent section.

The profound difference in the hibernating ground squirrel's responses to chronic administration of morphine underscores the question as to where the sequence of events leading to the development of physical dependence may be broken. Our data (Figure 2) show that physical dependence on morphine fails to develop during deep hibernation (Beckman et al. 1981). These animals received morphine either through subcutaneous implantation of two 75-mg morphine sulfate pellets or directly into the brain via an icv cannula at the same dose parameters as those which produced a robust naloxone-precipitated abstinence syndrome in euthermic animals. Although the hibernating animals only received morphine following entrance into deep hibernation, they were tested for an abstinence syndrome during the euthermic period immediately

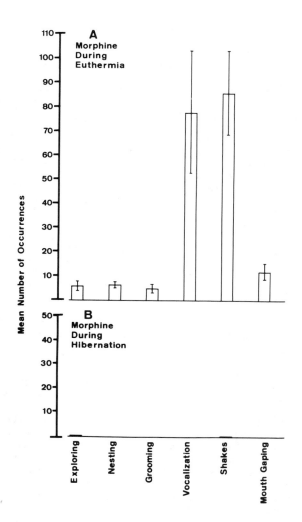

FIGURE 2. Quantified signs of abstinence precipitated by naloxone during (A) the nonhibernating (euthermic) state and (B) the hibernating state in ground squirrels implanted with morphine pellets. Brackets denote SEM. (From Beckman et al. 1981. copyright 1981 by AAAS).

following arousal. Whereas no abstinence syndrome was apparent, some of the animals did respond to morphine with a display of stereotyped behavior which began while the animals were starting to arouse (i.e., prior to naloxone administration) and continued into the post-arousal euthermic state. It is thus clear that, although morphine does not produce physical dependence in the hibernating state (at least at the dose parameters that we tested), it does evoke a strong response in the CNS.

PROPERTIES OF THE CNS DURING THE STATE OF HIBERNATION

Whereas the euthermic ground squirrel presents itself as a model of subtle modulation of opioid physical dependence, the hibernating ground squirrel is a model of the full extent of that modulation, in which the phenomenon disappears with a change in the state of the brain. Entrance into hibernation begins during sleep and is characterized by a striking reduction of body temperature and metabolic rate that reaches maximum depression during deep hibernation. It is so characteristic a feature that we commonly identify the departure of the euthermic state by the fall in these two variables. Thus, whereas internal temperature during euthermia is regulated at approximately 38°C, during deep hibernation in natural conditions, internal temperature decreases to nearly 0°C (Wang 1978).

Current evidence clearly indicates that the entrance into hibernation is controlled by the CNS and suggests that this control is manifest by an increase in central inhibitory level. For example, heart and respiratory rates, which are depressed during hibernation, begin to decline prior to any significant decrease in body temperature during euthermia (Lyman 1958; Strumwasser 1959a). Likewise the amplitude of the EEG has been observed to begin declining before any significant fall in body temperature occurred (Wunnenberg et al. 1978). As the entrance into hibernation progresses, the amplitude of the EEG continues to decrease (Strumwasser 1959a; Shtark 1970; Walker et al. 1977), and changes in the frequency distribution of the EEG occur with the decline in body temperature (South et al. 1969; Shtark 1970). Observations taken from multiple EEG recording sites within the same animal suggest that suppression of EEG activity is first evidenced in the cerebral cortex, followed by the midbrain reticular formation, thalamus and, lastly, in areas of the limbic system (notably in the hippocampus and hypothalamus) (Shtark 1970).

Studies of the CNS regulator of body temperature provide additional evidence for a controlled entry into hibernation. During entrance into hibernation, the threshold hypothalamic temperature for activating an increase in metabolic rate was demonstrable at all times, but at increasingly lower levels as time progressed (Heller et al. 1977; Florant et al. 1978).

Electroencephalographic studies indicate that once animals achieve the resting state of hibernation, the level of electrical activity is similar to that of the entry phase. That is, the cortex remains electrically

216

depressed except for varying periods of increased EEG activity (South et al. 1969; Shtark 1970; Walker et al. 1977) and, similarly, the midbrain reticular formation displays long periods of silence that are punctuated by short bursts of spiking activity (Strumwasser 1959b; South et al. 1969; Shtark 1970). The limbic system appears to diverge from this picture of general electrical depression in that limbic structures (notably the hippocampus, septum, and hypothalamus) have been reported to display nearly continuous EEG activity throughout the hibernation bout (Strumwasser 1959b; South et al. 1969; Shtark 1970). This characteristic of limbic structures, contrasted with the relative electrical silence of cortical and midbrain areas, has prompted suggestions (South et al. 1972; Beckman and Stanton 1976) that the proposed increase in central inhibitory level accompanying the transition from the euthermic state to the hibernating mode (Luecke and South 1972; Hammel et al. 1973) is controlled by neurons within the limbic system.

More recent analysis of regional CNS metabolic activity using the ^{14}C-2-DG autoradiographic method in ground squirrels (Kilduff et al. 1982) confirms the earlier descriptions of a general decline in activity throughout the brain during hibernation. Of particular interest is the fact that not all structures undergo a similar reduction in activity. Those that undergo the smallest reduction in relative 2-deoxyglucose uptake, in comparison to euthermia, include the medial preoptic area, ventral hippocampus, locus coeruleus, suprachiasmatic nucleus, and the lateral septal nucleus. Presumably, these structures retain functional significance during deep hibernation. Likewise, in addition to the locus coeruleus and the suprachiasmatic nucleus, we might expect structures such as the dorsal tegmental nucleus, inferior colliculus, superior colliculus, and the habenular nucleus to perform important control functions during deep hibernation because this group of structures exhibits the greatest relative 2-deoxyglucose uptake. It is worth noting that these structures are components of the endogenous opioid system, as shown by the presence of opioid receptors (Hiller et al. 1973; Kuhar et al. 1973; Pert et al. 1975; Simon and Hiller 1978; Pearson et al. 1980; Duka et al. 1981) or endogenous opioid compounds (Watson et al. 1977; Matsukura et al. 1978; Gramsch et al. 1979; Dupont et al. 1980).

Evidence for the maintenance of control functions during hibernation has been provided by studies on the CNS thermoregulatory system which show that it retains functional activity and can defend the hibernating animal against decreases in internal temperature below a threshold level (Hammel et al. 1968; Heller and Colliver 1974). Similarly, work in our laboratory has demonstrated the activation of a mechanism that is capable of inhibiting disturbance-induced arousal from hibernation (Beckman et al. 1976b).

Studies of the responsiveness of the hibernating brain to the microinjection of putative neurotransmitters such as norepinephrine (NE), 5-hydroxytryptamine (5-HT), acetylcholine (ACh), and the neuropeptide thyrotropin-releasing hormone (TRH), have demonstrated that these compounds continue to exert a potent effect on the brain during this state (Beckman and Satinoff 1972; Beckman et al. 1976a; Stanton et al. 1980). Microinjection of low concentrations of these compounds into the hypothalamus, hippocampus, or midbrain reticular formation can activate small thermogenic responses or the trigger process for arousal from hibernation. Additional studies in our laboratory, using ACh microinjections into the midbrain reticular formation or the preoptic/anterior area of the hypothalamus, have demonstrated that the hibernating brain undergoes a decrease in excitability coincident with the entrance into hibernation. CNS responsiveness then begins a recovery towards euthermic levels of excitability as time in the hibernation bout elapses (Beckman and Stanton 1976; Stanton and Beckman 1977). Interestingly, the profile of the increase in responsiveness to ACh is different in the midbrain reticular formation as compared with the preoptic/anterior area of the hypothalamus. In the former structure, the increase in responsiveness is gradual and progressive, whereas in the latter structure it occurs more abruptly at the half-way point of the bout. This increased responsiveness is probably a reflection of the higher level of EEG (Strumwasser 1959b; South et al. 1969; Shtark 1970) and metabolic (Kilduff et al. 1982) activity observed during hibernation in the hypothalamus.

It is therefore clear, both from the maintenance of neural activity and from the physiological responses that actively maintain the state of hibernation against disruption, that the hibernating brain is a functionally intact system.

CHARACTERISTICS OF THE HIBERNATING CNS THAT MAY MEDIATE THE MODULATION OF PHYSICAL DEPENDENCE ON MORPHINE

From the foregoing description of the functional characteristics of the hibernating brain, it is apparent that a number of major differences from the euthermic brain could contribute to the blockade of morphine physical dependence. We have outlined (Beckman et al. 1981) four possibilities which merit early consideration in light of recent findings in nonhibernating species: a) restrictions in the intracerebral distribution of morphine following icv administration in the hibernating brain, b) differences in the turnover (synthesis, release, reuptake and/or degradation) of neurotransmitters or neuromodulators across the two states, c) differences in the characteristics of opioid receptors (changes in regional receptor density or ligand binding affinity), and d) low temperature-induced differences in the development of physical dependence that are associated with the conditions of deep hibernation.

Intracerebral Distribution of Morphine During Hibernation

It is conceivable that some of the characteristics of the state of hibernation, such as the widespread reduction in the level of function of physiological systems or possible changes in tissue characteristics (Beckman and Stanton 1982) could reduce the efflux of icv-administered compounds into the brain and/or restrict patterns of intracerebral distribution compared to the euthermic state. In consideration of this, we have begun to examine autoradiographically the intracerebral distribution of tritiated morphine following icv administration during hibernation. In these experiments, tritiated morphine was infused continuously into the lateral ventricle of hibernating ground squirrels for periods of 4 to 30 hours. Qualitative results obtained by visual inspection of the autoradiographs revealed that the radiolabeled compound did leave the ventricular space and diffuse widely into the brain. The zones of increased optical density were clearly evident in the cortex, lateral ventricles, third ventricle, caudate nucleus, dorsal hippocampus, amygdala, bed nucleus of the stria terminalis, septum, medial preoptic area, thalamic structures, the aqueduct of Sylvius, and the periaqueductal gray. These regions were among those identified in previous studies as being sites of importance to the development of physical dependence and the expression of naloxone-precipitated abstinence, as shown by regional 2-DG uptake in dependent and withdrawing animals (Wooten et al. 1982) and by the ability to modify the display of physical dependence following focal lesions or drug administration (Kerr and Pozuelo 1971; Herz et al. 1972; Wei et al. 1972; Wikler et al. 1972; Wei et al. 1973).

We are beginning to analyze these autoradiographic data using computer-assisted densitometry in order to improve the qualitative resolution and to quantify the magnitude of regional optical density. We are, in addition, in the preliminary stages of analyzing the regional content of brain areas displaying increased autoradiographic density to determine whether the radioactive label is associated with morphine or its metabolites. Thus, while yet qualitative, our data do not indicate any decrement in the intracerebral distribution of morphine in the hibernating brain following continuous icv infusion.

Changes in Neurotransmitter Turnover During Hibernation

The second feature of the hibernating CNS that may contribute to the state-dependent block of physical dependence concerns the changes that occur in neurotransmitter level or turnover during deep hibernation. The notion that these changes, described below, may be of significance to the development of physical dependence is derived from the literature on the effects of morphine administration on neurotransmitter level or turnover, as well as the effect of changes in the brain level or activity of putative neurotransmitters on physical dependence and tolerance. The catecholamines (NE and DA), 5-HT, and ACh have received the most attention.

The earlier literature describing morphine's effects on the brain levels of these compounds is contradictory in that morphine has been reported to increase (Gunne 1959; Akera and Brody 1968) and decrease (Vogt 1954; Gunne 1959; Maynert and Klingman 1962; Gunne 1963; Lee and Fennessy 1970) NE levels, to increase DA levels (Clouet and Ratner 1970) and to decrease (Lee and Fennessy 1970) or have no effect (Maynert et al. 1962; Sloan et al. 1962) on 5-HT levels in the brain. Similarly, morphine may increase the level of ACh (Large and Milton 1970; Domino and Wilson 1973) or, depending upon the dose administered, produce biphasic effects on ACh level (Vasco and Domino 1978). Other reports have described effects of morphine administration on the turnover of these compounds. In view of the data on morphine's effects on neurotransmitter content, it is not surprising that morphine administration has been reported to increase or decrease the turnover of NE (Costa et al. 1974; Gomes et al. 1976; Arbilla and Langer 1978; Bensemana and Gascon 1978), DA (Loh et al. 1972; Costa et al. 1974; Bensemana and Gascon 1978; Moleman and Bruinvels 1979), 5-HT (Bensemana and Gascon 1978; Snelgar and Vogt 1980; Vasko and Vogt 1982), and ACh (Vasco and Domino 1978). The heterogeniety of these effects is most probably due to methodological differences (species, dose, sites of administration). In any case, the major point established by these studies is that chronic morphine administration affects the dynamics of major neurotransmitter systems in the brain. It seems reasonable to assume that such changes would be reflected in a functionally significant change in the matrix of inputs received by neural networks within the CNS, thereby producing an altered output that underlies the development of physical dependence. This interpretation is supported by ample evidence for morphine-induced supersensitivity in monoamine-sensitive systems, particularly with respect to DA (Schulz and Herz 1977; Kromer and Steigemann 1982; Ritzmann et al. 1982; Rae and DeMorhes 1983).

The foregoing evidence established that chronic morphine administration produces changes in the turn-over of several neurotransmitter systems in the CNS and therefore supports the concept that physical dependence is, at least in part, a manifestation of these changes. If this is indeed the case, then experimental manipulation of neurotransmitter level or turnover should result in the modulation of physical dependence. The results of such experiments, while not conclusive, do provide some support for this notion. They show that decreases in 5-HT levels resulted in decreases (Way et al. 1968; Ho et al. 1972) or no change (Schwartz and Eidelberg 1970; Cheney and Goldstein 1971) in the intensity of the morphine abstinence syndrome and in diminished (Way et al. 1968; Ho et al. 1972) or unaltered (Cheney and Goldstein 1971) development of tolerance to morphine. Decreases in the level of catecholamines have been reported to have no effect on the development of tolerance (Bhargava et al. 1973) and to increase (Friedler et al. 1972) or decrease (Schwartz and Eidelberg 1970) the intensity of the morphine abstinence syndrome.

Given the matrix of intense responses that are elicited during the antagonist-precipitated withdrawal from morphine, it seems appropriate to characterize morphine-induced changes in neurotransmitter dynamics as a disruption of normal CNS function. Viewed from this perspective, the hibernating CNS is a particularly interesting model because the dynamics of several neurochemical systems are markedly changed from that observed in euthermia. Low levels of brain protein renewal during hibernation, and dramatic increases during arousal, have been measured in ground squirrels (Belik and Kracho 1961). In hibernating golden hamsters, brain cholinesterase activity is depressed, perhaps reflecting the decrease in electrical activity of the cortex (which is high in cholinesterase concen-tration in the euthermic state) (Robinson and Bradley 1963). In contrast, glutamic acid decarboxylase activ-ity, which is associated with the formation of GABA, increased in the brain of hibernating golden hamsters (Robinson and Bradley 1963). Measures of the turnover of NE and 5-HT during euthermia and hibernation gener-ally indicate that the activity of 5-HT systems is accelerated prior to entrance and during deep hiber-nation whereas that of NE-releasing systems is de-pressed prior to entrance and remains low during deep hibernation (Wang 1982).

As we have pointed out, evidence obtained from non-hibernating species clearly suggests that the development of morphine physical dependence may stem from the effects of alterations in neurotransmitter dynamics. The hibernating CNS also displays changes in neurotransmitter dynamics which may contribute to the failure of morphine to produce physical dependence during hibernation. For example, we note that although the transition from euthermia to hibernation is accompanied by changes in distribution and quantity of activity within the brain as well as changes in neurochemical parameters, brain function does not appear to be disrupted or functionally impaired. It is likely that the preservation of this functional integrity is dependent upon such changes which are themselves manifestations of the hibernator's adaptive specializations that buffer the CNS against the effects of otherwise disruptive conditions.

With this in mind, we studied the turnover of DA in the caudate nucleus of drug-naive ground squirrels during euthermia and hibernation, as a prelude to examining the effect of chronic morphine administration on DA turnover in these two states. As we noted earlier, morphine-induced changes in DA turnover, and supersensitivity of DA systems following chronic opioid administration, suggest that sustained perturbation of normal dopaminergic activity is an important component of opioid physical dependence. In our experiments, we stereotaxically implanted four ground squirrels with a unilateral push-pull cannula in the caudate nucleus and another unilateral (same side) cannula in the lateral ventricle (for eventual chronic infusion of morphine). Resting euthermic animals were tested in a plexiglass chamber (ambient temperature, Ta: 20-22 $^{\circ}$ C) over a 2-3 hr period in which successive 30-min caudate perfusates (perfusion rate: 20.6 μl/min) samples were collected. Animals were allowed free movement by means of a swivel coupling in the perfusion system. Hibernating animals were tested in their cotton nests (Ta: 5°C) for a similar period. Perfusion samples were analyzed for DA (free and conjugate forms) and its metabolites (3,4-dihydroxyphenylacetic acid [DOPAC], 3-methoxy-4-hydroxyphenylacetic acid [homovanillic acid, HVA], and 3-methoxy-4-hydroxyphenethanol [MOPET]) by high performance liquid chromatography with electrochemical detection (HPLC/EC). Conjugates of DA were cleaved by acid hydrolysis prior to HPLC/EC analysis.

Our results (summarized in schematic form in Figure 3) show clear differences between the euthermic and hibernating brain in the performance of the caudate DA system. Our data from the euthermic state are based on a total of 26 samples collected from 4 animals. Free DA was not detectable in 21 of the samples. It was present in 5 of the samples at a mean level of 3.9 pmol/30 min. HVA was detected consistently at high levels (12.1 pmole/30 min.) in all 26 samples. DOPAC

EUTHERMIA

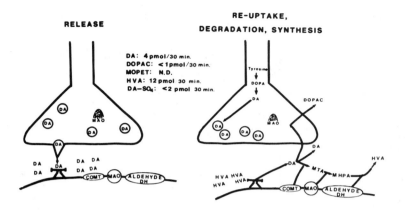

HIBERNATION

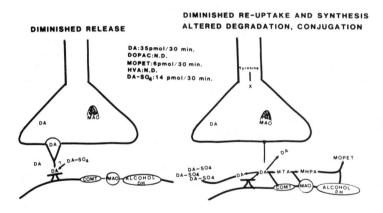

FIGURE 3. Caudate nucleus DA turnover during euthermia and hibernation in drug-naive ground squirrels. Upper half summarizes events of release, reuptake, degradation, and synthesis during euthermia as suggested by measurements of DA and its metabolites. Lower half summarizes these events during hibernation; note the shift in metabolism to the enzyme pathway utilizing alcohol dehydrogenase and the increased formation of conjugated DA (DA-SO$_4$). HVA was not detected in half of the samples collected during the early portion of the bout and in none of the samples obtained during the late portion of the bout.

was not detectable in 12 of the samples, but was present in 14 at a level of 0.9 pmol/30 min. Conjugated DA was not detected in 14 samples, but was present in 12 of the perfusates at a level of 1.9 pmol/30 min.

In contrast, results from the hibernating state (N=13 samples, 4 animals) showed that free DA was present in all samples at 35.0 pmol/30 min, but that HVA was not present in 10 samples. In 3 samples, HVA was detected at a level of 5.0 pmol/30 min. DOPAC was not detected in any of the samples. We did, however, detect MOPET in each sample, in quantities of 5.6 pmol/30 min. Conjugated DA was present in 7 of 13 samples at a level of 13.5 pmol/30 min.

Other interesting features of the hibernating DA system became apparent when these data were grouped according to the period of the hibernating bout in which they were collected. Early in the bout, levels of DA (in 7 out of 7 samples) averaged 22.2 pmol/30 min, whereas late-bout levels increased to 45.9 pmol/30 min (in 6 of 6 samples). The early-bout level of HVA in 3 samples was 5.0 pmol/30 min and was not detectable in 3 samples; late in the bout, HVA was not detectable in any of the 7 samples collected. MOPET was present during the early portion of the bout at a level of 4.7 pmol/30 min (6/6 samples) and during the late portion of the bout, it increased by 37% to 6.5 pmol/30 min (7/7 samples). Conjugated DA was not detectable in any of the 6 early-bout samples, but was consistently found in all 7 of the late-bout samples (13.5 pmol/30 min).

Thus, the data show that caudate perfusates from euthermic animals displayed consistent, high levels of HVA and very little (usually no) DA. This probably indicates a relatively constant and high turnover rate. It appears that the released DA was rapidly and efficiently converted to HVA through the normal route of DA metabolism, as the perfusates contained small amounts of DA and always contained HVA.

Caudate perfusates from the hibernating animals appeared quite different. The level of DA was approximately 10-fold higher than in euthermic animals and occurred in each perfusate sample (as opposed to euthermia wherein DA appeared in few samples). Furthermore, there was very little HVA present. DA metabolism continued to occur, however, albeit by a completely different route. Rather than being metabolized through the normal route to HVA, DA was converted preferentially to MOPET (where levels in each sample were about one-half the molar quantity of the euthermic levels of HVA), indicating a shift from aldehyde dehydrogenase to alcohol dehydrogenase. Thus, these data probably indicate that DA was still being released by caudate neurons (although we cannot say how the rate of release compared to that during euthermia), but was not converted as efficiently to a metabolite. Because DA appeared to be accumulating in the extracellular space, it is likely that overall turnover was less. However, DA turnover appeared to accelerate late in the bout, but remained qualitatively similar to that in the early portion of the hibernation bout.

Our data also suggest that DA conjugates may play an important role in the conservation of DA during hibernation. That is, conjugated DA appears to serve as a reservoir for the large amount of unmetabolized DA that accumulates during hibernation.

The results of these experiments suggest that the hibernating ground squirrel, in order to efficiently utilize the DA that is released from slowly firing caudate neurons, alters the metabolism of DA such that the synaptic concentration of DA is high enough to maintain a requisite level of tone in the DA pathway. This alteration appears to involve, at least in part, a shift in metabolism from HVA to MOPET and the use of conjugated DA (which is resistant to oxidative and methylating enzymes) as a storehouse for free DA. The resulting increase in the potential availability of free DA would serve as a buffer against the effects of opioid-induced decreases in DA release, thereby increasing the resistance of the dopaminergic system to opioid-induced dopamine supersensitivity. Assuming that DA supersensitivity is a component in the matrix of CNS changes that constitute opioid physical dependence, this adaptive change in DA metabolism could, in part, explain the failure of physical dependence to develop in the hibernating CNS. In order to test this hypothesis, we are beginning experiments to determine the effect of morphine administration during hibernation and euthermia on these parameters of DA metabolism.

There is another aspect to the concept that the development of morphine physical dependence involves alterations in the activity of CNS neurotransmitter systems. We have already noted that the experimental manipulation of central monoamine dynamics can influence physical dependence. Evidence has been presented in recent years that extends the concept of opioid-neurotransmitter interactions in physical dependence to another class of neuroactive compounds, the neuropeptides. Although there is some evidence to the contrary (Olson et al. 1982), the results of several studies on melanotropin-release inhibiting factor (MIF) and TRH favor an inhibitory influence of these compounds on opioid tolerance and physical dependence. For example, MIF has been reported to inhibit tolerance to the analgesic and cataleptic

225

effect of beta-endorphin (Bhargava 1981a) and to block beta-endorphin-induced increases in DA responsiveness (Bhargava 1981d). Other studies found that MIF can block morphine-induced increases in DA-responsiveness (Bhargava 1980a) and reduce tolerance to morphine-induced analgesia (Bhargava 1980a; Bhargava 1982), locomotor depression (Bhargava 1982), hypothermia (Bhargava 1981c), and catalepsy (Bhargava 1981c). Similarly, an analogue of MIF(cyclo[Leu-Gly]) has been reported to inhibit tolerance to morphine-induced analgesia (Ritzmann et al. 1982; Bhargava 1980a, 1981a, 1982) as well as some signs of morphine physical dependence, morphine-induced DA supersensitivity, and increases in the ligand affinity of striatal DA receptors (Ritzmann et al. 1982). TRH has been shown to block tolerance to the analgesic effects of morphine (Bhargava 1981b) and to exert an inhibitory effect on the development of morphine physical dependence (Bhargava 1980b). TRH and other peptide compounds have also been shown to antagonize opioid-induced responses. For example, TRH inhibited morphine-induced locomotor depression and decreases in body temperature (Bhargava et al. 1982), somatostatin inhibited beta-endorphin-induced adrenal medullary release of epinephrine (Van Loon et al. 1981), and cholesystokinin inhibited beta-endorphin-induced catalepsy in rats (Olson et al. 1982).

These findings are potentially relevant to the hibernating model system's reduced morphine dependence liability because changes in the brain levels of these and other neuroactive peptide compounds occur with hibernation. Thus, the level of TRH is lower in the brain of hibernating ground squirrels than in euthermic animals in all areas studied (cortex, septum, hippocampus, preoptic area, hypothalamus, thalamus, midbrain, and medulla) (Stanton et al. 1982). Curiously, TRH levels in the pineal gland increased dramatically during the late portion of the bout (Stanton et al. 1982). The levels of somatostatin, cholecystokinin, bombesin, and neurotensin were measured in five brain regions of hibernating and summer euthermic ground squirrels, with some interesting differences being displayed (Muchlinski et al. 1983). Somatostatin levels generally increased in hibernation in the thalamus and decreased in cortex, cerebellum, medulla, and hypothalamus, compared with average values measured during the summer season. Hibernation levels of cholecystokinin increased, relative to average summer values, in the cortex and cerebellum, tended to decrease in medulla and hypothalamus and showed no change in the thalamus. Hibernating levels of bombesin were lower than average summer euthermic levels in the hypothalamus, thalamus, and medulla but showed no changes in the cortex or cerebellum. Neurotensin levels were unchanged in the cortex during hibernation, but decreased in hypothalamus, thalamus, and medulla compared to summer animals. In another study, the content of met-enkephalin, leu-enkephalin, and ACTH was measured in whole-brain extracts obtained from hibernating and winter euthermic ground squirrels. The level of both met- and leu-enkephalin was increased, and that of ACTH decreased, in hibernating brain (Kramarova et al. 1983).

Whereas it is hazardous to infer particular changes in the overall turnover (thus, in substance release and alteration of neuronal activity) from data on changes in brain neurotransmitter or neuromodulator levels, it appears safe to assume that these results reflect changes, albeit unspecified, in the functional activity of these neuroactive compounds. This assumption appears to be particularly valid in the case of the increased levels of enkephalin. Recent work in our laboratory (Llados-Eckman and Beckman 1983) suggests that these increased levels reflect an increase in the functional activity of the endogenous opioid system during hibernation. We demonstrated that opioid blockade produced by continuous icv infusion of naloxone during hibernation produced a dose-dependent decrease in bout duration. These and other results (Margules et al. 1979; Kromer 1980) suggest that disruption of the baseline activity of endogenous opioid peptide systems during hibernation destabilizes the state, perhaps by interfering with a fundamental component of its controlling mechanism (Oeltgen et al. 1982).

As noted above, the proposed changes in functional activity of neuropeptides such as TRH, somatostatin, and cholesystokinin during hibernation could contribute to the blockade of the development of morphine physical dependence during this state. Another contributing factor, alluded to earlier, may involve an increase in the level of GABA in the hibernating brain (Robinson and Bradley 1963); inhibition of the degradation of GABA has been reported to attenuate physical dependence (Contreras et al. 1979).

When we proposed (Beckman et al. 1981) that changes in opioid binding might be a potential factor in explaining the resistance of the hibernating state to the development of physical dependence, our rationale was quite straightforward: if morphine binding decreased, either through increased competition with naturally available endogenous ligands or through a frank decrease in opioid binding sites, the potency of morphine (and, hence, physical dependence) would diminish. There is very recent evidence (Kramarova et al. 1983), as reviewed above, that enkephalin levels do increase during hibernation. Whether endorphin levels (or, more to the point, endorphin release) also increase during this state is still unknown.

227

Changes in the Characteristics of Opioid Binding

In considering the role that changes in opioid receptor parameters may play in the blockade of the development of physical dependence during hibernation, we have begun to study with Dr. James K. Wamsley regional brain opioid binding in hibernating and euthermic ground squirrels, using in vitro receptor autoradiography in conjunction with computer-assisted densitometry. In our initial studies, we have sought to avoid preferential labeling of specific opioid receptor subtypes and therefore have used a high concentration (4 nM) of tritiated dihydromorphine as the agonist ligand. The preliminary results show that, indeed, overall opioid binding does decrease in the hibernating brain, particularly in the dorsal aspects of the cerebral cortex, in the septum, hippocampus, thalamus, and in the amygdala. The decrease in intracerebral binding during hibernation is not, however, uniform. For example, binding in the rostral hypothalamus and the habenula remain comparable to that during the euthermic state. In addition, the overall decrease in binding cannot simply be ascribed to the low body temperatures associated with the hibernating state because the trend toward decreased binding is evident in euthermic winter animals, as compared to that observed in the brains of animals during the fall.

It is tempting to speculate that the decline in opioid binding in the winter euthermic and hibernating ground squirrel brain is due to a down-regulation of opioid receptors produced by the elevation of regional brain concentrations of endogenous opioids. Although it seems clear that the opposite phenomenon, up-regulation, occurs following chronic treatment with opioid antagonists such as naloxone or naltrexone (Lahti and Collins 1978; Bardo et al. 1982; Zukin et al. 1982), it remains uncertain whether chronic administration of opioid agonists reliably induces receptor down-regulation (Davis et al. 1975; Davis et al. 1979; Tsang and Ng 1980; Sivam et al. 1981).

Contribution of Low Body Temperature to Reduced Morphine Dependence Liablility During Hibernation

Although the evidence we have presented thus far suggests that hibernation-related adaptive changes in neurotransmitter or neuromodulator parameters (e.g., changes in DA metabolism or in opioid receptor binding) may provide the main source of stabilization against the development of morphine physical dependence, the potential role of low body temperature yet needs to be defined in the ground squirrel. Certainly, evidence obtained in nonhibernating species has identified a temperature-dependent component in the development of dependence and tolerance. Thus, lowered temperature

228

exerted a short-term (less than 4 hours) inhibition of dependence on normorphine in the isolated guinea pig ileum (Collier et al. 1981), and also blocked the development of tolerance to morphine depression of sensory evoked responses in mouse spinal cord-dorsal root ganglion explants (Crain et al. 1979).

In initial experiments, we have begun to compare the naloxone-precipitated abstinence syndrome in euthermic animals that have received continuous icv infusion of morphine (55 μg/μl/hr) with that displayed by post-arousal euthermic animals that had just completed receiving the same dosage of morphine, while hibernating at 20°C. Our initial results indicate that animals hibernating at this elevated temperature (usual hibernation temperature, 5°C) display a feeble abstinence syndrome that includes a few body shakes and vocalizations, and the occasional presence of milky dacryorrhea, chewing, dyspnea, eyetwitch, and forward, fanned tail during the 30-minute period following naloxone administration. One animal also displayed stereotypy, as observed previously in animals that received morphine during deep hibernation (Beckman et al. 1981). These data are too preliminary to adequately describe the effect of low temperature on the hibernation-induced block of physical dependence. They do, however, indicate that low body temperature may contribute to this phenomenon. Continuing work will determine its extent.

CONCLUSION

These studies on the ground squirrel have progressed to the point where it is clear that the hibernating model can make an important contribution to our understanding of the neural correlates of opioid physical dependence. Its unique advantage is that it permits a direct comparison of the performance of designated CNS systems following chronic opioid administration in states of high or low dependence liability. We can, therefore, identify changes in performance that do, or do not, correlate with the development of physical dependence and thereby describe the important determinants of morphine dependence. It is not inconceivable that the critical elements of the natural stabilizing mechanisms utilized by the hibernating CNS could be adapted for the therapeutic prevention of opioid physical dependence.

REFERENCES

Akera, T., and Brody, T.M. The addiction cycle to narcotics in the rat and its relation to catecholamines. _Biochem Pharmacol_, 17:675-688, 1968.

Arbilla, S., and Langer, S.Z. Morphine and β-endorphin inhibit release of noradrenalin from cerebral cortex but not dopamine from rat striatum. _Nature_, 271:559-561, 1978.

Bardo, M.T.; Bhatnagar, R.K.; and Gebhart, G.F. Differential effects of chronic morphine and naloxone on opiate receptors, monoamines, and morphine-induced behaviors in preweanling rats. _Develop Brain Res_, 4: 139-147, 1982.

Beckman, A.L.; Llados-Eckman, C.; Stanton, T.L.; and Adler, M.W. Physical dependence on morphine fails to develop during the hibernating state. _Science_, 212:1527-1529, 1981.

Beckman, A.L.; Llados-Eckman, C.; Stanton, T.L.; and Adler, M.W. Seasonal variation of morphine physical dependence. _Life Sci_, 30:147-153, 1982a.

Beckman, A.L.; Llados-Eckman, C.; Stanton, T.L.; and Adler, M.W. Differential effect of environmental temperature on morphine physical dependence and abstinence. _Life Sci_, 30:1013-1020, 1982b.

Beckman, A.L., and Satinoff, E. Arousal from hibernation by intrahypothalamic injections of biogenic amines in ground squirrels. _Am J Physiol_, 222:875-879, 1972.

Beckman, A.L.; Satinoff, E.; and Stanton, T.L. Characterization of midbrain component of the trigger for arousal from hibernation. _Am J Physiol_, 230: 368-375, 1976a.

Beckman, A.L., and Stanton, T.L. Changes in CNS responsiveness during hibernation. _Am J Physiol_, 231:810-816, 1976.

Beckman, A.L., and Stanton, T.L. Properties of the CNS during the state of hibernation. In: Beckman, A.L., ed. _The Neural Basis of Behavior_. New York: Spectrum, 1982. pp. 19-45.

Beckman, A.L.; Stanton, T.L.; and Satinoff, E. Inhibition of the trigger process for arousal from hibernation. _Am J Physiol_, 230:1018-1025, 1976b.

Belik,B., and Kracho, L.S. Protein metabolism in the brain of hibernating animals. _Ukrain Biochim Zhrl_ (Kiev), 33:684-692, 1961.

Bensemana, D., and Gascon, A.L. Relationship between analgesia and turnover of brain biogenic amines. _Can J Physiol Pharmacol_, 56:721-730, 1978.

Bhargava, H.N. Cyclo (leucylglycine) inhibits the development of morphine induced analgesic tolerance and dopamine receptor supersensitivity in rats. _Life Sci_, 27:117-123, 1980a.

230

Bhargava, H.N. The effects of thyrotropin-releasing hormone on the central nervous system responses to chronic morphine administration. Psychopharmacology, 68:185-189, 1980b.

Bhargava, H.N. Inhibition of tolerance to the pharmacological effects of human β-endorphin by prolyl-leucyl-glycinamide and cyclo (leucylglycine) in the rat. J Pharmacol Exp Ther, 218:404-408, 1981a.

Bhargava, H.N. Dissociation of tolerance to the analgesic and hypothermic effects of morphine by using thyrotropin releasing hormone. Life Sci, 29:1015-1020, 1981b.

Bhargava, H.N. The effects of peptides on tolerance to the cataleptic and hypothermic effects of morphine in the rat. Neuropharmacology, 20:385-390, 1981c.

Bhargava, H.N. Enhanced response to apomorphine in rats treated with multiple injections of human beta endorphin and its blockade by pro-leu-gly-NH and cyclo (leu-gly). Life Sci, 29:1945-1949, 1981d.

Bhargava, H.N. Hypothalamic peptide hormone, prolyl-leucyl-glycinamide and analog, inhibit tolerance to the analgesic and locomotor depressant but not to the locomotor stimulant effects of morphine in the mouse. Neuropharmacology, 21:227-233, 1982.

Bhargava, H.N.; Afifi, A.; and Way, E.L. Effect of chemical sympathectomy on morphine antinociception and tolerance development in the rat. Biochem Pharm, 22: 2769-2772, 1973.

Bhargava, H.N.; Matwyshyn, G.A.; Currie, B.L.; and Goebel, R.J. Structure activity relationship studies with hypothalamic peptide hormones II. Effects of thryotropin releasing hormone analogs on morphine-induced responses in mice. Life Sci, 30:711-718, 1982.

Cheney, D.L., and Goldstein, A. The effect of p-chlorophenylalanine on opiate-induced running, analgesia, tolerance, and physical dependence. J Pharmacol Exp Ther, 177:309-315, 1971.

Clouet, D.H., and Ratner, M. Catecholamine biosynthesis in brains of rats treated with morphine. Science, 168:854-856, 1970.

Collier, H.O.J.; Cuthbert, N.J.; and Francis, D.L. Effect of temperature on the induction of opiate dependence in guinea-pig isolated ileum. Br J Pharmacol, 73:300P-301P, 1981.

Contreras, E.; Tamayo, L.; and Quijoda, L. Effects of irreversible inhibition of GABA transaminase upon some morphine effects. Neuropharmacology, 18:309-313, 1979.

Costa, E.; Carenzi, A.; Guidotti, A.; and Revuelta, A. Narcotic analgesics and the regulation of neuronal catecholamine stores. In: Usdin, E., and Snyder, S., eds. Frontiers in Catecholamine Research 1973. London: Pergamon Press, 1974. pp. 1003-1010.

Crain, S.M.; Crain, B.; Finnigan, T.; and Simon, E.J. Development of tolerance to opiates and opioid peptides in organotypic cultures of mouse spinal cord. Life Sci, 25:1797-1802, 1979.

Dafny, N.; Brown, M.; Burks, T.F.; and Rigor, B.M. Patterns of unit responses to incremental doses of morphine in central gray, reticular formation, medial thalamus, caudate nucleus, hypothalamus, septum, and hippocampus in unanesthetized rats. Neuropharmacol, 18:489-495, 1979.

Davis, M.E.; Akera, T.; and Brody, T.M. Saturable binding of morphine to rat brain-stem slices and the effect of chronic morphine treatment. Res Commun Chem Path Pharmacol, 12:409-418, 1975.

Davis, M.E.; Akera, T.; and Brody, T.M. Reduction of opiate binding to brainstem slices associated with the development of tolerance to morphine in rats. J Pharmacol Exp Ther, 211:112-119, 1979.

Domino, E.F., and Wilson, A.E. Enhanced utilization of brain acetylcholine during morphine withdrawal in the rat. Nature, 243:285-286, 1973.

Duka, T.; Wuster, M.; Schubert, P.; Stoiber, R.; and Herz, A. Selective localization of different types of opiate receptors in hippocampus as revealed by in vivo autoradiography. Brain Res, 205:181-186, 1981.

Dupont, A.; Lepine, J.; Langelier, P.; Merand, Y.; Rouleau, D.; Vaudry, H.; Gros, C.; and Barden, N. Differential distribution of β-endorphin and enkephalins in rat and bovine brain. Reg Peptides, 1:43-52, 1980.

Florant, G.L.; Turner, B.M.; and Heller, H.C. Temperature regulation during wakefulness, sleep, and hibernation in marmots. Am J Physiol, 235:R82-R88, 1978.

Friedler, G.; Bhargava, H.; Quock, R.; and Way, E.L. The effect of 6-hydroxydopamine on morphine tolerance and physical dependence. J Pharm Exp Ther, 183:49-55, 1972.

Gomes, C.; Svensson, T.H.; and Trolin, G. Effects of morphine on central catecholamine turnover, blood pressure, and heart rate in the rat. Nauyn-Schmiedeberg's Arch Pharmacol, 294:141-147, 1976.

Gramsch, C.; Hollt, V.; Mehraein, P.; Pasi, A.; and Herz, A. Regional distribution of methionine-enkephalin- and beta-endorphin-like immunoreactivity in human brain and pituitary. Brain Res, 171:261-270, 1979.

Gunne, L. Noradrenaline and adrenaline in the rat brain during acute and chronic morphine administration and withdrawal. Nature, 184:1950-1951, 1959.

Gunne, L. Catecholamines and 5-hydroxytryptamine in morphine tolerance and withdrawal. Acta Physiol Scand, 58 (Suppl 204):1-91, 1963.

Hammel, H.T.; Dawson, T.J.; Abrams, R.M.; and Andersen, H.T. Total calorimetric measurements on *Citellus lateralis* in hibernation. *Physiol Zool*, 41:341-347, 1968.

Hammel, H.T.; Heller, H.C.; and Sharp, F.R. Probing the rostral brainstem of anesthetized, unanesthetized, and exercising dogs and of hibernating and euthermicground squirrels. *FedProc*, 32:1588-1597, 1973.

Heller, H.C., and Colliver, G.W. CNS regulation of body temperature during hibernation. *Am J Physiol*, 227:583-589, 1974.

Heller, H.C.; Colliver, G.W.; and Beard, J. Thermoregulation during entrance into hibernation. *Pflugers Arch*, 369:55-59, 1977.

Heller, H.C., and Poulson, T.L. Circannian rhythms-II. Endogenous and exogenous factors controlling reproduction and hibernation in chipmunks (*Eutamius*) and ground squirrels (*Spermophilus*). *Comp Biochem Physiol*, 33:357-383, 1970.

Herz, A.; Teschemacher, H.J.; Albus, K.; and Zieglgansberger, S. Morphine abstinence syndrome in rabbits precipitated by injection of morphine antagonists into the ventricular system and restricted parts of it. *Psychopharmacologia*, 26:219-235, 1972.

Hiller, J.M.; Pearson, J., and Simon, E.J. Distribution of stereospecific binding of the potent narcotic analgesic etorphine in the human brain: Predominance in the limbic system. *Res Commun Chem Pathol Pharmacol* 6:1052-1062, 1973.

Ho, I.K.; Lee, S.E.; Stolman, S.; Loh, H.H.; and Way, E.L. Influence of p-chlorophenylalanine on morphine tolerance and physical dependence and regional brain serotonin turnover studies in morphine tolerant-dependent mice. *J Pharmacol Exp Ther*, 182:155-165, 1972.

Kerr,F.W.L., and Pozuelo, J. Suppression of physical dependence and induction of hypersensitivity to morphine by stereotaxic hypothalamic lesions in addicted rats. *Mayo Clin Proc*, 46:653-665, 1971.

Kilduff, T.S.; Sharp, F.R.; and Heller H.C. [^{14}C] 2-deoxyglucose uptake in ground squirrel brain during hibernation. *J Neuroscience*, 2:143-157, 1982.

Kramarova, L.I.; Kolaeva, S.H.; Yukhananov, R.Y.; and Rozhanets, V.V. Content of DSIP, enkephalins, and ACTH in some tissues of active and hibernating ground squirrels (*Citellus suslicus*). *Comp Biochem Physiol*, 74C:31-33, 1983.

Kromer, W. Naltrexone influence on hibernation. *Experientia*, 36:581-582, 1980.

Kromer, W., and Steigemann, N. Opiate tolerance/dependence in the isolated guinea pig ileum is associated with an increased sensitivity to acetylcholine. *Pharmacology*, 25:294-296, 1982.

Kuhar, M.J.; Pert, C.B., and Snyder, S.H. Regional distribution of opiate receptor binding in monkey and human brain. _Nature_, 245:447-450, 1973.

Lahti, R., and Collins, R. Chronic naloxone results in prolonged increases in opiate binding sites in brain. _Eur J Pharmacol_, 51:185-186, 1978.

Large, W.A., and Milton, A.S. The effect of acute and chronic morphine administration on brain acetylcholine levels in the rat. _Br J Pharmac_, 38:451P-452P, 1970.

Lee, J.R., and Fennessy, M.R. The relationship between morphine analgesia and the level of biogenic amines in the mouse brain. _Eur J Pharmacol_, 12:65-70, 1970.

Leucke, R.H., and South, F.E. A possible model for thermoregulation during deep hibernation. In: South, F.E., Hannon, J.P., Willis, J.R., Pengelley, E.T., and Alpert, N.R., eds. _Hibernation and Hypothermia, Perspectives and Challenges_. Amsterdam: Elsevier, 1972. pp. 577-604.

Llados-Eckman, C., and Beckman, A.L. Reduction of hibernation bout duration by ICV infusion of naloxone in _Citellus lateralis_. _Soc Neurosci Abstr_, 9:796, 1983.

Loh, H.H.; Brase, D.A.; Sampath-Khanna, S.; Mar, J.B.; and Way, E.L. β-endorphin _in vitro_ inhibition of striatal dopamine release. _Nature_, 264:567-568, 1972.

Lyman, C.P. Oxygen consumption, body temperature and heart rate of woodchucks entering hibernation. _Am J Physiol_, 194:83-91, 1958.

Margules, D.L.; Goldman, B.; and Finck, A. Hibernation: An opioid-dependent state? _Brain Res Bull_, 4:721-724, 1979.

Matsukura, S.; Yoshimi, H.; Sueoka, S.; Kataoka, K., Ono, T.; and Ohgushi, N. The regional distribution of immunoreactive β-endorphin in the monkey brain. _Brain Res_, 159:228-233, 1978.

Maynert, E.W., and Klingman, G.I. Tolerance to morphine. I. Effects on catecholamines in the brain and adrenal glands. _J Pharmacol Exp Ther_, 135:285-295, 1962.

Maynert, E.W.; Klingman, G.I.; and Kaji, G.K. Tolerance to morphine. II. Lack of effects on brain 5-hydroxytryptamine and gamma-aminobutyric acid. _J Pharmacol Exp Ther_, 135:296-299, 1962.

Moleman, P., and Bruinvels, J. Morphine-induced striatal dopamine efflux depends on the activity of nigrostriatal neurones. _Nature_, 281:686-687, 1979.

Mrosovsky, N. The amplitude and period of circannual cycles of body weight in golden-mantled ground squirrels with medial hypothalamic lesions. _Brain Res_, 99:97-116, 1975.

Mrosovsky, N. Circannual cycles in hibernators. In: Wang, L.C.H., and Hudson, J.W., eds. _Strategies in Cold: Natural Torpidity and Thermogenesis_. New York: Academic Press, 1978. pp. 21-65.

Muchlinski, A.E.; Ho, F.J.; Chew, P.; and Yamada, T.
The concentrations of four neuropeptides in various
brain regions of summer active and hibernating
Spermophilus lateralis. Comp Biochem Physiol, 74:
185-189, 1983.

Oeltgen, P.R.; Walsh, J.W.; Hamann, S.R.; Randall,
D.C.; Spurrier, W.A.; and Myers, R.D. Hibernation
"trigger": Opioid-like inhibitory action on brain
function in the monkey. Pharmac Biochem Behav, 17:
1271-1274, 1982.

Olson, G.A.; Olson R.A.; Kastin, A.J.; and Coy, D.H.
Endogenous opiates: 1981. Peptides, 3:1039-1072,
1982.

Pearson, J.; Brandeis, L.; Simon, E.; and Hiller, J.
Radioautography of binding of tritiated diprenorphine
to opiate receptors in the rat. Life Sci, 26:1047-
1052, 1980.

Pengelley, E.T., and Fisher, K.C. The effect of
temperature and photoperiod on the yearly hibernating
behavior of captive golden-mantled ground squirrels
(*Citellus lateralis tescorum*). Canad J Zool, 41:
1103-1120, 1963.

Pert, C.B.; Kuhar, M.J.; and Snyder, S.H. Autoradiographic localization of the opiate receptor in rat
brain. Life Sci, 16:1849-1854, 1975.

Rae, G.A., and De Morhes, S. Supersensitivity to
noradrenaline in vas deferens from morphine-dependent
mice is confirmed. Eur J Pharmacol, 86:347-352,
352, 1983.

Ritzmann, R.F., Lee, J.M., and Fields, J.Z. Peptide
inhibition of morphine-induced dopaminergic supersensitivity. Life Sci, 31:2287-2290, 1982.

Robinson, J.D., and Bradley, M. Cholinesterase and
glutamic acid decarboxylase levels in the brain of
the hibernating hamster. Nature, 197:389-390, 1963.

Schulz, R., and Herz, A. Naloxone precipitated
withdrawal reveals sensitization to neurotransmitters
in morphine tolerant/dependent rats. Nauyn-
Schmiedeberg's Arch Pharmacol, 299:95-99, 1977.

Schwartz, A.S., and Eidelberg, E. Role of biogenic
amines in morphine dependence in the rat. Life Sci,
9:613-624, 1970.

Shtark, M.B. The Brain of Hibernating Animals. NASA
Technical Translation TTF-619, Washington, 1972.
Translation of Mozg Zimnespyashchekt. Novosibirsk,
Nauka Press, Siberian Branch, 1970.

Simon, E.J., and Hiller, J.M. The opiate receptors.
Ann Rev Pharmacol Toxicol, 18:371-394, 1978.

Sivam, S.P.; Nabeshima, T.; and Ho, I.K. Effects of
morphine administration on opiate receptor binding in
mice. Fed Proc, 40:289, 1981.

Sloan, J.W.; Brooks, J.W.; Eisenman, A.J.; and Martin,
W.R. Comparison of the effects of single doses of
morphine and thebaine on body temperature, activity,
brain and heart levels of catecholamines and
serotonin. Psychopharmacologia, 3:291-301, 1962.

Snelgar, R.S., and Vogt, M. Mapping, in the rat central nervous system, of morphine-induced changes in the turnover of 5-hydroxytryptamine. J Physiol, 314:395-410, 1980.

South, F.E.; Breazile, J.E.; Dellmann, H.D.; and Epperly, A.D. Sleep, hibernation and hypothermia in the yellow-bellied marmot (M. flaviventris). In: Mussachia, X.J., and Saunders, J.F., eds. Depressed Metabolism. New York: Elsevier, 1969. pp. 277-312.

South, F.E.; Heath, J.E.; Luecke, R.H.; Mihailovic, L.T.; Myers, R.D.; Panuska, J.A.; Williams, B.A.; Hartner, W.C.; and Jacobs, H.K. Status and role of the central nervous system and thermoregulation during hibernation and hypothermia. In: South, F.E., Hannon, J.P., Willis, J.R., Pengelley, E.T., and Alpert, N.R., eds. Hibernation and Hypothermia. Perspectives and Challenges. Amsterdam: Elsevier, 1972. pp. 629-633.

Stanton, T.L., and Beckman, A.L. Thermal changes produced by intrahypothalamic injections of acetylcholine during hibernation and euthermia in Citellus lateralis. Comp Biochem Physiol, 58A:143-150, 1977.

Stanton, T.L.; Winokur, A.; and Beckman, A.L. Reversal of natural CNS depression by TRH action in the hippocampus. Brain Res, 181:470-475, 1980.

Stanton, T.L.; Winokur, A.; and Beckman, A.L. Seasonal variation in TRH content of different brain regions and the pineal in the mammalian hibernator, Citellus lateralis. Reg Peptides, 3:135-144, 1982.

Stefano, G.B.; Kream, R.M.; Zukin, R.S.; and Catapane, E.J. Seasonal variation of stereospecific enkephalin binding and pharmacological activity in marine molluscs nervous tissue. In: Rozan, K.S., ed. Advances in Physiological Science Vol. 22, Neurotransmitters in Invertebrates. London: Pergamon Press, 1980. pp. 453-458.

Strumwasser, F. Thermoregulatory, brain and behavioral mechanisms during entrance into hibernation in the squirrel, Citellus beecheyi. Am J Physiol, 196:15-22, 1959a.

Strumwasser, F. Regulatory mechanisms, brain activity, and behavior during deep hibernation in the squirrel, Citellus beecheyi. Am J Physiol, 196:23-30, 1959b.

Tsang, D., and Ng, S.C. Effect of antenatal exposure to opiates on the development of opiate receptors in rat brain. Brain Res, 188:199-206, 1980.

Van Loon, G.R.; Appel, N.M.; and Ho, D. ß-endorphin-induced increases in plasma epinephrine, norepinephrine and dopamine in rats: Inhibition of adrenal medullary response by intracerebral somatostatin. Brain Res, 212:207-214, 1981.

Vasko, M.R., and Domino, E.F. Tolerance development to the biphasic effects of morphine on locomotor activity and brain acetylcholine in the rat. J Pharmacol Exp Ther, 207:848-858, 1978.

Vasko, M.R., and Vogt, M. Analgesia, development of tolerance, and 5-hydroxytryptamine turnover in the rat after cerebral and systemic administration of morphine. Neuroscience, 7:1215-1225, 1982.

Vogt, M. The concentration of sympathin in different parts of the central nervous system under normal conditions and after the administration of drugs. J Physiol, 123:451-481, 1954.

Walker, J.M.; Glotzbach, S.F.; Berger, R.J.; and Heller, H.C. Sleep and hibernation in ground squirrels (Citellus spp.): Electrophysiological observations. Am J Physiol, 233:R213-R221, 1977.

Wang, L.C.H. Energetic and field aspects of mammalian torpor: The Richardson's ground squirrel. In: Wang, L.C.H., and Hudson, J.W., eds. Strategies in Cold: Natural Torpidity and Thermogenesis. New York: Academic Press, 1978. pp. 109-145.

Wang, L.C.H. Hibernation and the endocrines. In: Lyman, C.P., Willis, J.S., Malan, A., and Wang, L.C.H., eds. Hibernation and Torpor in Mammals and Birds. New York: Academic Press, 1982. pp. 206-236.

Watson, S.J.; Akil, H.; Sullivan, S.; and Barchas, J.D. Immunocytochemical localization of methionine enkephalin: Preliminary observations. Life Sci, 21:733-738, 1977.

Way, E.L.; Loh, H.H.; and Shen, F. Morphine tolerance, physical dependence, and synthesis of brain 5-hydroxytryptamine. Science, 162:1290-1292, 1968.

Wei, E.; Loh, H.H.; and Way, E.L. Neuroanatomical correlates of morphine dependence. Science, 177:616-617, 1972.

Wei, E.; Loh, H.H.; and Way, E.L. Brain sites of precipitated abstinence in morphine dependent rats. J Pharmacol Exp Ther, 185:108-115, 1973.

Wikler, A.; Norrell, H.; and Miller, D. Limbic system and opioid addiction in the rat. Exptl Neurol, 34:543-557, 1972.

Wooten, G.F.; DiStefano, P.; and Collins, R.C. Regional cerebral glucose utilization during morphine withdrawal in the rat. Proc Natl Acad Sci, 79:3360-3364, 1982.

Wunnenberg, W.; Merker, G.; and Speulda, E. Thermosensitivity of preoptic neurons and hypothalamic integrative function in hibernators and non-hibernators. In: Wang, L.C.H., and Hudson, J.W., eds. Strategies in Cold: Natural Torpidity and Thermogenesis. New York: Academic Press, 1978. pp. 267-297.

Zukin, R.S.; Sugarman, J.R.; Fitz-Syage, M.L.; Gardner, E.L.; Zukin, S.R.; and Gintzler, A.R. Naltrexone-induced opiate receptor supersensitivity. Brain Res, 245:285-292, 1982.

ACKNOWLEDGEMENTS

The work reported here was supported by National
Institute on Drug Abuse grant DA-02254 and the Alfred
I. duPont Institute.

AUTHORS

Alexander L. Beckman, Ph.D.
Carmen Llados-Eckman, B.S.
Steven K. Salzman, Ph.D.
Toni L. Stanton, Ph.D.

Alfred I. duPont Institute, P.O. Box 269, Wilmington,
DE 19899

Neurophysiological Investigations of Opiate Tolerance and Dependence in the Central Nervous System

Steven Jon Henriksen

Most pharmacological studies investigating opiate- and opioid-induced tolerance, dependence or addiction liability have utilized in vitro bioassay systems or whole animal preparations. These studies, although critical for the elucidation of rank order potency series and the characterization of the variety of opiate receptor subtypes, have not led to the understanding of the cellular processes underlying opiate tolerance and dependence. More recently, studies using hybrid cell lines (see previous papers in this volume) and the investigation of opiate receptor up-or-down regulation (Zukin et al., this volume) have suggested important receptor ligand and second messenger processes that are candidates for participation in cellular events leading to the phenotype of the opiate-tolerant organism. Neurophysiological approaches have also been employed in the study of opiate and opioid neuropharmacology. These studies, using a variety of electrophysiological approaches at the cellular level, have begun to address those bioelectric events associated with acute and chronic drug exposure.

Electrophysiological Techniques: An Inherent Advantage For The Investigation Of Tolerance And Dependence:

(1) They allow the opportunity for real-time analysis of the cellular processes occurring during acute, chronic, and drug withdrawal conditions; (2) they provide a unique wide dynamic range of measured events exemplified by encephalographic and field potential analysis as well as analysis of intracellular events associated with synaptic and nonsynaptic processes; and (3) electrophysiological measurements can be made in several different in vitro and in vivo animal preparations of which each provides particular technical advantages for answering specific questions regarding mechanisms of opiate tolerance and dependence.

In this essay, I will review the evidence of the neurophysiological correlates of acute and chronic opiate (and opioid) exposure, and will discuss how these data generate hypotheses regarding the cellular mechanisms underlying these phenomena. This review is in no way meant to be exhaustive; rather, it has been focused solely on the central nervous system, and then only on particular examples from investigators using specific neurophysiological tools to study the mechanisms of tolerance.

Four considerations are important when discussing central neuronal responses to acute or chronic opiate treatment: (1) What is the nature of event being measured, i.e., is it evoked or spontaneous? (2) What is the time course of the alteration in the event recorded, and what is the stability of this effect?; (3) Can dependence be ascertained by precipitation with naloxone? and (4) Are the changes at the cellular level following chronic opiate exposure due to the same mechanisms that produce the acute effects of these drugs?

Encephalographic Analysis

The electroencephalograph to record spontaneously generated cortical bioelectric events has long been used as a tool to assess both acute and chronic effects of opiates (Khazan 1975). Systemic or intraventricular administration of acute doses of morphine, in numerous experimental animal species, results in a widespread cortical desynchrony and 4-10 Hz burst activity associated with behavioral stupor (Khazan et al. 1967; Khazan and Colasanti 1971; Nakamura and Winters 1973; Tortella et al. 1978). In addition, changes in cortical and subcortical electrical activity in response to repeated morphine administration has been investigated and electroencephalographic tolerance to opiates has been observed (Khazan et al. 1967; Teitelbaum 1976).

Multiple intracerebral injections of morphine into specific subcortical brain loci can result in electrographic tolerance at those injected sites (Teitelbaum et al. 1976). In addition, specific brain lesions have been shown to reverse electrographically assessed morphine tolerance (Teitelbaum et al. 1979).

In addition to those studies evaluating the action of opiates on the spontaneous electroencephalogram, other investigations have focused on the effects of opiates on evoked potentials in naive, tolerant and withdrawn animals (Straw and Mitchell 1964; Domino 1968; Gildenberg et al. 1976). These studies have demonstrated that particular components of stimulation-evoked potentials, and not others, are dramatically altered by acute opiate administration. These effects diminish on continued administration and therefore exhibit tolerance.

Studies such as these have demonstrated that the electroencephalographic technique is a valuable tool to monitor those cellular electrical events that parallel the development of behavioral tolerance to opiates. This approach has also been used to demonstrate more localized cerebral electrical changes associated with the opiate dependence cycle.

The same encephalographic techniques used to assess the acute and chronic effects of opiates on brain electrical activity have been applied to the study of the endogenous opioid peptides.

β-endorphin, methionine and leucine enkephalin, as well as several enkephalin derivatives, have been shown to have nonconvulsive epileptogenic properties when administered intraventricularly to rats (Henriksen et al. 1978; Urca et al. 1977; Neal and Keane 1978; Tortella et al. 1978). This epileptiform activity seems to have its origin in limbic structures (an area rich in opiate receptors) as determined by localized recording and 2-deoxyglucose techniques (figure 1). Another major opioid peptide, Dynorphin A (1-17), is not epileptogenic in rats, suggesting specific opiate receptor specificity for the generation of this activity (Henriksen et al. 1983).

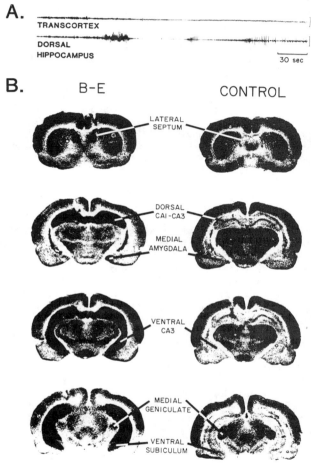

FIGURE 1. 2-DG. EEG traces and ^{14}C-2 deoxyglucose (2DG) auto-radiographic illustrations of the response to intraventricularly administered β-endorphin (B-E, 3 nM) in a representative rat. A) Electrographic tracing of ictal seizure episode elicited by B-E. B) ^{14}C-2DG autoradiographs of representative sections of control rat brain and a brain of a rat exhibiting a seizure following B-E. (Henriksen et al. 1983. © Alan R. Liss, Inc. 1983).

Visual inspection of the autoradiographs reveals a marked uptake of DG, bilaterally, in the dorsal and ventral hippocampus, posterior and ventral subiculum, dentate gyrus, lateral septum, and the posterior part of the medial nucleus of the amygdala (amygdala-hippocampal area). There was also a marked decrease of uptake bilaterally in the medial geniculate body.

The electrographic changes seen in the EEG following repeated ventricular or in situ administration of opioid peptides result in the development of tolerance to the effect of the peptide similar to opiates (Elazar et al. 1979). Figure 2 illustrates the development of tolerance to the epileptogenic action of a daily injection of β-endorphin (3 nM i.c.v.) in a rat.

These encephalographic studies provide important information regarding localized electrographic patterns associated with acute and chronic opioid/opiate administration. Therefore they suggest specific brain areas, and even nuclei, that are highly sensitive to the effects of these drugs. On the other hand, this experimental approach is unable to distinguish between a direct pharmacological effect and an indirect, secondary, effect of these drugs. Because of this technical limitation other neuropharmacological approaches have been employed to investigate more directly the action of narcotics and opioid peptides on single neurons.

Extracellular Analysis

1. Acute effects of opiates and opioid peptides

Prior to the knowledge of the endogenous opioid peptides or specific opiate receptors, most central pharmacological effects of systemically administered opiate alkaloids were attributed to their action on known transmitter systems (Clouet 1971; Way 1972; Way and Shen 1971; Clouet and Iwatsubo 1975). However, in their extensive review, Clouet and Iwatsubo (1975) could not attribute a causative role to any single transmitter system for the development of tolerance to opiates.

In an attempt to characterize more precisely the possible inter-action of opiates with other neurotransmitters, the neuropharma-cological technique of microiontophoresis combined with single cell recording has been employed. This approach has the important advantage of allowing the direct assessment of drug (or putative transmitter) efficacy on a single recorded neuron thereby allevi-ating the complication of indirect effects of systemically adminis-tered drugs. In addition, the effects of iontophoretically applied opiates (or, as we are now aware, opioid peptides) on cellular responses to other neurotransmitters can be evaluated. Early studies using this approach demonstrated complex neuronal actions of iontophoretically applied opiates. In the brainstem of the rat, iontophoretically applied morphine produced both excitatory (43%) as well as inhibitory (22%) actions on the spontaneous discharge of individual neurons (Bradley and Dray 1974). In addition, ionto-phoretically applied morphine was able to block, in many cases, the

CHANGES IN BETA-ENDORPHIN INDUCED ICTAL EPISODES FOLLOWING
REPEATED INJECTIONS

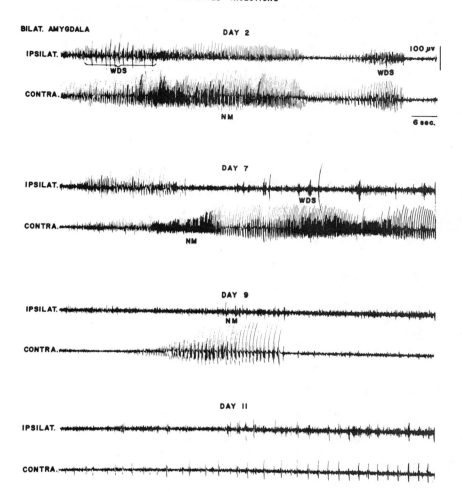

FIGURE 2. Endorphin Tolerance. Amygdala EEG traces taken from a rat injected once daily with β-endorphin (3 nM) intraventricularly. IPSILAT: refers to same side of the brain as the injection; CONTRA: refers to the opposite side from the injection. Note the slow but marked tolerance that develops to the ictal epileptiform events as recorded from the amygdala. WDS: wet-dog-shakes; NM=no movement.

normal excitatory response of these neurons to iontophoretically applied acetylcholine, noradrenaline and 5-hydroxytryptamine. On the other hand, the excitatory effect of glutamate on these neurons could not be blocked by morphine (Bradley and Dray 1974). In an attempt to assess the specificity of these morphine effects, it was found that only the depressions in brain stem unit activity were capable of being antagonized by naloxone, suggesting that the direct excitatory effects of morphine observed in a majority of the neurons tested was a nonspecific effect (Bramwell and Bradley 1974). In another important observation, these investigators rarely observed the phenomenon of tachyphylaxis (i.e., desensitization) to repeated iontophoretic applications of opiate and never observed such an effect to the inhibitory (i.e., specific) action of morphine.

Numerous other investigators have studied the action of opiates in other brain areas using the microiontophoretic technique. In general, these studies show that the specific (i.e., naloxone-reversible) effect of electrophoretically applied opiates is to depress the spontaneous activity of recorded neurons (Bradley and Dray 1974; Henry and Neuman 1975; Zieglgansberger and Bayerl 1975; Zieglgansberger et al. 1975; Satoh et al. 1976; Fry et al. 1980; but see Davies 1976). Figure 3 illustrates a representative example of the effect of normorphine, iontophoretically applied onto rat amygdala neurons.

Soon after the isolation, characterization, and synthesis of the first endogenous opioid peptide, neuropharmacologists began to evaluate this new, growing list of peptides for central opiate-like activity. Of paramount importance in these investigations has been the localization of opioid receptors through autoradiographic analysis (Goodman et al. 1980; Duka et al. 1981; Goodman and Snyder 1982) as well as the distribution of the endogenous opioid peptides thorough the use of immunohistochemical techniques (Bloom et al. 1977, 1978; Watson et al. 1977 and others).

In this way, the cellular physiologists have been able to direct their studies to those areas in the mammalian brain appropriate for each opiate receptor subtype being investigated as well as for the specific opioid peptide locally distributed. Early surveys of the response of neurons to iontophoretically applied opioid peptides suggested great similarities to what had previously been observed with opiate alkaloids (Nicoll et al. 1977; Siggins et al. 1978; Zieglgansberger et al. 1975; French and Siggins 1980). In most brain areas studied, the great majority of single neurons demonstrate naloxone-reversible inhibition of spontaneous discharge following electrophoresis of the enkephalins (either leucine or methionine) or β-endorphin (figure 4). A notable exception to this general inhibitory effect is observed in the hippocmapal formation where mostly excitatory effects are observed (Nicoll et al. 1980; and Zieglgansberger et al. 1979). These results supported earlier encephalographic data suggesting excitatory, epileptogenic, actions of intraventricularly administered opioid peptides on the hippocampal formation (Henriksen et al. 1978). Because of the unique excitatory actions of most opioid peptides on hippocampal neurons, a great number of investigators have focused their attention on this structure in an attempt to explain this paradox. Simply stated, it now appears that these opioid-induced excitatory effects

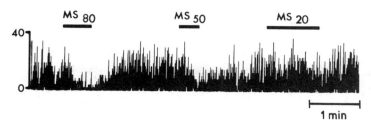

A. AMYGDALA

MS 80   MS 50   MS 20

40

0

1 min

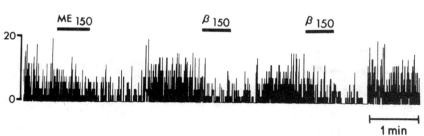

B. AMYGDALA

ME 150   β 150   β 150

20

0

1 min

FIGURE 3. Amygdala. Inhibitory effects of morphine (MS; panel A) on a single neuron in anterior central amygdala, and of methionine-enkephalin (ME) and β-endorphin (β; panel B) on a neuron in anterior basolateral amygdala. Apparent differences here in sensitivity of these neurons to the opiates or peptides were not consistently observed in other neurons. Note: the magnitude of response to MS in panel A is correlated with the iontophoretic current (French and Siggins 1980, © 1980 by Elsevier North Holland - Biomedical Press).

are most likely the result of an indirect disinhibitory action of the peptides on adjacent inhibitory interneurons (see Zieglgansberger et al. 1979).

These physiological data are supported by anatomical evidence suggesting the presence of opioid-containing neurons in close proximity to putative inhibitory interneurons (Gall et al. 1981).

2.   Extracellular effects of opiates and opioids in tolerant preparation

Microiontophoretic and micropneumatic techniques have been used to assess the cellular response to applied opioid peptides and opiates in animals previously made tolerant to opiate alkaloids. In most brain areas studied in tolerant rats, extracellular application of opiates and opioids results in a diminished responsiveness to their action compared to their effect in naive animals (Satoh et al. 1974, 1975, 1976; Zieglgansberger et al. 1976; Zieglgansberger and Fry 1976; Fry et al. 1979; Aghajanian 1978). In addition, cellular

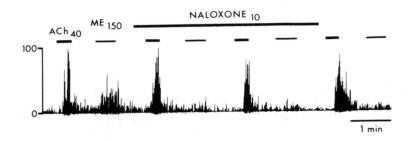

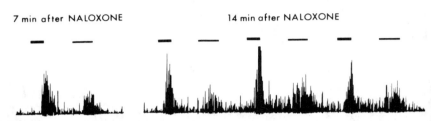

FIGURE 4. Excitatory action of methionine-enkephalin (ME) and
acetylcholine (ACh) in the hippocampus, and the blockade of the ME
action by iontophoretic naloxone. Thin bar indicates ME application and thicker bar, ACh application. Same neuron throughout
record. Note that firing rate and ACh response is not much
affected at 2-3 minutes of naloxone application, when ME responses
are totally blocked, but less selective naloxone effects emerge
later, when the ACh response is reduced by about 30% (French and
Siggins 1980, © 1980 by Elsevier North Holland - Biomedical Press).

dependence to morphine has been demonstrated by studies indicating
a higher incidence of excitatory responses to microiontophoreti-
cally administered naloxone has been observed for neurons recorded
in the medial thalamus (Frederickson et al. 1975), frontal cortex
(Satoh et al. 1976), locus coeruleus (Aghajanian 1978) and striatum
(Fry et al. 1980) of morphine-tolerant rats.

These studies offer strong evidence that both tolerance, as well as
dependence, to opiates and opioid peptides can be observed at the
single neuron level in the vertebrate CNS.

Recent studies have attempted to assess opioid tolerance and dependence using a CNS in vitro preparation, the hippocampal, or locus
coeruleus slice. This preparation offers several technical advantages over the in vivo preparation for the study of opiate tolerance and dependence. Of foremost importance is the ability to
accurately control drug concentration, which allows true pharmacological studies to be done with agonist and antagonist drugs.

As was previously discussed, opiates and opioids produce excitatory
effects in the hippocampal formation. In rat hippocampal slices,
opiates and opioid peptides potentiate the synaptic activation of

pyramidal neurons as revealed by a shift to the left in the input-output curves of monosynaptically evoked CA1 field potentials (Robinson and Deadwyler 1980; Corrigall et al. 1981; French and Zieglgansberger 1982; Valentino and Dingledine 1982; Robinson et al. 1982). Figure 5 illustrates the effect of normorphine and methionine-enkephalin on hippocampal slice CA1 field potentials in a slice obtained from a naive rat.

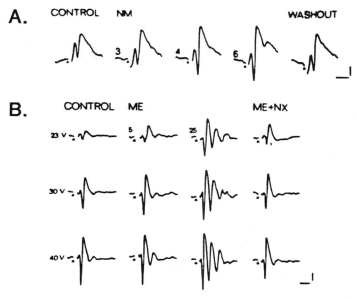

FIGURE 5. Effect of normorphine (NM, 1 µM) on the population spike evoked in hippocampal pyramidal cells (CA1) by stimulation of Schaffer collaterals. A. Spikes at several time points (3,4,6 minutes) after onset of opioid perfusion. Washout taken at 20 minutes after termination of drug application. Note the emergence of a secondary wave (6 minutes). Stimulus intensity was 40 V, duration 0.1 ms. Calibration: 1 mV, 5 ms. B. Effect of methionine-enkephalin (ME, 1 µM) at various time points (5, 25 minutes) and with different stimulus intensities (23,30,40 V). Note the large secondary and tertiary wave forms at the 25-minute time point. The responses to ME + NX were taken 5 minutes after the onset of perfusion of ME (1 µM) + naloxone (NX, 1 µM). Calibration: 1 mV, 5 ms (same recording and stimulation sites as in A) (French and Zieglgansberger 1982, © 1982 by Springer-Verlag).

Hippocampal slices obtained from rats made tolerant to morphine exhibit tolerance to morphine but not to opioids when challenged in vitro (French and Zieglgansberger 1982). These results suggest that, while both opiate agonists increase neuronal excitability of hippocampal pyramidal cells, this effect is likely to be mediated via different opiate receptor populations (figure 6).

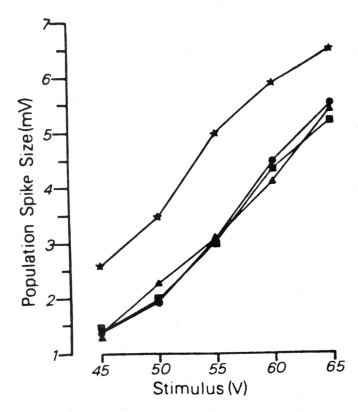

FIGURE 6. Effect of methionine-enkephalin (ME) and lack of effect of a high concentration of normorphine (NM) when applied to slices obtained from chronically morphinized rats:
●——● control; ✱——✱: ME, 5 μM; ▲——▲: NM, 5 μM; ■——■washout of Me response (French and Zieglgansberger 1982, © 1982 by Springer-Verlag).

In a recent study utilizing the locus coeruleus slice preparation (Andrade et al. 1983), tolerance was observed to the normal decrease in spontaneous firing of locus coeruleus neurons produced with acute administration of morphine. However, in contrast to what has been reported in in vivo studies (Aghajanian 1978), naloxone administered to the tolerant slice did not precipitate supranormal firing rates of locus coeruleus neurons. These results strongly suggest that, at least for noradrenergic locus coeruleus neurons in vitro, tolerance and dependence can be dissociated. It also suggests that dependence (withdrawal activation) in locus coeruleus neurons is mediated by factors present in vivo but not in vitro (i.e., extrinsic excitatory inputs to this area).

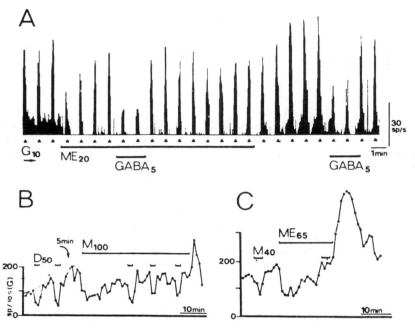

FIGURE 7. Acute desensitization to phoretically applied methionine-enkephalin. A: methionine-enkephalin (ME, 20 nA) reduces spontaneous and glutamate-induced (G, 10 nA/20 s) discharge activity. Despite ongoing application of ME, the firing rate increased again and showed a clear rebound after termination of drug application. The inhibitory action of GABA (5 nA) before (not shown), during and after ME application was not altered significantly. Applications are indicated by bars. Doses are indexed. B: ordinates in B and C give activity during pulses (10 s) of glutamate (10 nA). The applications were spaced 60 s apart. Microiontophoretic administration of D-Ala^2-D-Leu^5-enkephalin (D, 50 nA) causes inhibition which is not changed despite the desensitization to morphine (M, 100 nA). C: the inhibitory effect of morphine (M, 40 nA) was lost after the neuron was rendered insensitive to ME (65 nA). After termination of drug administration the neuron showed a marked rebound in its firing rate and reached control levels and sensitivity to morphine after about 15 minutes (Williams and Zieglgansberger 1981, © 1981 by Elsevier North Holland - Biomedical Press).

3. Acute desensitization to opiates/opioids

Cellular studies of opiate/opioid tolerance and dependence have the unique capability of accurately monitoring the developmental time course of subsensitivity to opiate agonists. Some investigations have suggested very short-term tolerance, or tachyphylaxis, to opiates can occur (Fry et al. 1980; Gahwiler 1981; Williams and Zieglgansberger 1981. Figure 7 illustrates an example of

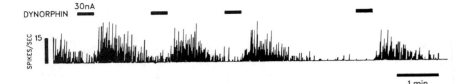

FIGURE 8. Dynorphin A(1-17), 30 nA, induces excitatory response in a CA3 hippocampal neuron recorded from anesthesized rat. Because space does not allow, this rate-meter represents only the last four of 50 dynorphin A 30-second pulses. No acute desensitization was observered.

desensitization of a frontal cortical neuron to a continuous iontophoretic pulse of methionine-enkephalin. In addition, in this same study, an apparent one-way cross-desensitization was observed for morphine and D-Ala-D-Leu-enkephalin (figure 7C).

Other studies in other brain areas failed to demonstrate acute tolerance to either opiates or opioids peptides. Figure 8 illustrates the effect of iontophoretically applied dynorphin on a rat hippocampal neuron and the lack of tachyphylaxis.

In addition, studies of opiate/opioid effect on hippocampal neurons in the slice preparation have failed to show any short-term tolerance to either agent (Valentino and Dingledine 1982; Robinson and Deadwyler 1980). In fact, even after 4-hours of superfusion with morphine (20 M), no diminution in the augmentation of the evoked population spike was observed.

It is possible that some of the earlier investigations demonstrating tachyphylaxis to opiates may have been confounded by technical problems associated with long-term ejection artifacts observed when using iontophoretic pipettes. The issue of acute tolerance to opiates and opioid peptides, therefore, remains unresolved.

Intracellular Analysis

Following the lead of in vivo pharmacological studies of the action of opiates and opioid peptides on single neurons in brain, several investigators recently have begun to investigate the intracellular processes associated with acute and chronic drug exposure. Recordings have been made from neurons penetrated in the hippocampal and locus coeruleus slice preparation (See Siggins and Zieglgansberger 1981; Masukawa and Prince 1982; Robinson and Deadwyler 1981; Nicoll et al. 1980; Dingledine 1980; Haas and Ryall 1980; Pepper and Henderson 1980; Williams et al. 1982). In the locus coeruleus slice preparation, methionine[5]-enkephalin, D-Ala[2]-D-Leu[5]-enkephalin (DADLE) and morphine produce a naloxone-sensitive increase in potassium conductance resulting in hyperpolarization of

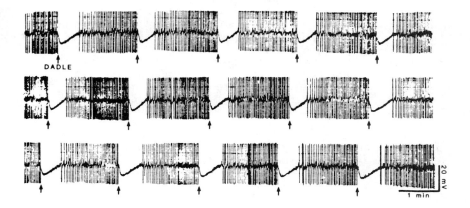

FIGURE 9. Enkephalin inhibits cell firing. The figure shows an intracellular recording from a spontaneously firing locus coeruleus neuron. DADLE was applied by a brief (50 ms) pulse of pressure (70 kN M^{-2}, 10 p.s.i.) to a pipette positioned just above the brain slice at the time indicated by the arrows. The cell hyperpolarized and the action potential discharge was inhibited. The pen recorder did not reproduce the full action potential amplitude, which was 70-100 mV among different neurons. These recordings were made from a completely submerged slice of pons (thickness 300 M) continuously superfused with a solution of the following composition (nM): NaCL 126, KCl 2.5, $CaCl_2$ 2.4, NaH_2PO_4 1.2, $MgCl_2$ 1.3, $NaHCO_3$ 25, glucose 11, which was equilibrated at $37^{\circ}C$ with 95% O_2, 5% CO_2 (Williams et al. 1982, © 1982 by MacMillan Journals Ltd.).

the cell and cessation of spontaneous firing (Williams et al. 1982; North and Williams 1983; see figure 9). Note the lack of acute desensitization to this response.

In contrast, pyramidal cells penetrated in the hippocampal slice preparation show little or no direct transmembrane effects of either morphine or several opioid peptides. On the other hand these agents do alter synaptic responses to afferent stimulation, which is consistent with a modulatory action, of opioids in this structure (Masukawa and Prince 1982; Siggins and Zieglgansberger 1981). As yet, there exists no consensus as to the exact mechanisms by which opioids alter these hippocampal synaptic potentials but most studies suggest a reduction of recurrent and feed forward inhibitory post-synaptic potentials (IPSPs) implying a disinhibitory mechanism. This interpretation is also suggested by extracellular studies previously discussed.

One recent study has investigated the changes in transmembrane properties and sensitivity to opiates following prolonged exposure to morphine (Williams and North 1983). In this interesting study, intracellular recordings were made from locus coeruleus neurons in the slice preparation after three treatment paradigms: (1) recordings made from slices cut from naive rats and superfused with morphine for 8-12 hours, (2) recordings made from slices taken from rats previously implanted with morphine pellets and superfused with morphine; and (3) recordings made from slices taken from pelleted rats but superfused in a morphine-free solution. In "naive" locus coeruleus slices, normorphine (1-3 M) produced the usual hyperpolarization of these neurons; however, the hyperpolarization lasted for as long as the superfusion continued (up to 12 hours). That is, no tolerance was observed to the hyperpolarizing effect of normorphine in this time period. Neurons recorded from pelleted rats showed only mild tolerance to the hyperpolarizing action of superfused normorphine (3-10-fold less potent). In studies taken from pelleted rats, naloxone caused a depolarization of recorded neurons and the return to baseline of the spontaneous firing rate. These studies indicate that no acute tolerance to normorphine is seen during 8-12 hours of perfusion in the locus coeruleus slice. In addition, only minimal tolerance is observed in the slices taken from pelleted rats. This is to be compared to strong behavioral and cellular tolerance seen in vivo with the same treatment schedule. Therefore, at least for neurons in this preparation, much of those observed signs of tolerance and dependence seen in vivo must derive from a larger neural net influencing secondarily the excitability of locus coeruleus neurons. Studies such as these intracellular investigations will be very important to follow for neurons from other brain areas where acute tolerance has been observed.

SUMMARY

In this essay I have presented several examples of cellular neuro-physiological approaches used to investigate opiate tolerance and dependence. In many ways, these central nervous system studies parallel earlier investigations carried out in in vitro preparations and cell culture systems reviewed by others in this volume. The examples presented here have demonstrated that opiate/opioid tolerance and dependence are observed at all levels of electro-physiological analysis. Moreover, recent studies utilizing the locus coeruleus slice preparation have shown the feasibility of separating the processes underlying opiate tolerance and those of dependence (Andrade et al. 1983). Several important issues remain unresolved: (1) Can acute tolerance to opiates/opioids be demon-strated in all preparations (and in all brain areas studied) or is this phenomenon, in part, due to technical shortcomings of ionto-phoresis? (2) What are the characteristics of the subpopulations of opioid receptor agonists and their differential ability to alter, in naive or tolerant preparations, synaptic and nonsynaptic processes in neurons? and (3) What are the intracellular events associated with dependence on other brain areas known to contain neurons that are post-synaptic to endogenous opioid peptides? In addition, what is the relationship, at the synaptic level, of opioid-induced synaptic activity and the cascade of intracellular events coupled to "second messenger" processes? Are these intra-cellular processes ubiquitous for all opioid agonist subtypes or are regional as well as intracellular coupling mechanisms heterogeneous?

Many of these questions currently remain unanswered. However, taking our lead from investigators using molecular approaches to study receptor function (see Sigworth 1982; Walker et al. 1982; Taylor et al. 1983; Dunn et al. 1983 and others vis-a-vis muscarinic ACh receptor), "opioid" physiologists are likely to play a major role in elucidating and characterizing endogenous ligand/receptor interactions in the coming years.

REFERENCES

Aghajanian, G. Tolerance of locus coeruleus neurones to morphine and suppression of withdrawal response by clonidine. Nature, 276:186-187, 1978.

Andrade, R., Vandermaelen, C. and Aghajanian, G. Morphine tolerance and dependence in the locus coeruleus: single cell studies in brain slices. European J Pharmacol, 91:161-169, 1983.

Bloom, F., Battenberg, E., Rossier, J., Ling, N., Leppaluoto, J., Vargo, T. and Guillemin, R. Endorphins are located in the intermediate and anterior lobes of the pituitary gland not in the neurophyphysis. Life Sci, 265:49-51, 1977.

Bloom, F.E., Battenberg, E., Rossier, J., Ling, N. and Guillemin, R. Neurons containing beta-endorphin in rat brain exist separately from those containing enkephalin: immunocyto-chemical studies. Proc Natl Acad Sci USA, 75:1591-1595, 1978.

Bradley, P.B. and Dray, A. Morphine and neurotransmitter substances: microiontophoretic study in the rat brain stem. Br J Pharm, 50:47-55, 1974.

Bramwell, G.J. and Bradley, P.B. Actions and interactions of narcotic agonists and antagonists on brain stem neurons. Brain Res, 73:167-170, 1974.

Clouet, D.H. The alteration of brain metabolism by narcotic analgesic drugs. In: Lajtha, A., ed. Handbook of Neuro-chemistry. Vol. 6 New York: Plenum Press, 1971. pp.479-508.

Clouet, D.H. and Iwatsbo, K. Mechanisms of tolerance to and dependence on narcotic analgesic drug. Ann Rev Pharm, 15:49-70, 1975.

Corrigall, W., Linseman, M.A., Lucato, R. and Elliott, M. Differential tolerance to the effects of morphine on evoked activity in the hippocampal slice. Life Sci, 28:1613-1620, 1981.

Davies, J. Effects of morphine and naloxone on renshaw cells and spinal interneurons in morphine dependent and non-dependent rats. Brain Res, 113:311-326, 1976.

Dingledine, R. Enkephalins excitatory action on hippocampal neurons cannot be explained by attenuation of recurrent inhibition. Neurosci Abstr, 6:612, 1980.

Domino, E.F. Effects of narcotic analgesics on sensory input, activating system and motor output. Res Pull Ass Nerv Ment Pis, 46:150-155, 1968.

Duka, T., Wuster, M., Schubert, P., Stolber, R. and Herz, A. Selective localization of different types of opiate receptors in hippocampus as revealed by in vitro autoradiography. Brain Res, 205:181-186, 1981.

Dunn, S., Conti-Tronconi, B. and Raftery, M. Separate sites of low and high affinity for agonists on torpedo californice acetylcholine receptor. Biochemistry, 22:2512-2518, 1983.

Elazar, Z., Motles, E., Ely, Y. and Simantov, R. Acute tolerance to the excitatory effect of enkephalin microinjections into hippocampus. Life Sci, 24:541-548, 1979.

Frederickson, R.C.D., Norris, F.H. and Hewes, C.R. Effects of naloxone and acetylcholine on medial thalamic and cortical units in naive and morphine dependent rats. Life Sci, 17:81-82, 1975.

French, E. and Siggins, G. An iontophoretic survey of opioid peptide actions in the rat limbic system: In search of opiate epileptogenia mechanisms. Reg Pep, 1:127-146, 1980.

French, E. and Zieglgansberger, W. The excitatory response of in vitro hippocampal pyramidal cells to normorphine and methionine-enkephalin may be mediated by different receptor populations. Exp Brain Res, 48:238-244, 1982.

Fry, J.P., Zieglgansberger, W. and Herz, A. Specific versus nonspecific actions of opioids on hippocampal neurones in the rat brain. Brain Res, 163:295-305, 1979.

Fry, J.P. Herz, A. and Zieglgansberger, W. A demonstration of naloxone-precipated opiate withdrawal on single neurons in the morphine-tolerant/dependent rat brain. Brit J Pharmac, 68:585-592, 1980.

Fry, J.P., Zieglgansberger, W. and Herz, A. Tachyphylaxis to enkephalin-tolerance and dependence at the single neuron level? In: Ryall and Kelley, eds. Iontophoresis and Transmitter Mechanisms in the Mammalian Central Nervous System, Elsevier, 1978. pp. 323-325.

Fry, J.P., Zieglgansberger, W. and Herz, A. Development of acute opioid tolerance and dependence in rat striatal neurons. Naunyn Schmiedebergs Arch Pharmacol, 313:145-149, 1980.

Gahwiler, B.H. Development of acute tolerance during exposure of hippocampal explants to an opioid peptides. Brain Res, 217:196-200, 1981.

Gall, C., Brecha, N., Chaung, K.J. and Karten, H.I. Localization of enkephalin-like immunoreactivity to identified axonal and neuronal populations of the rat hippocampus. J Comp Neurol, 198:335-350, 1981.

Gildenberg, P., Murthy, K.S., Adler, M. and Frost, E.A. The effect of morphine on evoked potentials in naive, tolerant and withdrawn rats. In: Opiates and Endogenous Opioid Peptides. Amsterdam: Elsevier Biomedical Press, 1976, pp. 247-256.

Goodman, R.R., Snyder, S., Kuhar, M. and Young, W.S. III. Differentiation of delta and mu opiate receptor localizations by light microscopic autoradiography. Proc Natl Acad Sci USA, 77:6239-6243, 1980.

Goodman, R. and Snyder, S. k opiate receptors localized by autoradiography to deep layers of the cerebral cortex: relation to sedative effects. Proc Natl Acad Sci USA, 79:5703-5707, 1982.

Haas, H. and Ryall, R. Is excitation by enkephalins of hippocampal neurons in the rat due to presynaptic of activation or to disinhibition? J Physiol, 308:315-330, 1980.

Henriksen, S.J., Bloom, F.E., McCoy, F., Ling, N. and Guillemin, R. Beta-endorphin induces nonconvulsive limbic seizures. Proc Natl Acad Sci USA, 75:5221-5225, 1978.

Henriksen, S., Chouvet, G., McGinty, J. and Bloom, F. Neuropeptides and the epilepsies: Current Perspectives. In: Epilepsy: An Update on Research and therapy. Nistico, D., Perry,& Meinardi, eds. Progress in Clinical and Biological Research, V. 24. New York: Alan R. Liss, 1983. pp. 105-120.

Henry, J.L. and Neuman, R.S. Morphine depression of dorsal horn neurons in the cat. Proc Canad Fed Biol Soc, 17:158, 1975. '

Khazan, N. Implications and significance of EEG and sleep-awake activity in the study of experimental drug dependence on morphine. In: Ehrenpreis, S. and Neidle, A., eds. Methods in Narcotic Research. New York: Marcel Dekker, Inc., 1975. pp. 173-215.

Khazan, N., Weeks, J.R. and Schroeder, L.D. Electroencephalographic electromyographic and behavioral correlates during a cycle of self-maintained morphine addiction in the rat. J Pharmacol Exp Ther, 155:521-531, 1967.

Khazan, N. and Colasanti, B. EEG correlates of morphine challenge in post-addict rats. Psychopharmacologia, 22:56-63, 1971.

Masukawa, L. and Prince, D. Enkephalin inhibition of inhibitory input to CA1 and CA3 pyramidal neurons in the hippocampus. Brain Res, 249:271-280, 1982.

Nakamura, J. and Winters, W.D. Attenuation of the morphine EEG continuum following a repeat dose within 16 days: delayed tolerance in the rat. Neuropharm, 12:607-617, 1973.

Neal, H. and Keane, P.E. The effects of local microinjections of opiates and enkephalins into the forebrain on the electro-corticogram of the rat. Electroenceph Clin Neurophysiol, 45:655-665, 1978.

Nicoll, R., Siggins, G., Ling, N., Bloom, F. and Guillemin, R. Neuronal actions of endorphins and enkephalins among brain region: A comparation microiontophoretic study. Proc Natl Acad Sci USA, 74:2584-2588, 1977.

Nicoll, R., Alger, B. and Jahr, C. Enkephalin blocks inhibitory pathways in the vertebrate CNS. Nature, 287:22-25, 1980.

North, R. and Williams, J.T. Opiate activation of potassium conductance inhibitory calcium action potentials in rat locus coeruleus neurons. Br J Pharmac, 80:225-228, 1983.

Pepper, C.M. and Henderson, G. Opiates and opioid peptides hyperpolarize locus coeruleus neurons in vitro. Science, 209:394-596, 1980.

Peri, R. and Meinardix, H., eds. Epilepsy: An update on Research and Therapy. New York: Alan Liss, Inc., 1983. pp. 105-120.

Robinson, J., Dunlap, C.E. III and Deadwyler, S. Differences in opiate-induced synaptic excitability of hippocampal slices prepared from tolerant rats. Exper Neurol, 77:590-598, 1982.

Robinson, J.H. and Deadwyler, S. Morphine excitation: effects on field potentials recorded in the in vitro hippocampal slice. Neuropharmacology, 19:507-514, 1980.

Robinson, J.H. and Deadwyler, S.A. Intracellular correlates of morphine excitation in the hippocampal slice preparation. Brain Res, 224:375-383, 1981.

Satoh, M., Zieglgansberger, W., Fries, W. and Herz, A. Opiate agonist-antagonist interaction at cortical neurones of naive and tolerant/dependent rats. Brain Res, 82:378-382, 1974.

Satoh, M., Zieglgansberger, W. and Herz, A. Interaction between morphine and putative excitatory neurotransmitters in cortical neurones in naive and tolerant rats. Life Sci, 17:75-80, 1975.

Satoh, M., Zieglgansberger, W. and Herz, A. Actions of opiates upon single unit activity in the cortex of naive and tolerant rats. Brain Res, 115:99-110, 1976.

Siggins, G.R.,Zieglgansberger, W., French, E., Ling, N. and Bloom, F. Opiate and opioid peptides may excite hippocampal (HPC) neurons (HPN) by inhibiting adjacent inhibitory interneurons. Neurosci Abstr, 4:414, 1978.

Siggins, G.R. and Zieglgansberger, W. Morphine and opioid peptides reduce inhibitory synaptic potentials in hippocampal pyramidal cells in vitro without alteration of membrane potential. Proc Natl Acad Sci USA, 78:5235-5339, 1981.

Sigworth, F. Fluctuation in the current through open ACh-receptor channels. Biophys J, 37:309a, 1982.

Straw, R.N. and Mitchell, C.L. The effects of morphine, pentobarbital, pentazocine and nalorphine on bioelectric potentials evoked in the brain stem of the rat by electrical stimulation of the tooth pulp. J Pharmacol Exp Ther, 146:7-15, 1964.

Taylor, P., Brown, R. and Johnson, D. The linkage between ligand occupation and response of the nicotinic acetylcholine receptor. In: Current Topics in Membranes and Transport. Vol. 18. New York: Academic Press, 1983. pp. 407-443.

Teitelbaum, H., Catravas, G. and McFarland, W.L. Reversal of morphine tolerance after medial and thalamic lesions in the rat. Science, 185:449-451, 1979.

Teitelbaum, H., Blosser, J. and Catravas, G. Bilateral electro-encephalographic response and unilateral tolerance to unilateral intracerebral morphine injections. Nature, 260:158-159, 1976.

Tortella, F.C., Moreton, J.E. and Khazan, N. Electroencephalo-graphic and behavioral effects of D-Ala^2-methionine-enkepha-linamide and morphine in the rat. J Pharm Exp Therap, 206:636-643, 1978.

Urca, G., Frenk, H., Liebeskind, J.C. and Taylor, A.N. Morphine and enkephalin: analgesia and epileptic properties. Science, 197:83-96, 1977.

Valentino, R. and Dingledine, R. Pharmacological characterization of opioid effects in the rat hippocampal slice. J Pharmacol Exp Therap, 223:502-509, 1982.

Walker, J., Takeyasu, K. and McNamee, M. Activation and inactivation kinetics of torpedo californica acetylcholine receptor in reconstituted membranes. Biochemistry, 21:5384-5389, 1982.

Watson, S.J., Akil, H., Sullivan, J. and Barchas, J.D. Immunocyto-chemical localization of methionine enkephalin: preliminary observation. Life Sci, 21:733-738, 1977.

Way, E.L. Role of serotonin in morphine effects. Fed Proc, 31:113-120, 1972.

Way, E.L. and Shen, F.H. Catecholamine and 5-hydroxytryptamine. In: Clouet, D., ed. Narcotic Drugs Biochemical Pharmacology. New York: Plenum Press, 1971, pp. 229-253.

Williams, J.T. and Zieglcansberger, W. Neurons in the frontal cortex of the rat carry multiple opiate receptors. Brain Res, 226:304-308, 1981.

Williams, J.T., Egan, T.M. and North, D. Enkephalin opens potassium channel on mammalian central neurons. Nature, 229:74-77, 1982.

Williams, J. and North, R.A. Tolerance to opiates in locus coeruleus actions? Abst International Narcotic Res Conf, 49, 1983.

Zieglgansberger, W. and Bayerl, J. Interference of microelectro-phoretically applied substances with the depolarizing action of glutamate and acetylcholine. Pflugers Arc ges Physiol, 355 (Suppl):R170, 1975.

Zieglgansberger, W., Satoh, M. and Bayerl, J. Actions of micro-electrophoretically applied opiates on cortical and spinal neurons. Naunyn-Schmiedebergs Arch exp Path Pharmacol, 287:(Suppl)R16, 1975.

Zieglgansberger, W. and Fry, J.P. Actions of enkephalin on cortical and striatal neurons of naive and morphine tolerant/dependent rats. In: Kosterlitz, H.W., ed. Opiates and Endogenous Opioid Peptides. Amsterdam: Elsevier/North Holland Biomed. Press, 1976. pp. 213-238.

Zieglgansberger, W., Fry, J.P., Herz, A., Moroder, L. and Wunsch, E. Enkephalin-induced inhibition of cortical neurons and the lack of this effect in morphine tolerant/dependent rats. Brain Res, 115:160-164, 1976.

Zieglgansberger, W., French, E., Siggins, G. and Bloom, F. Opioid peptides may excite hippocampal pyramidal neurons by inhibiting adjacent inhibitory interneurons. Science, 205:415-417, 1979.

AUTHOR

Steven J. Henriksen, Ph.D.
Scripps Clinic and Research Foundation
Department of Basic and Clinical Research
Division of Preclinical Neuroscience and Endocrinology
10666 North Torrey Pines Road
La Jolla, California 92037

Spinal Cord Tissue Culture Models for Analyses of Opioid Analgesia, Tolerance and Plasticity

Stanley M. Crain

I. MODELS OF OPIOID FUNCTIONS USING FRESHLY ISOLATED TISSUES OR CELL CULTURES

In vitro preparations of freshly isolated guinea pig ileum and mouse vas deferens have provided simple model systems for bio-assays of opioid agonists and antagonists (Kosterlitz and Waterfield 1975; Kosterlitz and Hughes 1977). The validity of these models rests on demonstrations of close correlation between the agonist potencies of opioid agents as measured by their ability to depress electrically induced contractions and: 1) their analgesic potencies in man (Kosterlitz et al. 1973); 2) their relative opiate receptor binding potencies in rat brain homogenates as well as in guinea pig ileum (Creese and Snyder 1975; Simon 1976). Although peripheral nerve muscle preparations may be limited in their usefulness for analyses of the specific opioid systems within the CNS (e.g. Van Neuten et al. 1976; Ward and Takemori 1976a,b), they have indeed provided valuable insights into some of the cellular mechanisms involved in opioid tolerance and dependence. Studies of isolated guinea pig ileum during chronic exposure to opioids for periods up to 24 hours (e.g. Hammond et al. 1976; Collier et al. 1980, 1981a,b; North and Karras 1978a,b; North and Zieglgansberger 1978; North and Vitek 1979; Johnson and North 1980; see reviews by Duggan 1980; North 1979; Collier 1980)[1] have demonstrated that some of the basic phenomena characteristic of opioid tolerance and dependence-withdrawal in the CNS can be elicited in isolated neurons. (See, however, discussion in Sect. III-A on differences in the opioid tolerance properties observed in freshly isolated preparation of myenteric neurons innervating peripheral muscle vs. dorsal root ganglion neurons co-cultured with spinal cord.) The data obtained by North and co-workers from myenteric ganglia suggest that significant components of opioid tolerance and dependence may be mediated by plastic changes in the bioelectric excitability and propagative properties of individual neurons (see, however, results with brainstem slices, below)--whereas Collier has emphasized the possible role of "an hypertrophy of the cyclic AMP system in these neurons in response to inhibition by opiate of a neuronal adenylate cyclase" (see below).

Freshly isolated slices or strips of neonatal spinal cord with attached dorsal root ganglia (DRGs) (Otsuka and Konishi 1974) have provided useful preparations for electrophysiologic analyses of the acute effects of opioids on primary afferent networks of the CNS (Suzue and Jessell 1980; Hentall and Fields 1983). Furthermore, intracellular recordings of neurons in slices from adult rat spinal cord have recently demonstrated that morphine and D-ala-D-leu enkephalin (DADLE) can directly hyperpolarize dorsal-horn interneurons by opening membrane K^+ channels (Yoshimura and North, 1983), in addition to previous evidence from cell cultures that opioids may depress the release of transmitter from nociceptive DRG fibers (see below and Sect. II, III). However, studies of the long-term effects during chronic exposure to opioids require maintenance of these isolated neural tissues under more stable conditions such as those provided by tissue culture techniques (see Sect. III). For example, no signs of tolerance to the hyperpolarizing action of opiates on locus ceruleus neurons were detected when freshly isolated slices of normal rat brainstem were exposed to normorphine for 8-12 hours (Williams and North 1983), whereas slices prepared from morphine-tolerant rats were 3- to 10-fold less sensitive to opiates as determined by similar electrophysiologic tests. Since the degree of tolerance to the hyperpolarizing action of opiates on locus ceruleus neurons was, nevertheless, small compared to the tolerance assessed in these rats by behavioral tests, the authors suggested that "tolerance (and dependence) observed in experiments which examine the behavior of complex networks of neurons results from or is amplified by an adaptive process which occurs in transmission between cells" (Williams and North 1983).[2]

Cultures of dissociated fetal rodent spinal cord neurons and DRG cells (Ransom et al. 1977) have also been fruitfully used to analyze physiologic mechanisms of action of opioids. With intracellular recording techniques, MacDonald and Nelson (1978) demonstrated that etorphine depressed excitatory postsynaptic potentials (EPSPs) elicited in spinal cord cells by activation of co-cultured DRG cells. Statistical analysis of the quantal parameters for the DRG-evoked EPSPs in cord neurons revealed that etorphine reduced EPSP quantal content at this synapse without altering quantal size, thereby indicating a presynaptic depressant action. The data suggested that etorphine may have a direct depressant effect on transmitter release at the DRG-cord synapse, but partial blockade of spike propagation into the presynaptic terminals could not be ruled out. Analyses by Mudge et al. (1979) in cultures of dissociated DRG neurons provided more direct evidence that opioids depress transmitter release, possibly by decreasing the influx of Ca^{++} across the membrane of the DRG presynaptic terminal (see Sect. III-C).

Although no studies of the effects of chronic opioid exposure of dissociated DRG or cord neurons have been reported, cultures of dissociated mouse neuroblastoma x glioma hybrid cells, which show high stereospecific opiate binding levels (Klee and Nirenberg (1974), develop significant alterations in cyclic nucleotide and adenylate cyclase levels during chronic exposure to opiates. Whereas acute exposure of these cells to opioids results in inhibition of adenylate cyclase and a decreased cyclic AMP level after chronic exposure to morphine, basal levels of adenylate cyclase increase so that higher concentrations of opiates are required to produce decrements in cyclic AMP (Sharma et al. 1975a). These workers suggested a provocative model for tolerance and dependence, based on their demonstrations of sequential early inhibition and compensatory increase in adenylate cyclase activity and cyclic AMP levels during chronic opiate exposure (Klee et al. 1975; Sharma et al. 1975b; Lampert et al. 1976; see also Traber et al. 1975, and reviews by Hamprecht 1977 and Collier 1980).[3] No correlative electrophysiological data have been reported on alterations in dissociated neuroblastoma x glioma cells during chronic exposure to opioids. However, electrophysiological analyses of myenteric neurons in the guinea pig ileum (Karras and North 1979), dorsal-horn neurons in cat spinal cord (Duggan and Griersmith 1979), and dorsalhorn networks in mouse cord-ganglion explants in culture (see Sect. II; Crain, unpublished observations) have not detected any signs of altered sensitivity to opiates during acute exposure to cyclic nucleotides or phosphodiesterase inhibitors (see reviews by Duggan 1980 and Collier 1980). These physiological data do not, however, preclude possible alterations in cyclic AMP functions in neurons during development of tolerance and dependence following chronic exposure to opiates (see Sect. III-B).

Although these cultures of tumor-derived cells do not develop sufficient organization to permit analyses of mechanisms involved in the specific physiologic effects of opioids on synaptic networks of the CNS, recent biochemical studies of these cells by Sharma and Khanna (1982) have, nevertheless, provided interesting clues to a possible role of vitamin C in the development of opioid tolerance. They reported that introduction of ascorbate (1-5mM) attenuated the delayed etorphine-induced compensatory increase in cyclic AMP levels (tested at 4 hrs of incubation) without effecting the short-term (15 min) inhibitory response of these neuroblastoma cells to the drug. Prompted by the data obtained from this in vitro model system, co-administration of high levels of vitamin C (~1mg/kg) with morphine in mice was shown to "suppress the development of tolerance and physical dependence on the drug without significantly affecting its analgesic properties" (Khanna and Sharma 1983).

In addition to the enhancement of adenylate cyclase activity and cyclic AMP levels in these neuroblastoma cells during chronic exposure to opioids, Dawson et al. (1979) have shown that a stereo-specific dose-dependent, naloxone-reversible inhibition of the biosynthesis of membrane glycosphingolipid and glycoprotein also occurred within 24 hours. It is not yet clear whether these opiate-induced cell-surface changes are a consequence of cyclic nucleotide changes or vice versa.

262

II. SPINAL CORD TISSUE CULTURE MODELS OF OPIOID ANALGESIA

Cultures of organized explants of fetal mouse spinal cord cross-sections with attached sensory dorsal-root ganglia (DRGs) (Crain and Peterson 1974; Crain 1976) have been particularly useful for analyses of cellular mechanisms underlying opioid analgesia and tolerance (Crain et al. 1977, 1978, 1979, 1982b). Single focal DRG stimuli evoke prominent negative slow-wave responses restricted to dorsal regions of spinal cord explants (Fig. 1A,D), arising abruptly after latencies of 2-3 msec, with amplitudes up to 2 mv, and often lasting more than 500 msec (Crain and Peterson 1974). These potentials resemble primary afferent depolarization (PAD) and secondary sensory-evoked synaptic network responses in dorsal cord in situ (e.g. Eccles, 1964). Simultaneous recordings in ventral cord regions generally show small positive or polyphasic slow-wave potentials and spike barrages, after latencies of 5-10 msec (Fig. 1).

DRG-evoked 'PAD' responses in dorsal cord are generally maintained or augmented in the presence of 1 mM γ-aminobutyric acid (GABA), whereas most other synaptic network discharges in the cord explants are rapidly depressed (Crain and Peterson, 1974). In contrast to the enhancing effects of GABA on sensory-evoked dorsal-horn network responses in cord-DRG explants, these responses are selectively depressed by acute exposure to low concentrations of morphine and other opiates (Crain et al. 1977). Introduction of 0.1-1 μM morphine into the culture leads to marked and sustained depression of major components of the DRG-evoked, PAD-like, slow-wave responses in dorsal cord within a few min, whereas ventral cord discharges are either unaltered or enhanced (Fig. 1B). A series of opioid peptides with a wide range of analgesic potencies produced similar selective depressant effects on the sensory-evoked dorsal-horn network discharges of cord-DRG explants (Table 1) (Crain et al. 1978), at concentrations remarkably proportionate to their potency in the intact animal. After return to control medium, restoration of opioid-depressed dorsal cord responses gradually occurs during periods of 30-60 min (Fig. 1C). Exposure to opiate antagonists, e.g. naloxone (10-100 nM) or diprenorphine (1-10 nM), prevents development of the characteristic depression of sensory-evoked dorsal cord responses by these opiates and opioid peptides (Fig. 1D) (Crain et al. 1977, 1978), whereas they are ineffective against the acute effects of non-opioid-receptor-mediated depressant agents, e.g. high-Mg^{++}, xylocaine, serotonin (see Sect. III-B).

The depressant effects of opiates and opioid peptides on dorsal cord explant responses were often markedly reduced or prevented when the Ca^{++} level was raised to 5mM, especially in the presence of 0.1mM 4-aminopyridine (4-AP) (Fig. 2) (Crain et al. 1982a). Receptor assays showed that 0.1mM 4-AP ± 5mM Ca^{++} had no effect on stereospecific opiate binding, indicating that the antagonist actions of these agents in our cultures do not occur at the level of the opiate receptor. 4-AP has been shown to markedly potentiate synaptic transmitter release by depressing

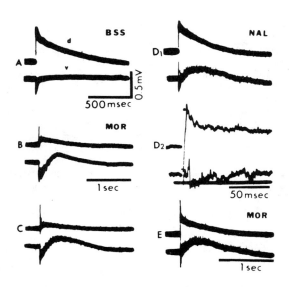

FIGURE 1

*Selective opiate depression of sensory-evoked dorsal-horn network
responses in cord-DRG explant (4 weeks in vitro). **A**: Short-latency
negative slow-wave potential in dorsal cord (d) and small longer-
latency, positive slow-wave response in ventral cord (v) are evoked
by a single large DRG stimulus. **B**: 5 min after introduction of
morphine (1µM), major components of the dorsal cord responses
have disappeared. In contrast, the ventral cord response is enhanced. **C**: 10 min after return to BSS, the dorsal cord response
to DRG stimuli remains small, and the ventral cord discharge is
still large. **D1**: 3 min after introduction of naloxone (3µM) the
dorsal cord slow-wave response is restored and enhanced; short-
latency components are seen at faster sweep (**D2**). **E**: 20 min after
return to BSS, 1µM morphine partly depresses DRG-evoked dorsal
cord response (more complete depression occurred after increase to
10µM morphine). Note: Upward deflection indicates negativity at
recording electrode; onset of stimulus is indicated by first
sharp pulse or break in baseline of each sweep. All records in
Figs. 1-4 show maximal response evoked by large stimuli with standard placements of recording microelectrodes within the cord and
stimulating electrodes within the DRG tissue. BSS is balanced salt
solution consisting of (in mmol/l distilled water) of NaCl, 137;
KCl, 5.5; KH_2PO_4, 0.4; $CaCl_2$, 1.3; $MgCl_2$, 0.5; $MgSO_4$, 0.4; Na_2HPO_4,
0.3; $NaHCO_3$, 4.2; and glucose, 5.5 (From Crain et al. 1977.
© 1977, Elsevier Biomedical Press.)*

TABLE 1

Comparison of depressant potency in vitro and analgesic potency in situ for a series of opioid peptides

Compound	Effective depressant concentration (μM) in vitro[a]	Molar potency ratios	
		Sensory network depressant potency in vitro	Analgesic potency in rodents in situ[b]
Tyr-gly-gly-phe-met	10	1	1
Tyr-gly-gly-phe-leu	10	1	1
Tyr-D-ala-gly-phe-met	0.1-1.0	10-100	100;700
Tyr-D-ala-gly-phe-D-leu	0.02	500	≈1000
D-ala-tyr-gly-gly-phe-met [D-Met2,Pro5]-enkephalinamide	≫10	≪1	≪1
[D-ala2-MePhe4,Met-(0)5-ol]-enkephalin (Sandoz FK 33-824)	0.005-0.01	1000-2000	2000
β-Endorphin	0.002-0.005	2000-5000	30,000
α-Endorphin	0.1	100	200-1000
	1.0	10	<1
Morphine	0.3	30	30

[a] Molar concentration required to produce marked and sustained depression (>50%) of sensory-evoked dorsal-horn network responses in explants of mouse spinal cord with attached dorsal root ganglia. All of these opiate depressant effects were prevented by naloxone (0.01-0.1 μM) or diprenorphine (0.001-0.01 μM).

[b] Determined by tail-flick test after intracerebral, intraventricular, or spinal subarachnoid injections (see references to in situ studies in Crain et al. 1978).

(From Crain et al. 1978. © 1978, Elsevier Biomedical Press.)

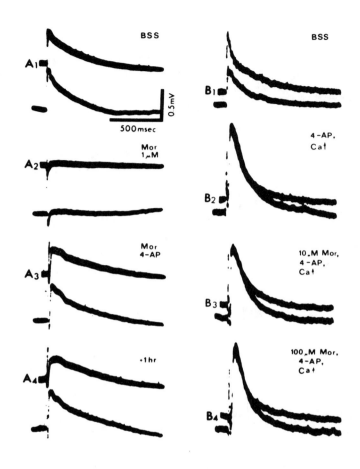

FIGURE 2

*Antagonism by 4-aminopyridine (4-AP) of the depressant effects
of morphine on sensory-evoked dorsal-horn network responses in
cord-DRG explants. (A_1): Characteristic short-latency negative
slow-waves are evoked in two sites in dorsal cord by DRG stimulus.
(A_2): Dorsal cord responses are blocked after 10 min in 1μM
morphine. (A_3): Cord responses gradually recover after addition
of 0.1 mM 4-AP along with 1μM morphine and can still be elicted
one hour later (A_4). (B): Dorsal horn responses in another
explant (B_1) are remarkably enhanced in 0.1 mM 4-AP + 5 mM Ca^{++}
(B_2). (B_3): Cord responses are not significantly attenuated
after 10 min exposure to 10μM morphine + 0.1 mM 4-AP + 4 mM Ca^{++},
nor after 10 min in 100μM morphine + same 4-AP/Ca^{++} levels (B_4).
(From Crain et al. 1982a. © 1982, Pergamon Press Inc.)*

membrane K^+ conductance during depolarization of nerve terminals, thereby prolonging the presynaptic spike and enhancing Ca^{++} influx (e.g. Illes and Thesleff 1978). Furthermore, 4-AP antagonized the depression of synaptic transmission in spinal cord produced by high Mg^{++} or EGTA (Galindo and Rudomin 1978) and the depressant effects of adenosine on cerebral neurons (Perkins and Stone 1980; Stone 1981a). The effects of 4-AP and high Ca^{++} on cord-DRG cultures are in good agreement with studies in the mouse vas deferens where similar concentrations of these agents were shown to reverse the inhibitory action of morphine on neuromuscular transmission (Illes et al. 1980; Stone 1981a). Although these effects of 4-AP and high Ca^{++} on cord-DRG cultures do not clearly distinguish between presynaptic or postsynaptic mechanisms of opiate depressant action on afferent cord networks, a primary action of opioids at presynaptic DRG terminals in the dorsal horn appears to be more probable (see below) but does not preclude direct inhibitory effects on cord interneurons (Yoshimura and North 1983; Murase et al. 1982). Either mode of opioid action could probably be overcome by 4-AP/high Ca^{++}-enhanced transmitter release, as in studies of botulinum- or curare-blocked motor endplates (Kim et al. 1980). Nevertheless, our in vitro results demonstrate that the depressant effects of opiates on afferent spinal cord networks involve relatively restricted physiological actions that can be readily antagonized by Ca^{++}, even in the presence of extremely high opioid concentrations (Crain et al. 1982a). The effects of increased Ca^{++} concentration on the opioid-sensitivity of the sensory-evoked responses in cord-DRG explants are in agreement with the suppression of opiate analgesic effects in situ by intracerebroventricular injections of calcium (Kakunaga et al. 1966; Harris et al. 1975) and the reversal of morphine analgesia in rats by injections of 4-AP (Tung and Brandom 1981). They are also consonant with evidence that the depressant effects of opioids may be due to interference with Ca^{++} conductance in presynaptic terminals, thereby impeding transmitter release (see Sect. III C; also Dunlap and Fischbach 1978; Macdonald and Nelson 1978).

The development of opiate-sensitive DRG-evoked responses restricted to dorsal-horn regions of our cord explants is in good agreement with microelectrophoretic injection of morphine into the substantia gelatinosa in cat spinal cord, resulting in selective depression of cell responses to noxious, but not tactile, stimuli (Duggan et al. 1977). Furthermore, physiologic analyses of these opioid networks in vitro and in situ correlate well with binding assays showing that high levels of stereospecific opiate receptors develop in the dorsal-horn regions of the adult monkey spinal cord (Lamotte et al. 1976) and in our fetal mouse cord-DRG explants (Hiller et al. 1978b). In addition, we have demonstrated that even higher levels of receptors develop in the neuritic outgrowth of isolated DRG cultures (Hiller et al. 1978a). The latter assays provided the first direct evidence that opiate receptors are located on DRG nerve fibers which are destined to establish presynaptic afferent connections with the spinal cord (see also Lamotte et al. 1976; Fields et al. 1980).

III.   CORD TISSUE CULTURE MODELS OF OPIOID TOLERANCE AND
PLASTICITY

A.   Development of Tolerance in Cord-DRG Explants During
Chronic Exposure to Opiates and Opioid Peptides

Most in vitro analyses of tolerance to opiates have utilized
peripheral neurons or neuroblastoma cells (as noted in Sect. I).
Our electrophysiologic experiments during chronic exposure of
cord-DRG explants to opiates and opioid peptides (Crain et al.
1979) have provided the first demonstration that isolated mammalian
CNS tissues can, indeed, develop marked tolerance after several
days of chronic exposure in vitro. Earlier studies of tolerance
in chronic spinal dogs by analyses of spontaneous and reflex activities during chronic morphine exposure and hyperactivity of
these reflexes after withdrawal of morphine (Wikler and Frank 1948;
Wikler 1953; Wikler and Carter 1953) suggest that this cord-DRG
explant model is reasonable and likely to provide significant
insights into some of the complex problems of opiate addiction.

Following exposure of cord-DRG explants to low levels of morphine
(1 μM) for 2 or more days (at 35°C), the initial opiate-depressant
effects on sensory-evoked dorsal-horn network responses disappeared
and characteristic dorsal cord responses could again be evoked by
DRG stimuli in the presence of morphine-- even after large increases in concentration (up to 100-fold: Fig. 3B2,3) (Crain et
al. 1979). These manifestations of tolerance to opiates could
still be observed for 2 days after transfer to drug-free culture
medium, and characteristic sensitivity to opiates returned during
the subsequent few days. The stereospecificity of these opiate-
tolerance effects was demonstrated by the fact that chronic exposure of cord-DRG explants to 1 μM levorphanol produced similar
tolerance to opiates as occurred after 1 μM morphine, whereas
chronic exposure to 1 μM dextrorphan was ineffective.

Tolerance also developed after chronic exposure of cord-DRG
explants to low concentrations (10 nM) of the synthetic enkephalin
analog, {D-ala^2, MePhe^4, Met-(0)5-ol}-enkephalin (Sandoz FK 33-824),
consonant with the tolerance that occurs in rodents following daily
injections of this potent, long-lasting analgesic (Roemer et al.
1977). Acute application of this opioid peptide to our explants
depressed DRG-evoked dorsal cord responses at levels as low as
1 nM (Table 1) (Crain et al. 1978). Furthermore, tolerance developed after chronic exposure of cord-DRG explants to opioid
peptides (0.1-1 μM) that bind predominantly to delta-type
receptors, e.g. D-ala-D-leu enkephalin (DADLE) (Wuster et al.
1979; Kosterlitz et al. 1980) as well as to mu-type receptors, .
e.g., tyr-D-ala-gly-N-Me-Phe-Gly-ol (DAGOL) (Handa et al. 1981).
Morphine-tolerant cultures showed cross-tolerance to FK 33-824,
met-enkephalin, DADLE, and β-endorphin when tested at concentrations up to 10-fold higher than required to produce acute depressant effects on naive cord-DRG explants. On the other hand,
cultures rendered tolerant to FK33-824 (at 0.01 μM) showed un-

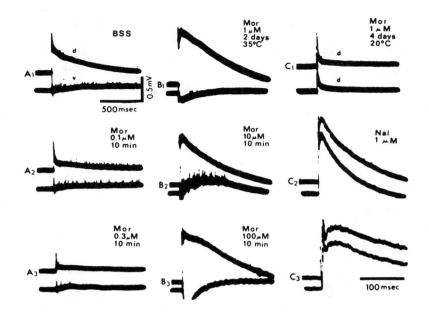

FIGURE 3

Development of tolerance to acute opiate-depressant effects
on sensory-evoked dorsal-horn network response in cord-DRG explants (3 weeks in vitro). A_1: Short-latency negative slow-wave is
evoked in dorsal cord (d) by DRG stimulus. A_2: Within 10 min in
0.1 µM morphine, dorsal cord response is attenuated, whereas
ventral cord discharge (v) shows little change. A_3: In 0.3 µM
morphine, dorsal cord slow-wave response is almost abolished.
(No recovery occurred during exposure to 0.3-1 µM morphine for
several hrs.) B_1: Large dorsal-cord network response is evoked in
another cord-DRG explant after chronic exposure to 1 µM morphine
for 2 days at 35°C (cf. $A_2, _3$). B_2: Dorsal cord response remains
large even after increasing morphine concentration to 10 µM.
(Ventral cord discharges were often enhanced at high opiate
levels.) B_3: Even after increase to 100 µM morphine dorsal cord
response shows no further attenuation (10 min test; partial depression developed after longer exposure at 100 µM level). C_1:
Only small dorsal-horn responses can be evoked in another explant
(2 sites) after exposure to 1 µM morphine for 4 days at 20°C,
resembling attenuation after acute exposure to morphine (cf. A_2).
C_2: 1 µM naloxone restores characteristic dorsal cord response
within a few min; same recording sites as in C_1. Sharp rising
phases of these DRG-evoked dorsal cord responses are shown at
faster sweep (C_3). (From Crain et al. 1979. © 1979, Pergamon
Press Inc.)

269

usually strong cross-tolerance to morphine; dorsal cord responses could still be evoked even after acute exposure to high levels of morphine (about 100 μM), or 1,000-fold higher than the depressant level required to depress cord responses in a naive explant (i.e., cross-tolerance ratio = 1,000).

In contrast to the high degree of selective tolerance to specific types of opiate receptors (delta vs. mu) that has been observed in mouse vas deferens (Schulz et al. 1980)[5], preliminary tests on cord-DRG explants chronically exposed to either DADLE or DAGOL (at 0.01-1 μM) have often shown evidence of at least some degree of cross tolerance to agonists binding to other receptor subtypes including the kappa agonists, dynorphin and ethylketocyclazocine (Chang et al. 1981; Chavkin et al. 1982; Kosterlitz et al. 1981) However, cross-tolerance ratios were often much lower than in tests made with agonists binding to similar opiate receptor subtypes. The variability observed in these cross-tolerance tests may be due in part to marked heterogeneities in the distribution of opiate receptor subtypes that develop in the DRG neurons (Werz and Mac-donald, 1982a,b, 1983),as well as the cord neurons, explanted from various levels of the neuraxis into these cultures. In guinea pig ileum tissue, where cross-tolerance was observed between delta and mu agonists, Schulz et al. (1981) interpreted these data as support for "the notion that these drugs act via a common receptor, possibly a mu-receptor type" (see alternative views in Sect. III-B).

The tolerant state did not develop if morphine was prevented from binding to the opiate receptors by concomitant chronic exposure to low levels of naloxone (0.1μM). Within an hour after removal of naloxone from the culture medium, morphine produced character-istic depressant effects on dorsal cord responses. Furthermore, when the incubation temperature was lowered to <25°C, no evidence of tolerance was detected after sustained exposure to 1 μM morphine (as long as 7 days). Dorsal cord synaptic network res- ponses remained depressed in these cord-DRG cultures during chronic incubation in 1 μM morphine at 20°C (Fig. 3C_1); the opiate sensitivity tests were carried out after returning the cultures to 35°C. However, characteristic sensory-evoked cord responses were rapidly restored after introduction of 0.1-1 μM naloxone (Fig. 3 $C_{2,3}$), demonstrating that the depression of dorsal cord responses in these cultures was opiate-mediated and not merely due to metabolic deficits resulting from incubation at suboptimal temper-ature. Control 2-week-old cultures incubated in regular media at 20°C for 1 week showed no significant electrophysiologic deficits. The data indicate that a temperature-dependent metabolic change occurs in the neurons of these mouse cord-DRG explants after 2 days of chronic exposure to morphine at 35°C leading to a sustain-ed decrease in sensitivity to opiate-depressant effects (Crain et al. 1979).[4] These results are compatible with evidence that tolerance to opiates in rats is blocked by inhibitors of protein and RNA synthesis (Cox and Osman 1970); more critical tests are required to characterize the specific molecular alterations that may underlie the development of tolerance in neurons.

The temperature-dependence of the opiate-tolerance mechanism in our mouse spinal cord-DRG explants is in contrast to the opiate tolerance which develops in myenteric neurons of freshly isolated guinea pig ileum within 1 day after incubation in 1 µM morphine at 4°C (Hammond et al. 1976) and at $21-24^\circ$C (North and Karras 1978 a,b). These differences in temperature requirements may be due to differences in processes involved in the development of tolerance in central vs. peripheral neurons and they may provide clues to some of the molecular mechanisms underlying the development of tolerance in CNS neurons. It should also be noted that the tolerance observed following the 1-day morphine exposure of freshly isolated guinea pig ileum preparations disappeared within a few hours after transfer to drug-free medium (Hammond et al. 1976), whereas our cord-DRG explants continued to show tolerance effects for several days after return to regular culture medium. The marked tolerance to opiates that develops in cord-DRG explants may also be enhanced due to the relatively immature stage of these fetal mouse tissues during the period of chronic exposure in vitro as observed in neonatal mice at 1-2 weeks of age (Nicak and Kohut 1978).

As noted above, in the presence of 4-AP and high Ca^{++} acute introduction of morphine to cord-DRG cultures at concentrations as high as 100-1,000 times the level required to depress afferent cord responses in regular medium is ineffective (Fig. 2B), resembling the tolerance observed in these explants several days after chronic exposure to opiates (Fig. 3B). These results are consonant with evidence suggesting that neurons may become tolerant during chronic exposure to opioids by developing higher levels of intra-cellular calcium in their presynaptic terminals (e.g. Harris et al. 1977; Yamamoto et al. 1978; Huidobro-Toro et al. 1981)--as occurs during acute 4-AP/high Ca^{++} exposure of naive explants--thereby overcoming opioid inhibitory effects produced at presynaptic, and perhaps also at postsynaptic, sites (Crain et al. 1982a).

It is generally considered to be unlikely that tolerance to morphine is caused by down-regulation of opiate receptors since most analyses in vivo have not detected alterations in the number nor the affinity of these receptors after chronic treatment with morphine (e.g. Pert and Snyder 1976; Chang et al. 1981; Bardo et al. 1982). Nevertheless, Davis et al. (1975, 1979) reported a significant decrease in opiate binding after development of analgesic tolerance in rats when the assays were made on thin slices of brainstem tissue rather than on brain homogenates, and Kirby (1983) observed decreased opiate binding in the spinal cord of young rats that had been chronically exposed to morphine during the last half of gestation. Furthermore, chronic incubation of aggregating brain cells cultured with etorphine appeared to induce a down-regulation of mu and kappa opiate receptors (Lenoir et al. 1983), in extension of previous evidence demonstrating down-regulation of delta receptors following 4-hour DADLE exposures of cultured neuroblastoma-glioma hybrid cells (Chang et al. 1982; Simantov et al. 1982) and freshly isolated rat hippocampal slices (Chang et al. 1983). In view of the ambiguities in the data on possible receptor down-regulation following chronic exposure of CNS tissues to opiate agonists, cord-DRG explants may provide a useful system to determine if opiate receptors do, in fact, undergo significant alterations during the development of tolerance, just as we have demonstrated up-regulation during chronic exposure of these explants to opiate antagonists (see Sect. III-D).

Marked increases in the spike-firing rate of opiate-tolerant myenteric neurons occurred in the guinea pig ileum preparation after agonist removal, or after introduction of an antagonist (North and Karras 1978 a,b). This was interpreted as evidence of opiate-dependence in the ileum preparation (see also Hammond et al. 1976). Although we have not detected such increased spike-firing in our CNS explants, we have observed that the sensory-evoked dorsal-horn network responses in opiate-tolerant cultures were generally much larger in amplitude (e.g. Fig. 3B), and could often be recorded over larger areas of the dorsal cord, than the responses evoked in control cultures. The generation of unusually large amplitude dorsal cord responses during chronic exposure to opiates may, indeed, be an expression of dependence following development of tolerance to the opioid level available to the neurons in these cultures. Furthermore, in tolerant cord-DRG explants that did not show unusually large amplitude sensory-evoked dorsal cord responses, acute exposure to naloxone often produced marked increases (up to 50%) in the amplitude of these responses. {Naloxone also enhanced dorsal cord responses in some of our naive cord-DRG explants (Crain et al. 1977), but the effects in these untreated cultures were generally smaller and more variable}.

B. Cross-Tolerance to 5-Hydroxytryptamine in Morphine-Tolerant Cord-DRG Explants

Explants that had become tolerant to morphine after chronic exposure for >2 days often developed a significant degree of cross-tolerance to the depressant effect of serotonin (5-HT) on dorsal-horn network responses (Crain et al. 1982b), as well as to other opioid peptides (Crain et al. 1979). In some morphine-tolerant explants (Fig. $4B_1$) 3- to 10-fold increases in the usual 5-HT concentration were required in order to produce depression of the dorsal cord responses comparable to that in naive explants (Fig. $4B_{2,3}$ versus $4A_{2,3}$ and Fig. 5). In contrast, morphine-tolerant explants did not show cross-tolerance to other types of agents that depressed cord responses, e.g. high Mg^{++}, xylocaine, alcohol. Moreover, acute exposure of morphine-tolerant explants to naloxone (1 μM) further attenuated the effects of 5-HT so that the minimum depressant levels of 5-HT were often increased up to 30-fold (Fig. $4B_{5,6}$ and Fig. 5).

Increasing the extracellular Ca^{++} concentration from the usual 1 mM to 5 mM level or introduction of 4-AP markedly antagonized the depressant effects of 5-HT on DRG-evoked cord responses, so that 5-HT concentrations comparable to those used on morphine-tolerant explants were required to depress naive explants. Furthermore, exposure of cord-DRG explants to 4-AP in the presence of

272

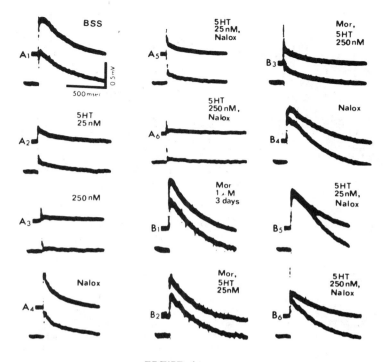

FIGURE 4

*Depressant effects of 5-HT on sensory-evoked dorsal-horn network
responses in fetal mouse spinal cord-DRG explants (A) and
development of cross-tolerance to 5-HT after chronic exposure to
morphine (B). (A_1): Short-latency negative slow-waves are evoked in
two regions of dorsal cord by DRG stimulus. (A_2): Cord responses
are markedly depressed after 10 min in 25 nM 5-HT (in other
cultures levels as low as 3 nM were effective). (A_3): After
several min in 250 nM 5-HT, responses are almost completely blocked. (A_4): Cord responses recover in BSS (+ 1 µM naloxone).
($A_{5,6}$): Similar 5-HT-induced depression of cord responses occurs
in presence of 1 µM naloxone (cf. $A_{5,6}$ and $A_{2,3}$). (5-HT antagonists
methysergide and cyproheptadiene were ineffective as naloxone
up to 10 µM.) (B_1): After 3-day exposure to 1 µM morphine,
tolerance develops and dorsal-horn responses can be evoked in the
presence of morphine. (B_2): Relatively little attenuation of the
cord responses occurs in this opiate-tolerant explant after 10 min
in 25 nM 5-HT (+ morphine) (cf. A_2). (B_3): A significant cord response can still be evoked even after 5 min in 250 nM 5-HT (cf. A_3).
(B_4): Cord response recovers within 5 min after adding 1 µM naloxone
to bathing fluid. (B_5): No depression of cord response occurs
after 10 min in 25 nM 5-HT in the presence of naloxone (cf. A_2,B_2)
and a response can still be elicited even after 10 min in 250 nM
5-HT (cf. A_3,B_3). (From Crain et al. 1982b. © 1982, Pergamon
Press Inc.)*

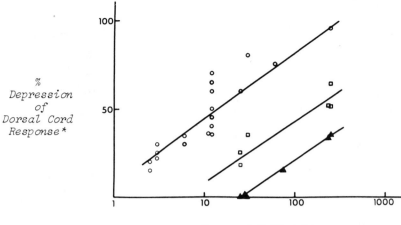

Conc. of 5-HT (nM)

FIGURE 5

Shift in 5-HT dose-response curve after chronic exposure of cord-DRG explants to morphine. O , Naive explant in BSS; ◘ , morphine-tolerant explant in BSS (after 3 days in 1 µM morphine); ▲ , shortly after exposure of morphine-tolerant explant to naloxone (1 µM). (*Based on response data in Fig. 4 and similar tests in >20 cultures) (From Crain et al. 1982b. © 1982, Pergamon Press Inc.)

5 mM Ca^{++} was even more effective in preventing the usual depressant effects of 5-HT -- as well as morphine (Fig. 2)-- on cord responses. In the presence of 4-AP/high Ca^{++}, large dorsal cord responses could still be evoked after introduction of concentrations of 5-HT about 10- to 100-fold higher than required to produce comparable depression in control medium (Crain et al. (1982b).

Our in vitro results are consonant with evidence that 5-HT administration near the cell bodies of dorsal horn neurons and in the substantia gelatinosa of the cat reduced the excitation of these neurons by noxious stimuli (Headley et al. 1978; Belcher et al. 1978) and depressed spinal segmental nociceptive reflexes (Bell and Matsumiya 1981). Furthermore, depression of opiate-sensitive dorsal-horn network responses by bath perfusion with 5-HT provides an in vitro model that correlates well with analgesia produced in the rat by intrathecal administration of 5-HT (Yaksh and Wilson 1979). The absence of naloxone-antagonism of 5-HT depressant effects on DRG-evoked cord responses in naive explants indicates that the 5-HT effects are not mediated by opioid receptors in these cultures, in agreement with studies of 5-HT-induced antinociception and analgesia in situ (Headley et al. 1978; Bell and Matsumiya 1981; Yaksh and Wilson 1979). Similarly, the absence of methysergide- and cyproheptadine-antagonism of the depressant

274

effects of 5-HT on DRG-evoked cord responses suggests that these effects may not be mediated by 5-HT receptors. Alternatively, another type of 5-HT receptor may be involved (e.g. Peroutka et al. 1981). Further studies are required to clarify the mode of action of 5-HT in producing these potent depressant effects on dorsal-horn responses and the remarkable similarities in the effects of 5-HT and opiates on the responses of both naive and opiate-tolerant explants. In cultures of dissociated chick DRG neurons where 5-HT and opiates attenuate the duration of Ca^{++}-mediated soma action potentials, the effects of 5-HT also failed to be antagonized by methysergide (Dunlap and Fischbach 1978). These data suggest that 5-HT may block neuronal components of dorsal-horn networks at similar regions to those that are depressed by opiates, e.g. presynaptic DRG nerve terminals where abundant opiate receptors are located (see above; and related studies of 5-HT effects in situ by Belcher et al. 1978; Carstens et al. 1981). Furthermore the marked attenuation of the depressant effects of both 5-HT and opioids on cord-DRG explants by high Ca^{++} and 4-AP (Crain et al. 1982a,b) raises the possibility that cross-tolerance to 5-HT and to other types of opioid peptides in morphine-tolerant explants (see Sect. III-A) may result from a more generalized physiological alteration in presynaptic components of dorsal-horn networks {e.g., enhanced Ca levels (Harris et al. 1977; Yamamoto et al. 1978; Huidobro-Toro et al. 1981)} that renders them tolerant to a broad spectrum of agents whose depressant actions are mediated by interference with Ca^{++}-dependent synaptic transmitter release (Crain 1984).

Finally, the marked increase in degree of cross-tolerance to 5-HT after acute introduction of naloxone in morphine-tolerant cord-DRG cultures may be an expression of opiate dependence, possibly mediated by the same mechanism underlying naloxone-enhancement of the amplitude of sensory-evoked dorsal-horn responses observed in opiate-tolerant explants (Crain et al. 1979). Both of these naloxone-elicited alterations may reflect the onset of hyperexcitability properties in dorsal-horn networks associated with sudden withdrawal from chronic exposure to opiates (see reviews by Duggan 1980; Wikler 1980; Johnson and North 1980).[6]

These interpretations have been strengthened by recent studies of the effects of Mn^{++} on opioid-tolerant explants. In previous tests with elevated Mg^{++} concentrations, no clearcut evidence of cross-tolerance to this Ca^{++}-antagonist had been detected (as noted above). Mn^{++} is much more potent than Mg^{++} in selectively competing with Ca^{++} for a common site on presynaptic membrane in neuromuscular junctions (Meiri and Rahamimoff 1972; Balnave and Gage 1973) and other synapses (e.g. Nichols and Nakajima 1975). At concentrations of about 1mM, Mn^{++} produces negligible depressant effects on postsynaptic membrane conductances or action potentials, and it appears to act primarily in blocking excitation-secretion coupling mechanisms in presynaptic terminals (Nichols and Nakajima 1975). In preliminary tests on cord-DRG cultures, introduction of 1mM Mn^{++} often produced much weaker depressant effects on opioid-tolerant vs. naive explants, especially after acute addition

of naloxone, resembling the effects of 5-HT on these cultures
(see above).

C. Alterations in Presynaptic DRG Functions in Cord-DRG
Explants Monitored by Intracellular Recordings from DRG Neurons

Analyses by Mudge et al. (1979) in cultures of dissociated chick
embryo DRG neurons demonstrated that D-ala [2] enkephalinamide
inhibited the K^+-evoked (Ca^{++}-dependent) release of substance
P from these DRG cells. Furthermore, enkephalin also decreased
the duration and magnitude of the Ca^{++} component of the spike
recorded in the DRG perikarya without affecting the resting
membrane potential or resting membrane conductance. Since Ca^{++}
spikes in perikarya appear to be generated by specialized membranes
with high densities of Ca^{++} channels comparable to those present
in the less accessible presynaptic terminal membrane (Stinnakre
and Tauc 1973), the data suggest that opioids may depress synaptic
transmitter release by decreasing the voltage-dependent influx of
Ca^{++} across the active membrane of the DRG terminal as well as
the perikaryon.

Our extracellular bioelectric recordings of DRG-evoked dorsal-horn
responses in cord-DRG explants during chronic opioid exposure have
demonstrated that tolerance to the depressant effects of opioids
develops after 2-3 days in vitro. A mechanism that may possibly
underlie this sustained decrease in responsiveness to opioids is
that some functional alteration occurs in the presynaptic DRG
terminals in the dorsal cord which attenuates the effectiveness
of the postulated opioid-induced depression of voltage-dependent
Ca^{++} influx in these terminals (see Section III-B). For example,
an increased density of Ca^{++} channels uncoupled to opiate receptors might develop in DRG terminals during chronic exposure
to opioids, or voltage-dependent Ca^{++} influx might become much
larger due to altered ionic concentration gradients or conductances across the membrane of DRG terminals (as may occur during
acute introduction of 4-AP and high Ca^{++} in naive cord-DRG
cultures ; Fig. 2). We are attempting to test this hypothesis by
carrying out intracellular electrophysiologic recordings from DRG
neuron perikarya in cord-DRG explants during chronic exposure to
opiates to determine whether significant alterations in Ca^{++}-
mediated components of DRG action potentials, or other evidence
of enhanced Ca^{++}-mediated functions, can be detected in tolerant
explants. In order to establish baselines for evaluating
possible alterations in DRG functions that may develop in tolerant
explants, we have carried out intracellular recordings from DRG
neuron perikarya in organotypic cord-DRG explants (grown for 3-5
weeks in regular culture media) during acute application of
opioids (Chalazonitis and Crain 1983). Intracellular recordings
were made with beveled micropipettes (40-80 MΩ) on DRG neuron
somas (20-50 μm diam) (Fig. 6A). Opiate agonists were tested on
DRG spikes evoked in a BSS containing 5 mM Ca^{++} and 5 mM Ba^{++} in
order to enhance inward current through Ca^{++} channels and block
delayed voltage-dependent K^+ channels. A "hump" developed in the
repolarizing phase of the spike under these conditions (Fig. 6B)
which was blocked by 5-10 mM Co^{++}, confirming Ca^{++} mediation of

276

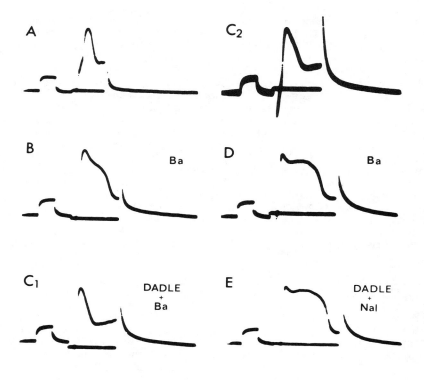

FIGURE 6

*Exposure to DADLE results in sustained attenuation of the duration
of the action potential of a DRG neuron in an explant of mouse
spinal cord with attached DRGs (2 months in vitro). (A): Typical
somatic action potential is evoked by intracellular depolarizing
current during initial perfusion of culture with BSS containing
5.4mM Ca^{++}. (B): After addition of 5mM Ba^{++} to the high-Ca^{++} BSS,
the duration of the action potential increased more than 3-fold;
note prominent 'hump' on repolarizing phase. (C_1): By 2 min after
bath perfusion with 10µM DADLE (in high-Ca^{++}, high-Ba^{++} BSS) the
duration of the action potential was sharply reduced and remained
short as long as the agonist was present (4-10 min tests). (C_2):
After 5 min in DADLE, action potential duration was still attenuated (8 superimposed sweeps at 0.1Hz). (D): After return to high-
Ca^{++}, Ba^{++} BSS, action potential became markedly prolonged again.
(E): Introduction of 10µM DADLE in the presence of 3µM naloxone
was ineffective in altering the action potential. Calibration
bars: 20mV and 5 msec. (Unpublished data from Chalazonitis and
Crain 1983 and in preparation).*

this hump. Opiate agonists were bath-perfused (0.5 ml/min) for test periods up to 10 min. In about 80% of the neurons in isolated DRG explants, the duration of the Ca^{++} component of the action potential was reduced by about 50% in the presence of DADLE at 10 μM (Fig. 6C; Table 2). These effects were reversed after return to Ca^{++}-Ba^{++} BSS and prevented by perfusion of naloxone (3 μM) together with DADLE. This widespread distribution of opioid-sensitive neuron perikarya in relatively mature, organotypic DRG explants is similar to the large fraction of opioid-sensitive cells (ca. 75%) observed in dissociated chick and mouse embryo DRG cultures (Mudge et al. 1979; Werz and Macdonald 1982a). On the other hand, no significant alterations in the action potentials generated by adult mouse DRG neurons were detected during acute application of opioid to freshly isolated ganglia (Williams and Zieglgansberger 1981; see also North 1979). The marked difference in opioid sensitivity of DRGs in these in vitro vs. in situ studies may reflect normal developmental changes that occur in at least some types of DRG perikarya during establishment of synaptic connections with cord neurons or, alternatively, the in vitro results may be due to abnormal opioid hypersensitivity resulting from isolation of these embryonic cells and their maintenance in a relatively immature state. In order to clarify this ambiguity, we compared the opioid sensitivity of sensory neurons in organotypic explants of DRGs attached to spinal cord (Fig. 1) vs. isolated DRG explants. These tests showed that a significantly smaller fraction of DRG neuron somas were sensitive to DADLE when grown attached to spinal cord vs. isolated DRGs: 51% vs. 78% (Table 2; Chalazonitis and Crain 1983). Furthermore, recordings made 8-16 days after dorsal-root transection in 2-to 3-week-old cord-DRG explants revealed that 84% of these decentralized DRG neurons were opioid-sensitive (Table 2). Although the duration of the Ca^{++} hump of the somatic DRG action potential was significantly shorter in attached vs. isolated cultures, some of the opiate-insensitive neurons still generated prominent Ca^{++} humps. This suggests that a decrease in functional opiate receptors rather than in Ca^{++} channels may underly the observed decrease in opioid-sensitive DRG somas in DRG-cord explants. The data obtained thus far are consistent with the hypothesis that as the central terminals of fetal DRG neurites participate in the formation of opioid synaptic networks within the dorsal-horn region of DRG-cord explants the opioid sensitivity of the perikaryal region of these DRG neurons may decrease (Chalazonitis and Crain 1983).

During maturation opiate receptors on DRG neuron somas may decrease in number or they may become non-functional, e.g. by uncoupling from Ca^{++} channels in the soma membrane, whereas at embryonic stages, opiate receptors may be distributed all over the surface of DRG neurons just as acetylcholine receptors are distributed all along embryonic un-innervated muscle fibers (Diamond and Miledi 1962). Perhaps opiate receptors are translocated during maturation to the terminal regions of DRG neurites as these neurites establish synaptic connections in the spinal cord, analogous to the clustering of ACh receptors during formation of

TABLE 2

Opioid-Sensitivity of DRG Neurons Grown
Either Attached to Cord or Alone

Type of explant	DRG neurons with opioid-sensitive Ca^{++}-mediated action potentials[a]			
	Explants tested	DRG neuron somas tested	Opioid-sensitive neurons[b]	
	n	n	n	Fraction
Isolated DRG	36	49	38	78%
DRG attached to cord	58	67	34	51%*
DRG-cord, 8-16 days after dorsal-root transection in vitro	17	19	16	84%

[a]Tests made by bath-perfusion of 10µM D-ala-D-leu enkephalin (DADLE) during intracellular recordings in BSS containing 5mM Ca^{++} and 5mM Ba^{++} (at 3-5 weeks in vitro; see text).

[b]Neurons showing marked reduction (about 50%) in duration of Ca^{++} component of action potential during exposure to DADLE (see text).

*This fraction is significantly lower than that of the isolated DRG population (x^2 test: p < 0.005) and from the DRG population that had been decentralized (p < 0.01).

(Unpublished data from Chalazonitis and Crain 1983 and in preparation.)

neuromuscular junctions. Alternatively, opiate receptors might still be present on many DRG somas--as evidenced by autoradiographic localization of ^{3}H-etorphine on some types of adult DRG neurons (Ninkovic et al. 1982)--but the distribution of Ca^{++} channels on these somas may decrease during maturation (Matsuda et al. 1978; Yoshida and Matsuda 1979; Spitzer 1979) or these channels may no longer be regulated by linkage with opiate receptors. These ambiguities may be clarified by more systematic intracellular recordings from DRG neurons at different stages of maturation in cultures of DRG-cord explants and is isolated DRG explants, and by correlative autoradiography of opiate receptor distributions on these DRG neurons. Studies of these types of plasticity in opioid networks during development of DRG-cord synapses or after decentralization of DRG neurons may also provide insights into mechanisms underlying plastic alterations in opiate receptor distributions that occur following chronic pharmacologic interventions (see Sect. III-D).

We have demonstrated that about 50% of the DRG neuron perikarya in mature cord-DRG explants still show marked sensitivity to opiates (Table 2) under culture conditions where reliable tolerance develops in dorsal cord afferent networks after chronic opioid exposure. Intracellular recording from these DRG perikarya during chronic exposure of cord-DRG explants to opiates may, therefore, lead to significant clues to alterations in DRG functions that may play a role in the development of opioid tolerance and dependence in the dorsal horn of the spinal cord[6]. Although such data are not yet available, we have observed an interesting type of short-term "desensitization" during intracellular recordings from about 30% of the opioid-sensitive DRG neurons in both cord-DRG and isolated DRG explants. In these neurons, after an initial reduction (~50%) in the duration of the DRG action potential within 2-3 minutes after introduction of DADLE, the characteristic Ca^{++}-hump progressively reappeared and the action potential regained its original width during the following 5-6 minutes, even though the agonist was still present (Chalazonitis and Crain 1983, and unpublished observations). In the rest of the DRG neurons, the opioid-induced decrease in the duration of the Ca^{++}-hump was stably maintained (during 4-10 min tests). It will be of interest to determine if this desensitization is temperature-dependent and fails to occur at 20°C, as in the "acute tolerance" studies of hippocampal explants exposed to FK 33-824 (Gahwiler 1981) and in our long-term tolerance test on cord-DRG explants (Crain et al. 1979). We have not observed signs of desensitization in our previous extracellular recordings of DRG-evoked dorsal-horn field potentials in cord-DRG explants exposed to DADLE (or morphine) for periods up to several hours, and the transitory depressant effects of DADLE on DRG neuron perikarya may, therefore, be a type of tachyphyllaxis[2] unrelated to cellular processes mediating long-term opioid tolerance.

D. Opiate Receptor Upregulation During Chronic Exposure of Cord-DRG Explants To Opiate-Antagonists

Chronic administration of naloxone in rats resulted in enhanced morphine-induced analgesia (Tang and Collins 1978) and an increased number of opiate binding sites in brain tissue (Lahti and Collins 1978). Chronic naloxone treatment of guinea pigs also led to increased opiate binding in the ileum and brainstem and enhanced sensitivity to opiate-depressant effects on the isolated ileum preparation (Schulz et al. 1979). These preliminary reports of enhanced opiate binding after chronic naloxone have been confirmed and extended by Zukin et al. (1982), using improved assay techniques and controls, demonstrating that chronic naltrexone in rats resulted in a nearly two-fold increase in brain opiate receptor number (the actual increase ranged widely in specific regions of the CNS) (see Zukin et al., this volume).

Since high levels of stereospecific opiate receptors develop in fetal mouse cord-DRG explants (Hiller et al. 1978 a,b; see Sect. II), we used this system to examine the mechanism underlying the regulation of opiate receptors in response to chronic antagonists (Tempel et al. 1983). Cord-DRG explants were grown for two weeks, and then exposed to naloxone (10μM) for an additional week. Assays of cultures exposed to naloxone for 1 week revealed a 50% increase in ^{3}H-dihydromorphine binding (Tempel et al. 1983) relative to that in either control cultures (Table 3) containing regular nutrient media or 10μM (+)naloxone {the (+)enantiomer of naloxone which does not bind to opiate receptors (Ijima et al. 1978)}. In order to answer the question as to whether antagonist-induced

TABLE 3

Opiate Receptor Upregulation During Chronic Exposure

of Cord-DRG Cultures to Naloxone

Drug Exposure*		No. of Assays**	Opiate Receptor Binding § (fmoles bound per mg protein)	% Change in Binding Relative to Control
Agents(s)	Period (days)			
Control medium	-	8	100	-
Naloxone (10μM)	0-1	3	100	0
"	2	2	125	+25%
"	5	2	150	+50%
"	7	4	151	+51%
(+)Naloxone (10μM)	7	1	88	-12%
Naloxone (10μM)+ cyclohexamide (1μM)	5	1	93	+50% §§
Cyclohexamide (1μM)	5	1	62	-

*Cultures were grown in regular medium for 2 weeks prior to drug exposure

**For each assay, 7-9 cultures were pooled, homogenized and washed free of residual naloxone

§ Aliquots of homogenates were incubated in ^{3}H-dihydromorphine (5nM) ± levorphanol (10μM)

§§ %change in binding relative to cyclohexamide control; 1μM cyclohexamide blocked >90% of protein synthesis in cord-DRG cultures (measured by incorporation of ^{14}C-leucine into total protein)
(Unpublished data from Tempel, Crain, Simon and Zukin 1983, and in preparation.)

receptor upregulation requires the synthesis of new receptors, cultures were exposed to naloxone (10μM) together with cycloheximide (1μM), a relatively selective inhibitor of protein synthesis, for 5 days at 35°. These conditions blocked protein synthesis by greater than 90% in cord-DRG explants, as measured by incorporation of ^{14}C-leucine into total protein, yet upregulation of opiate receptors still occurred (Table 3). This result suggests that upregulation may be due to an unmasking of previously-existing receptors. No significant change in receptor density was observed following 1 day of naloxone treatment; a modest increase was observed after 2 days; and maximal upregulation, after 5 days of chronic exposure (Table 3). The maximal increase of 50% was quite comparable to the 52% increase observed in assays of spinal cord after chronic naltrexone in situ (Tempel and Zukin, in preparation; see also Zukin et al. 1982 and this volume). These data demonstrate the feasibility of utilizing cord-DRG explants as an in vitro model system for analyses of cellular mechanisms underlying the plasticity of opioid networks during chronic exposure to opioid antagonists, as well as agonists (see Sect. III-A). Attempts are also being made to detect electro-physiologic evidence of opioid supersensitivity in correlation with experimental upregulation of these receptors as observed in situ by Tang and Collins (1978), Schulz et al. (1979), Zukin et al. (this volume); see, however, Bardo et al. (1982) .

IV. CONCLUDING REMARKS

Electrophysiologic analyses of dissociated DRG and cord neurons have provided valuable insights into some of the primary effects of opioids on transmitter release and conductance changes at DRG terminals and cord-DRG synapses (Sect. I and III-C). However, many important aspects of sensory-evoked dorsal-horn network functions mediating opioid analgesia, tolerance and dependence may be difficult to study in randomly dispersed, monolayer arrays of DRG and cord neurons in dissociated cultures. Cord-DRG explants, on the other hand, provide a specific opioid-sensitive network of CNS and DRG neurons which can maintain not only an organized set of physiological properties, but also an organotypic multi-layered geometrical arrangement of neuron perikarya and fiber tracts clearly related to the original body axes of the explanted tissue (Crain 1976; Crain et al. 1978; Crain 1980, 1984). Studies with organotypic CNS explants can, therefore, bridge the gap between experiments in the whole animal -- which are often difficult to analyze because of the large number of complex interacting networks -- and experiments in cell cultures of relatively disorganized, but more accessible, arrays of dissociated neurons.

Our experiments with cord-DRG explants show the potentialities of this model system for analyses of cellular mechanisms associated with opioid tolerance (Sect. III) and they provide a foundation for more systematic experiments with these tissue culture models to gain further insights into physico-chemical factors that regulate development of tolerance and dependence during chronic exposure to opioids.

Furthermore, developmental studies of the effects of opioids in cultures of immature fetal CNS tissues may be useful in relation to problems arising in the human fetus during maternal narcotic addiction. Finally, analyses of factors leading to increased opiate receptor levels and possible opioid supersensitivity in cord-DRG explants after chronic exposure to naloxone at various stages of maturation provide an opportunity to correlate studies of opioid tolerance with the more general problem of plasticity in opioid systems of the CNS.

FOOTNOTES

[1]See reviews by Herz, Tucker, Klee, Loh and Wuster (this volume).
[2]See review by Henriksen (this volume).
[3]See reviews by Tucker, Klee, Loh and Wuster (this volume).
[4]See review by Beckman (this volume).
[5]See review by Herz (this volume).
[6]Hyperexcitability in opioid-tolerant cord-DRG explants observed after sudden withdrawal of opiates may, indeed, be mediated by compensatory alterations in the cord, as well as DRG, neurons of these complex dorsal-horn networks (see reviews by Herz and Wuster, this volume). Similarly, emphasis in this review on presynaptic DRG factors that may be involved in opioid analgesia and tolerance does not, of course, preclude a significant role for postsynaptic cord neurons (e.g. Williams and North 1983).

REFERENCES

Balnave, R.J., and Gage, P.W. The inhibitory effect of manganese on transmitter release at the neuromuscular junction of the toad. Brit. J. Pharmacol, 47: 339-352, 1973.

Bardo, M.T., Bhatnagar, R.K., and Gebhart, G.F. Differential effects of chronic morphine and naloxone on opiate receptors, monoamines, and morphine-induced behaviors in preweanling rats. Dev. Brain Res, 4: 139-147, 1982.

Belcher, G., Ryall, R.W., and Schaffner, R. The differential effects of 5-hydroxytryptamine, noradrenaline and raphe stimulation on nociceptive and non-nociceptive dorsal-horn interneurones in the cat. Brain Res, 151: 307-321, 1978.

Bell, J.A., and Matsumiya, T. Inhibitory effects of dorsal-horn and excitant effects of ventral horn intraspinal micro-injections of norepinephrine and serotonin in the cat. Life Sci, 29: 1507-1514, 1981.

Carstens, E., Klumpp, D., Randic, M., and Zimmerman, M. Effects of iontophoretically applied 5-hydroxytryptamine on the excitability of single primary afferent C- and A-fibers in the cat spinal cord. Brain Res, 220: 151-158, 1981.

Chalazonitis, A., and Crain, S.M. Opioid-sensitivity of neurons in organotypic cultures of fetal mouse dorsal root ganglion (DRG) explants grown either attached to spinal cord or in isolation. Soc. Neurosci Abstr, 9: 943, 1983.

Chang, K.J., Hazum, E., and Cuatrecasas, P. Novel opiate binding
sites selective for benzomorphan drugs. Proc. Nat. Acad. Sci.
USA, 78: 4141-4145, 1981.

Chang,K.J., Eckel, R.W., and Blanchard S.G. Opioid peptides
induce reduction of enkephalin receptors in cultured neuroblastoma
cells. Nature,296: 446-448, 1982.

Chang, K.J., Cuatrecasas, P., Valentino, R.J., Bostock, E.,
King, M.E., and Dingledine, R. Down-regulation of opiate receptors
in the hippocampal slice after prolonged incubation with δ-agonist
but not μ-agonists. INRC Symp. Abstr:L-30,1983(Life Sci,33:333-336).

Chavkin, C., James, I.F., and Goldstein, A. Dynorphin is a specific
endogenous ligand of the κ opioid receptor, Science, 215: 413-415,
1982.

Collier, H.O.J. Cellular site of opiate dependence. Nature, 283:
625-629, 1980.

Collier, H.O.J., Cuthbert, N.J. and Francis, D.L. Tolerance,
dependence and quasi-dependence in the guinea-pig isolated ileum.
In: Way, E.L., ed. Endogenous and Exogenous Opiate Agonists
and Antagonists. Oxford: Pergamon Press, 1980. pp. 509-512

Collier, H.O.J., Cuthbert, N.J., and Francis, D.L. Clonidine
dependence in the guinea-pig isolated ileum. Brit. J. Pharmacol,
73: 443-453, 1981a.

Collier, H.O.J., Cuthbert, N.J., and Francis, D.L. Model of
opiate dependence in the guinea-pig isolated ileum. Brit. J.
Pharmacol, 73: 921-932, 1981b.

Cox, B.M., and Osman, O.H. Inhibition of the development of
tolerance to morphine in rats by drugs which inhibit ribonucleic
acid or protein synthesis. Brit. J. Pharmacol., 38: 157-170, 1970

Crain, S.M. Neurophysiologic Studies in Tissue Culture. New York,
Raven Press, 1976.

Crain, S.M. Development of specific sensory-evoked synaptic networks
in organized CNS tissue cultures. In: Giacobini, E., Vernadakis, A.,
and Shahar, A., ed. Tissue Culture in Neurobiology. New York:
Raven Press, 1980. pp. 169-185.

Crain, S.M. Development and plasticity of specific sensory synaptic
networks in fetal mouse spinal cord cultures. In: Tsukada, Y., ed.
Perspectives of Neuroscience:from Molecule to Mind. Tokyo: Univ.
of Tokyo Press, 1984.(in press)

Crain, S.M., and Peterson, E.R. Enhanced afferent synaptic functions
in fetal mouse spinal cord-sensory ganglion explants following NGF-
induced ganglion hypertrophy. Brain Res, 79: 145-152, 1974.

Crain, S.M., Crain, B., Peterson, E.R., and Simon, E.J. Selective
depression by opioid peptides of sensory-evoked dorsal-horn network responses in organized spinal cord cultures. Brain Res,
157: 196-201, 1978.

Crain, S.M., Crain, B., Finnigan, T., and Simon, E.J. Development
of tolerance to opiates and opioid peptides in organotypic cultures
of mouse spinal cord. Life Sci, 25: 1797-1802, 1979.

Crain, S.M., Peterson, E.R., Crain, B., and Simon, E.J. Selective
opiate depression of sensory-evoked synaptic networks in dorsal-horn
regions of spinal cord cultures. Brain Res, 133: 162-166,
1977.

Crain, S.M., Crain, B., Peterson, E.R., Hiller, J.M., and Simon, E.J. Exposure to 4-aminopyridine prevents depressant effects of opiates on sensory-evoked dorsal-horn network responses in spinal cord cultures. Life Sci, 31: 235-240, 1982a.

Crain, S.M., Crain, B., and Peterson, E.R. Development of cross-tolerance to 5-hydroxytryptamine in organotypic cultures of mouse spinal cord-ganglia during chronic exposure to morphine. Life Sci, 31: 241-247, 1982b.

Creese, Il, and Snyder, S.H. Receptor binding and pharmacological activity of opiates in the guinea pig intestine. J. Pharmacol. exp. Ther, 194: 205-219, 1975.

Davis, M.E., Akera, T., and Brady, T.M., Saturable binding of morphine to rat brain-stem slices and the effect of chronic morphine treatment. Res. Commun. Chem. Path. Pharmacol, 12: 409-418, 1975.

David, M.E., Akera, T., and Brody, T.M. Reduction of opiate binding to brainstem slices associated with the development of tolerance to morphine in rats. J. Pharmacol. exp. Ther, 211: 112-119, 1979.

Dawson, G., McLawhon, R., and Miller, R.J. Opiates and enkephalins inhibit synthesis of gangliosides and membrane glycoproteins in mouse neuroblastoma cell line N4TG1. Proc. Natl. Acad. Sci. USA, 76: 605-609, 1979.

Diamond, J., and Miledi, R. A study of foetal and new-born rat muscle fibres. J. Physiol, (London) 162: 393-408, 1962.

Duggan, A.W. Single neurone studies related to opiate tolerance and dependence. Proc. Austral. Physiol. and Pharmacol. Soc, 11: 15-19, 1980.

Duggan, A.W., and Griersmith, B.T. Methyl xanthines, adenosine 3', 5'-cyclic monophosphate and the spinal transmission of nociceptive information. Brit. J. Pharmacol, 67: 51-57, 1979.

Duggan, A.W., Hall, J.G., and Headley, P.M. Suppression of transmission of nociceptive impulses by morphine: Selective effects of morphine administered in the region of the substantia gelatinosa. Brit J Pharmacol, 61:65-76, 1977.

Dunlap, K., and Fischbach, G.D. Neurotransmitters decrease the calcium component of sensory neurone action potentials. Nature, 276:837-839, 1978..

Eccles, J.C. The Physiology of Synapses. Berlin, Springer-Verlag, 1964.

Fields, H.L., Emson, P.C., Leigh, B.K., Gilbert, R.F.T., and Iversen, L.L. Multiple opiate receptor sites on primary afferent fibres. Nature, 284: 351-353, 1980.

Gahwiler, B.H. Development of acute tolerance during exposure of hippocampal explants to an opioid peptide. Brain Res, 217: 196-200, 1981.

Galindo, J., and Rudomin, P. Facilitation of synaptic activity in the frog spinal cord produced by 4-aminopyridine. Neurosci. Letters, 19: 299-304, 1978.

Hammond, M.D., Schneider, C., and Collier, H.O.J. Induction of opiate tolerance in isolated guinea pig ileum and its modification by drugs. In: Kosterlitz, H.W. ed. Opiates and Endogenous Opioid Peptides. Amsterdam: Elsevier, 1976, pp.169-178. pp. 169-178.

Hamprecht, B. Structural, electrophysiological, biochemical, and pharmacological properties of neuroblastoma-glioma cell hybrids in cell culture. In:Bourne, G.H., Danielli, J.F., and Jeon, K.W., eds. International Review of Cytology. New York: Academic Press, 1977. pp. 99-170.

Handa, B.K., Lane, A.C., Lord, J.A.H., Morgan, B.A., Rance, M.J., and Smith, C.F.C. Analogues of βLPH 61-64 possessing selective against activity at μ-opiate receptors. Eur. J. Pharmacol, 70: 531-540, 1981.

Harris, R.A., Loh, H.H., and Way, E.L. Effects of divalent cations, cation chelators and an ionophore on morphine analgesia and tolerance. J. Pharmacol. exp. Ther, 195: 488-498, 1975.

Harris, R.A., Yamamoto, H., Loh, H.H. and Way, E.L. Discrete changes in brain calcium with morphine analgesia, tolerance-dependence, and abstinence. Life Sci,20: 501-506, 1977.

Headley, P.M., Duggan, A.W., and Griersmith, B.T. Selective reduction by noradrenaline and 5-hydroxytryptamine of nociceptive responses of cat dorsal-horn neurons. Brain Res, 145: 185-189, 1978.

Hentall, I.D., and Fields, H.L. Actions of opiates, substance P, and serotonin on the excitability of primary afferent terminals and observations on interneuronal activity in the neonatal rat's dorsal horn in vitro. Neuroscience, 9: 521-528, 1983.

Hiller, J.M., Simon, E.J., Crain, S.M., and Peterson, E.R. Opiate receptors in cultures of fetal mouse dorsal root ganglia (DRG) and spinal cord: Predominance in DRG neurites. Brain Res, 145: 396-400, 1978.

Hiller. J.M., Simon, E.J., Crain, S.M., and Peterson, E.R. Opiate receptor distribution in organized cultures of fetal mouse spinal cord and dorsal root ganglia. In: Van Ree, J.M., and Terenius, L., eds. Characteristics and Function of Opioids. Amsterdam: Elsevier/North Holland Press, 1978. pp. 477-478.

Huidobro-Toro, N.P., Hu, J., and Way, E.L. Calcium antagonism of the inhibitory effect of normorphine on the ileum of the morphine-tolerant and nontolerant guinea pig. J. Pharmacol. exp. Ther, 218: 84-91, 1981.

Ijima, I., Minamikawa, J., Jacobson, A.E., Brassi, A., and Rice, K.C. Studies in the (+)-morphinan series 5. Synthesis and biological properties of (+)-Naloxone. J. Med. Chem, 21: 398-400, 1978.

Illes, P., and Thesleff, S. 4-Aminopyridine and evoked transmitter release from motor nerve endings. Brit. J. Pharmacol, 64: 623-629, 1978.

Illes, P., Zieglgansberger, W., and Herz, A. Calcium reverses the inhibitory action of morphine on neuroeffector transmission in the mouse vas deferens. Brain Res, 191: 511-522, 1980.

Johnson, S.M., and North, R.A. Membrane potential changes in neurones undergoing withdrawal from opiates. Brain Res, 190: 559-563, 1980.

Kakunaga, T., Kaneto, H., and Hano, K. Pharmacologic studies on analgesics. VII. Significance of the calcium ion in morphine analgesia. J. Pharmacol. exp. Ther, 153: 134-141, 1966.

Karras, P.J., and North, R.A. Inhibition of neuronal firing by opiates: evidence against the involvement of cyclic nucleotides. Brit. J. Pharmacol, 65: 647-652, 1979.

Khanna, N.C., and Sharma, S.K. Megadoses of vitamin C prevent the development of tolerance and physical dependence on morphine in mice. Life Sci, 33:401-404, 1983.

Kim, Y.I., Golaner, M.M., and Sanders, D.B. Facilitatory effects of 4-aminopyridine on normal neuromuscular transmission. Muscle and Nerve, 3: 105-111, 1980.

Kirby, M.L. Changes in {^{3}H}naloxone binding in spinal cord of rats treated prenatally with morphine. Neuropharmacol, 22: 303-307, 1983.

Klee, W.A., and Nirenberg, M. A neuroblastoma χ glioma hybrid cell line with morphine receptors. Proc. natl. Acad. Sci. USA, 71: 3474-3477, 1974.

Klee, W.A., Sharma, S.K., and Nirenberg, M. Opiate receptors as regulators of adenylate cyclase. Life Sci, 16: 1869-1874, 1975.

Kosterlitz, H.W., and Hughes, J. Peptides with morphine-like action in the brain. Brit. J. Psychiat, 130: 298-304, 1977.

Kosterlitz, H.W., and Waterfield, A.A. In vitro models in the study of structure-activity relationships of narcotic analgesics. Ann. Rev. Pharmacol, 15: 29-47, 1975.

Kosterlitz, H.W., Waterfield, A.A. and Berthoud, V. Assessment of the agonist and antagonist properties of narcotic analgesic drugs by their actions on the morphine receptor in the guinea pig ileum. In: Braude, M.C., Harris, L.S., May, E.L., Smith, J.P., and Villarreal, J.E., eds. Advances in Biochemical Psychopharmacology, Vol. 8, Narcotic Antagonists. New York: Raven Press, 1973. pp. 319-334.

Kosterlitz, H.W., Lord, J.A.H., Paterson, S.J., and Waterfield A.A. Effects of changes in the structure of enkephalins and of narcotic analgesic drugs on their interactions with μ- and δ-receptors. Brit. J. Pharmacol, 68: 333-342, 1980.

Kosterlitz, H.W., Paterson, S.J., and Robson, L.E., Characterization of the κ-subtype of the opiate receptor in the guinea-pig brain. Brit. J. Pharmacol, 73: 939-949, 1981.

Lahti, R., and Collins, R. Chronic naloxone results in prolonged increases in opiate binding sites in brain. Eur. J. Pharmacol, 51: 185-186, 1978.

Lamotte, C., Pert, C.B., and Snyder, S.H. Opiate receptor binding in primate spinal cord: distribution and changes after dorsal root section. Brain Res, 112: 407-412, 1976.

Lampert, A., Nirenberg, M., and Klee, W.A. Tolerance and dependence evoked by an endogenous opiate peptide. Proc. natl Acad. Sci. USA, 73: 3165-3167, 1976.

Lenoir, D., Barg, J., and Simantov, R. Down-regulation of opiate receptors in serum-free cultures of aggregating fetal brain cells. Life Sci, 33:337-340, 1983.

Macdonald, R.L., and Nelson, P.G. Specific opiate-induced depression of transmitter release from dorsal root ganglion cells in culture. Science, 199: 1449-1451, 1978.

Matsuda, Y., Yoshida, S., and Yonezawa, T. Tetrodotoxin sensitivity and Ca component of action potentials of mouse dorsal root ganglion cells cultured in vitro. Brain Res, 154: 69-82, 1978.

Meiri, U., and Rahamimoff, R. Neuromuscular transmission: Inhibition by manganese ions. Science, 176:308-309, 1972.

Mudge, A.W., Leeman, S.E., and Fischbach, G.D. Enkephalin inhibits release of substance P from sensory neurons in culture and decreases action potential duration. Proc. natl. Acad. Sci. USA, 76: 526-530, 1979.

Murase, K., Nedeljkov, V., and Randic, M. The actions of neuropeptides on dorsal-horn neurons in the rat spinal cord slice preparation an intracellular study. Brain Res, 234: 170-176, 1982.

Nicak, A., and Kohut, A. Development of tolerance to morphine and pethidine in rats is dependence on age. Activitas Nervosa Superior (Praha), 20: 231-235, 1978.

Nichols, R.A., and Nakajima, Y. Effects of manganese and cobalt on the inhibitory synapse of the crustacean stretch receptor neuron. Brain Res, 86: 493-498, 1975.

Ninkovic, M., Hunt, S.P., and Gleave, J.R. Localization of opiate and histamine H_1-receptors in the primate sensory ganglia and spinal cord. Brain Res, 241: 197-206, 1982.

North, R.A. Opiates, opioid peptides and single neurones. Life Sci, 24: 1527-1546, 1979.

North, R.A., and Karras, P.J. Opiate tolerance and dependence induced in vitro in single myenteric neurones. Nature, 272: 73-75, 1978a.

North, R.A., and Karras, P.J. Tolerance and dependence in vitro. In: Van Ree, J.M., and Terenius, L., eds. Characteristics and Function of Opioids. Amsterdam: Elsevier/North Holland Press, 1978. pp. 25-36b.

North, R.A., and Vitek, L. The effect of chronic morphine treatment on excitatory junction potentials in the mouse vas deferens. Brit. J. Pharmacol, 68: 399-406, 1979.

North, R.A., and Zieglgansberger, W. Opiate withdrawal signs in single myenteric neurones. Brain Res, 144: 208-211, 1978.

Otsuka, M., and Konishi, S. Electrophysiology of mammalian spinal cord in vitro. Nature, 252: 733-735, 1974.

Perkins, M.N. and Stone, T.W. 4-aminopyridine blockade of neuronal depressant responses to ATP. Brit. J. Pharmacol, 70: 525-428, 1980.

Peroutka, S.J., Lebovitz, R.M., and Snyder, S.H. Two distinct central serotonin receptors with different physiological functions. Science, 212: 827-829, 1981.

Pert, C., and Snyder, S. Opiate receptor binding-enhancement of opiate administration in vivo. Biochem. Pharmacol, 25: 847-853, 1976.

Ransom, B.R., Neale, E., Henkart, M., Bullock, P.N., and Nelson, P.G. Mouse spinal cord in cell culture. 1. Morphology and intrinsic neuronal electrophysiologic properties. J. Neurophysiol, 40: 1132-1150, 1977.

Roemer, D., Buescher, H.H., Hill, R.C., Pless, J., Bauer, W., Cardinaux, F., Closse, A., Hauser, D., and Hugenin, R. A synthetic enkephalin analogue with prolonged parenteral and oral analgesic activity. Nature, 268: 547-549, 1977.

Schulz, R., Wuster, M., and Herz, A. Supersensitivity to opioids following chronic blockade of endorphin activity by naloxone. Naun. Schmied. Arch. Pharmacol, 306: 93-96, 1979.

Schulz, R., Wuster, M., Krenss, H., and Herz, A. Selective development of tolerance without dependence in multiple opiate receptors
of mouse vas deferens. Nature, 285: 242-243, 1980.

Schulz, R., Wuster, M., Rubini, P., and Herz, A. Functional opiate
receptors in the guinea-pig ileum: Their differentiation by
means of selective tolerance development. J. Pharmacol. exp. Ther,
219: 547-550, 1981.

Sharma, S.K., and Khanna, N.C. Ascorbate suppresses the opiate-
induced compensatory increase in cyclic AMP in neuroblastoma
x glioma hybrid cells. Biochem. J, 208: 43-46, 1982.

Sharma, S.K., Nirenberg, M., and Klee, W.A. Morphine receptors
as regulators of adenylate cyclase activity. Proc. natl. Acad.
Sci. USA, 72: 590-594, 1975a.

Sharma, S.K., Klee, W.A., and Nirenberg, M. Dual regulation of
adenylate cyclase accounts for narcotic dependence and tolerance.
Proc. nat. Acad. Sci. USA, 72: 3092-3096, 1975b.

Simantov, R., Baram, D., Levy, R., and Nadler, H. Enkephalin and
α-adrenergic receptors: Evidence for both common and differentiable regulatory pathways and down-regulation of the enkephalin
receptor. Life Sci, 31: 1323-1326, 1982.

Simon, E.J. The opiate receptors. Neurochemical Res, 1: 3-28,
1976.

Spitzer, N.C. Ion channels in development. Ann. Rev. Neurosci,
2: 363-397, 1979.

Stinnakre, J., and Tauc, L. Calcium influx in active aplysia
neurones detected by injected aequorin. Nature (New Biol.),
242: 113-115, 1973.

Stone, T.W. Physiological roles for adenosine and adenosine 5'-
triphosphate in the nervous system. Neuroscience, 6: 523-555,
1981a.

Stone, T.W. The effects of 4-aminopyridine on the isolated vas
deferens and its effects on the inhibitory properties of adenosine,
morphine, noradrenaline and γ-aminobutyric acid. Brit. J.
Pharmacol, 73: 791-796, 1981b.

Suzue, T., and Jessell, T. Opiate analgesics and endorphins inhibit
rat dorsal root potential in vitro. Neurosci. Lett, 16: 161-166
1980.

Tang, A.H., and Collins, R.J. Enhanced analgesic effects of
morphine after chronic administration of naloxone in the rat.
Eur. J. Pharmacol, 47: 473-474, 1978.

Tempel, A., Crain, S.M., Simon, E.J., and Zukin, R.S. Opiate
receptor upregulation in explants of spinal cord-dorsal root
ganglia. Soc. Neurosci. Abstr, 9: 327, 1983.

Traber, J., Gullis, R. and Hamprecht, B. Influence of opiates on
the levels of adenosine 3':5'-cyclic monophosphate in neuroblastoma
x glioma hybrid cells. Life Sci, 16: 1863-1868, 1975.

Tung, A.S., and Brandom, B. W. 4-Aminopyridine reversal of
morphine analgesia. Soc. Neurosci. Abstr, 7: 798, 1981.

Van Neuten, J.M., Janssen, P.A.J., and Fontaine, J. Naloxone
reverses inhibitory effects of fatigue and of compounds not
related to narcotic analgesics in the guinea-pig ileum. Arch.
int. Pharmacodyn, 220: 349-350, 1976.

Ward, A., and Takemori, A.E. Studies on the narcotic receptor in
the guinea-pig ileum. J. Pharmacol. exp. Ther, 199: 117-123,
1976a.

Ward, A., and Takemori, A.E. Effect of 6-hydroxydopamine and 5,6-dihydroxytryptamine on the response of the coaxially stimulated guinea-pig ileum to morphine. J. Pharmacol. exp. Ther, 199: 124-130, 1976b.

Werz, M.A. and Macdonald, R.L. Opioid peptides decrease calcium-dependent action potential duration of mouse dorsal root ganglion neurons in cell culture. Brain Res, 239: 315-321, 1982a.

Werz, M.A., and Macdonald, R.L. Heterogeneous sensitivity of cultured dorsal root ganglion neurones to opioid peptides selective μ-and δ-opiate receptors. Nature, 299: 730-732, 1982b.

Werz, M.A., and Macdonald, R.L. Dynorphine specifically decreased calcium-dependent action potential duration in cultured primary sensory neurons. INRC Symp, Abstr: P-84, 1983.

Wikler, A. Opiate Addiction. Psychological and Neuro-physiological Aspects in Relation to Clinical Problems. Illinois: C.C. Thomas, 1953.

Wikler, A. Opioid Dependence. New York: Plenum Press, 1980.

Wikler, A., and Carter, R.L. Effects of single doses of N-allylnormorphine on hindlimb reflexes of chronic spinal dogs during cycles of morphine addiction. J. Pharmacol. exp. Ther, 109: 92-101, 1953.

Wikler, A., and Frank, K. Hindlimb reflexes of chronic spinal dogs during cycles of addiction to morphine and methadon. J. Pharmacol. exp. Ther, 94: 382-400, 1948.

Williams, J.T. and North, R.A. Tolerance to opiates in locus coeruleus neurones? INRC Symp, Abstr: P-49, 1983.

Williams, J., and Zieglgansberger, W. Mature spinal ganglion cells are not sensitive to opiate receptor mediated action. Neurosci. Lett, 21: 211-216, 1981.

Wuster, M.R., Schulz, R., and Herz, A. Specificity of opioids towards the μ-, δ- and ε-opiate receptors. Neurosci. Lett, 15: 193, 1979.

Yaksh, T.L., and Wilson, P.R. Spinal serotonin terminal system mediates antinociception. J. Pharmacol. exp. Ther, 208: 446-453, 1979.

Yamamoto, H., Harris, R.A. Loh, H.H., and Way, E.L. Effect of acute and chronic morphine treatments on calcium localization and binding in brain. J. Pharmacol. exp. Ther, 205: 255-264, 1978.

Yoshida, S., and Matsuda, Y. Studies on sensory neurons of the mouse with intracellular-recording and horseradish peroxidase-injection techniques. J. Neurophysiol, 42: 1134-1145, 1979.

Yoshimura, M., and North A.R. Substantia gelatinosa neurones hyperpolarized in vitro by enkephalin. Nature, 305: 529-530, 1983.

Zukin, R.S., Sugarman, J.R., Fitz-Syage, M.L., Gardner, E.L., Zukin, S.R., and Gintzler, A.R. Naloxone-induced opiate super-sensitivity. Brain Res, 245: 285-292, 1982.

ACKNOWLEDGEMENTS

This work was supported by a research grant from the National
Institute on Drug Abuse (DA-02031). Collaborative research with
Drs. Eric J. Simon and Jacob M. Hiller (New York University) was
supported by NIDA grant DA-00017 (to E.J.S.). Collaborative
research with Drs. R. Suzanne Zukin and Ann Tempel (at Einstein)
was supported by NIDA grants DA-01843 and DA-00069 (to R.S.Z.).

The cord-DRG cultures used in these studies were prepared by Edith
E. Peterson. Tissue culture facilities were kindly provided by
Dr. Murray B. Bornstein. Bea Crain provided skillful technical
assistance in carrying out many of the electrophysiologic
experiments.

AUTHOR

Stanley M. Crain, Ph.D.
Departments of Neuroscience and Physiology, and the
Rose F. Kennedy Center for Research on
Mental Retardation and Human Development
Albert Einstein College of Medicine
Bronx, New York   10461

NOTE ADDED IN PROOF

Following the discussions at the NIDA Symposium (Boston, Nov. 1983) on Dr. Collier's hypothesis regarding the possible roles of adenylate cyclase (AC)/cyclic AMP in opioid tolerance and dependence, attempts were initiated to utilize forskolin, a selective activator of AC(Seamon and Daly), to facilitate evaluation of the effects of increased AC/cAMP levels on the sensitivity of cord-DRG explants to opiates (see above: Sect. I). When naive explants were treated with forskolin (10-50μM) for 10-30 min prior to and during exposure to 0.3μM morphine, the usual depressant effects on dorsal-horn responses often failed to occur (10-30 min tests) (Crain et al, 1984). Dibutyryl cAMP (10mM) or the more potent analog, dioctanoyl cAMP(0.1mM), produced a similar degree of "tolerance" to opiates as 10μM forskolin. With high levels of forskolin (50μM), even concentrations of morphine up to 10μM were far less effective in depressing cord responses. These anti-opiate effects of exogenous cAMP and forskolin are probably both mediated by increases in intracellular cAMP. The onset of opioid-"tolerance" in cAMP-or forskolin-treated cord-DRG explants provides the first electrophysiologic support for the hypothesis that neurons may develop tolerance/dependence during chronic opioid exposure by a compensatory enhancement of their AC/cAMP system following initial opioid-depression of AC activity (see review by Collier, 1980). Previous evidence relied primarily on behavioral tests (Ho et al. 1973; Collier et al. 1975) and biochemical analyses in cell cultures (Sharma et al. 1975). It will be of interest to determine if dorsal-horn tissues of cord-DRG explants do, in fact, develop increased AC/cAMP levels as they become tolerant during chronic exposure to opiates.

ADDITIONAL REFERENCES

Crain, S.M., Crain, B. and Peterson, E.R. Cyclic AMP or forskolin produces rapid "tolerance" to the depressant effects of opiates on sensory-evoked dorsal-horn responses in spinal cord-dorsal root ganglion (DRG) explants. Soc. Neurosci Abstr 10 (in press).
Ho, I.K., Loh, H.H. and Way, E.L. Cyclic adenosine monophosphate antagonism of morphine analgesia. J Pharmacol Exp Ther, 185:336-345, 1973.
Seamon, K.B. and Daly, J.W. Forskolin: a unique diterpene activator of cyclic AMP-generating systems. J Cyclic Nucleotide Res, 7:201-224, 1981.

Experimental Approaches Toward Determining the Neuronal Circuits Most Affected by Chronic Opiate Administration

Robert Elde

INTRODUCTION

A wide variety of studies have explored the expression of tolerance to opiates at behavioral, cellular and molecular levels. However, very little is known concerning the anatomical identity of neuronal systems that are most affected by chronic opiate administration. Since the discovery of opiate receptors and the characterization of opioid peptides, a great deal of information has been gathered concerning the regional distribution of opiate binding sites as well as the distribution of neuronal cell bodies, fibers and terminals that contain enkephalins, endorphins and dynorphins. It has been hypothesized that the activity of neurons that bear opiate receptors is likely to be perturbed by chronic opiate adminstration, perhaps by alterations in receptor number or affinity (Klee et al., Law et al., Zukin et al, this volume). In addition, it has been suggested that the activity of opioid neurons themselves may be altered in the tolerant state, perhaps through receptor-mediated autofeedback mechanisms. It is also quite possible that the major effects of chronic opiate administration are expressed by neurons that are regulated by the above classes of neurons, but separated from them by one or more synaptic connections (Wuster and Costa, this volume). Moreover, it has not been established if chronic opiate administration leads to chronic excitation or inhibition of the affected neuronal circuits.

PREVIOUS STUDIES

Little is known of the neuroanatomical substrates of opiate tolerance because of limitations inherent to techniques used to measure neuronal activity. Microelectrode physiological methods provide precise records of neuronal activity of single cells or small groups of cells over times that range from milliseconds to minutes. Chronic or periodic recording from chronically implanted electrodes may extend the period for recording of activity to several days. However, the number of neurons that can be sampled by these methods is very small. Considering the large number of brain regions and the large number of neurons within each region, it is clear that unit recording of neuronal activity is not an adequate method for sampling the entire nervous system for the effects of chronic opiate administration on neuronal activity.

Electroencephalographic methods overcome some of the limitations of microelectrode recording in that large regions of brain can be measured for net neuronal activity. However, the neuroanatomical resolution of these methods is poor.

Introduction of the autoradiographic method for detecting regional accumulation of radiolabeled 2-deoxyglucose provided the technical means to survey the entire brain for changes in glucose utilization. Regional deoxyglucose accumulation has been found to closely parallel neuronal activity during the time of exposure to deoxyglucose, the duration of exposure usually being an hour or less (Sokoloff et al. 1977).

Several studies have been reported on the effects of opiate administration on 2-deoxyglucose accumulation. Lightman and colleagues (1982) found that acute morphine produced a naloxone-reversible increase in glucose utilization in the posterior lobe of the pituitary. Chronic administration of morphine also produced an increase in glucose utilization in the posterior pituitary, although a subsequent acute challenge with morphine produced a decrease in glucose utilization. Wooten and colleagues (1982) surveyed regional glucose utilization in the di- and telencephalon of morphine-dependent rats and in rats in which withdrawal was precipitated with naloxone. Optical densitometry of autoradiograms from morphine-dependent animals revealed significant increases in some regions, significant decreases in other regions and no change in glucose utilization in other regions (table 1).

These data are of considerable interest, however it is important to note that the relative activity of neurons as measured in these studies may not genuinely reflect the sites most prominent in expressing the tolerant state. In the first place, it is debatable whether or not a genuine state of tolerance was achieved during the periods of measurement, since the morphine injections were halted or morphine pellets were removed some hours prior to infusion of radiolabeled deoxyglucose. Thus, it is possible that some of the changes in deoxyglucose accumulation could be due to early phases of withdrawal from the tolerant state. Secondly, at least some of the changes in glucose utilization may reflect the morphine-treated animals' behavioral response to the handling that was necessary for cannulae insertion and deoxyglucose administration.

It is important to stress that limitations inherent to the deoxyglucose method produce difficulties for the design of experiments that will differentiate changes in glucose utilization that are directly attributable to a drug's action from those which occur as secondary effects. General hypoxia secondary to opiate-induced respiratory depression represents another example of possible counfounding effects that may be detected by the deoxyglucose method. Wuster and colleagues (1981) attempted to

TABLE 1

Regions with Changes in Brain Glucose Utilization
after Chronic Morphine Treatment*

Increased

Medial preoptic area, lateral preoptic area, bed nucleus stria
terminalis, preoptic magnocellularis, parasubiculum, subiculum,
medial entorhinal cortex, lateral entorhinal cortex; CA-1 pyramidal
layer, CA-1 striatum radiatum, perforant path, dentate gyrus, CA-3
pyramidal layer, CA-2.

Decreased

Frontal motor cortex, medial frontal cortex; striatum; thalamic
anterior ventral nucleus; medial habenula nucleus.

---

*Data from Wooten et al. (1982)

avoid the effects of opiate-induced respiratory depression by
studying glucose utilization in an in vitro whole brain perfusion
system. Whereas such an approach may provide information on the
sites of acute effects of opiates, it is unlikely to provide
information on the sites where the chronic effects of opiate
administration may be manifest.

Recent work on levels of enzymes involved in brain energy metabolism
suggests an alternate approach for studying the sites involved in
the expression of tolerance to opiates. Wong-Riley (1979) and
colleagues (Wong-Riley et al. 1978; Wong-Riley and Welt 1980) have
explored the intensity of histochemically-revealed cytochrome
oxidase activity as a function of neuronal activity. When auditory,
visual and somatosensory systems were denervated, cytochrome oxidase
staining intensity was shown to decrease within neurons as far as
several synapses distal to the site of sensory deprivation. Using
more quantitative assays, several other enzymes related to energy
metabolism were shown by Dietrich and colleagues (1981) to be
significantly depressed within specific targets of whisker afferent
pathways after cauterization of whiskers. Thus, there is striking
evidence that long-term inactivation of neuronal pathways leads to
decreases in energy-related enzyme levels.

Kageyama and Wong-Riley (1982) have further reported that the level
of cytochrome oxidase staining within hippocampal neurons correlates
positively with the known spontaneous activity of those neurons.
That is, spontaneously active neurons have higher levels of
cytochrome oxidase activity than those which are tonically silent.
Most importantly, Dietrich and colleagues (1982) have demonstrated
increases in levels of three energy metabolism-related enzymes in
cortical barrel fields that are the targets of intact whisker
afferents in animals in which other whisker afferents had been
removed. The authors suggest this is the first demonstration of an
increase of energy-related enzymes in brain in response to chronic,

295

experimental stimulation of a pathway. As they point out, however, these changes are not without biological precedent, since similar long-term changes in levels of enzymes of energy metabolism are observed in skeletal muscle as a function of exercise and disuse (see Karpati and Engel 1968, Holloszy and Booth 1976).

Metabolic enzyme histochemistry provides a possible means to detect changes in neuronal activity that are manifest and maintained over a period of weeks. The technique is attractive for identification of sites affected by chronic opiate administration, since transient phenomena that may accompany handling and treatment of animals are unlikely to be detected. In contrast to the deoxyglucose method, enzyme histochemistry does not require intensive manipulation of animals (such as restraint, intravenous cannulation and injection) immediately prior to and during the time of the measurement. Thus, it can be expected that neurons identified by enzyme histochemistry as most altered by chronic exposure to opiates will represent those neurons that are responsible for the physiological and behavioral expression of tolerance.

PILOT STUDIES

An experiment was conducted to compare the intensity of cytochrome oxidase staining in brains of animals chronically exposed to morphine and in brains from control animals. Morphine was made available to Swiss-Webster mice ad libitum in drinking water that contained 10% sucrose (Khavari and Risner 1973). During the first 16 days, mice consumed an average of 69 mg morphine sulfate/kg/day. During the last 9 days the concentration of morphine was doubled resulting in mean consumption of 146 mg/kg/day. Control mice received sucrose drinking water for 25 days. At several intervals during the study, tolerance was assessed in cohorts by naloxone-precipitated withdrawal. Brains of mice were fixed by vascular perfusion with 4% formaldehyde. Frozen sections sampling the entire neuraxis were processed for cytochrome oxidase activity according to Wong-Riley and Welt (1980). Specificity controls for staining were obtained by inclusion of sodium azide in the incubation media. Staining patterns and density were examined and, in limited areas to date, quantified by optical densitometry.

Cytochrome oxidase staining was heterogeneous within the brain. Staining for this enzyme complex appeared to be specific since inclusion of the electron transport inhibitor, sodium azide, prevented staining. The intensity of staining in many regions did not appear to differ between morphine-treated and control mouse brains (figures 1 and 2). However, in certain discrete regions such as the mammillary nuclei, a striking decrease in the staining intensity was observed in morphine treated animals (74% of control, $p < 0.05$; figures 1 and 2). Decreases in staining in

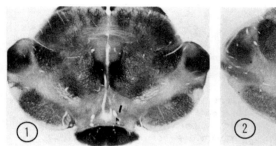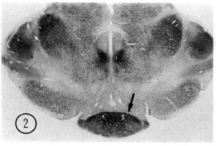

FIGURES 1 and 2. Photomicrographs of coronal sections of rat midbrain after processing for cytochrome oxidase histochemistry. Many regions in vehicle control (figure 1) and chronic morphine-treated animals (figure 2) exhibit similar staining intensity. However, the mammillary nuclear complex (arrows) of the morphine-treated animals was strikingly decreased in staining intensity.

morphine-treated mice were apparent in some other regions. No increases in cytochrome oxidase staining were noted in morphine-treated mice.

This pilot study demonstrates the feasibility of using enzyme histochemistry to determine sites where neuronal activity is most altered as a consequence of chronic morphine administration. Previous reports (Dietrich et al. 1981, 1982) have suggested that levels of enzymes involved in energy metabolism change only over a time course of several weeks. This phenomenon is exploited by enzyme histochemistry and thereby avoids detection of transiently occurring events. Thus histochemical detection of metabolic enzymes has an advantage over the 2-deoxyglucose method in that it is less susceptible to revealing changes in neuronal activity that are actually a consequence of periodic handling of the animal or responses to manipulation of the animal in the period immediately prior to sacrifice.

However, cytochrome oxidase histochemistry is unlikely to demonstrate all of the sites involved in tolerance to morphine. As noted above, neither this pilot study nor previous studies in other systems have noted increases in levels of cytochrome oxidase. The findings of Dietrich and colleagues (1982) suggest that increases as well as decreases of malate dehydrogenase or citrate synthase may be histochemically demonstrable. Thus histochemical study of these enzymes may be more appropriate to determine the variety of changes in neuronal activity which occur as a consequence of long-term perturbation by opiates.

SUMMARY AND FUTURE QUESTIONS

The investigation of neuroanatomical substrates, through which opiate tolerance and dependence phenomena are manifest, now appears to be feasible. Histochemical processing of brains to reveal certain enzymes of energy metabolism is likely to identify neurons most involved in the tolerant state. The following specific questions can be addressed.

1. Is the net activity of neurons bearing opiate receptors altered by chronic opiate administation? Are neurons bearing different classes of opiate receptors differentially affected? Are neurons that produce opioid peptides affected? Do opioid neurons in discrete regions, or those producing particular opioid peptides, differ in their activity during chronic exposure to morphine? Is the net effect inhibition or excitation?

2. What neurotransmitters are produced by neurons most affected by chronic exposure to morphine? Such inquiry may suggest the use of new therapeutic means of countering the untoward effects of tolerance to opiates.

3. Which neurons in the brain are principally involved in the manifestation of withdrawal from chronic opiates? Which neurotransmitters do they contain and which receptors do they bear? Such data may suggest new therapeutic means of countering the untoward effects of withdrawal from opiates.

REFERENCES

Dietrich, W.D., Durham, D., Lowry, O.H., and Woolsey, T.A. Quantitative histochemical effects of whisker damage on single identified cortical barrels in the adult mouse. J Neuroscience, 1:929-935, 1981.

Dietrich, W.D., Durham, D., Lowry, O.H., and Woolsey, T.A. "Increased" sensory stimulation leads to changes in energy-related enzymes in the brain. J Neuroscience, 2:1608-1613, 1982.

Holloszy, J.O. and Booth, F.W. Biochemical adaptations to endurance exercise in muscle. Annu Rev Physiol, 38:273-291, 1976.

Kageyama, G.H., and Wong-Riley, M.T.T. Histochemical localization of cytochrome oxidase in the hippocampus: Correlation with specific neuronal types and afferent pathways. Neuroscience, 7:2337-2361, 1982.

Karpati, G., and Engel, W.K. Correlative histochemical study of skeletal muscle after suprasegmental denervation, peripheral nerve section and skeletal fixation. Neurology, (N.Y.) 18:681-692, 1968.

Khavari, K.A., and Risner, M.E. Opiate dependence produced by ad libitum drinking of morphine in water, saline, and sucrose vehicles. Psychopharmacologia, 30:291-302, 1973.

Lightman, S., Hunt, S.P., and Iversen, L.L. Effects of opiates and osmotic stimuli on rat neurohypophyseal metabolic activity monitored with [3H]-2-deoxyglucose. Neuroendocrinology, 35:104-110, 1982.

Sokoloff, L., Reivich, M., Kennedy, C., Des Rosiers, M.H., Patlak, C.S., Pettigrew, K.D., Sakurada, O., and Shinohara, M. The (^{14}C)-deoxyglucose method for the measurement of local cerebral glucose utilization: Theory, procedure, and normal values in the conscious and anaesthetized albino rat. J Neurochem, 28:897-916, 1977.

Wong-Riley, M.T.T. Changes in the visual system of monocularly sutured or enucleated cats demonstrable with cytochrome oxidase histochemistry. Brain Res, 171:11-28, 1979.

Wong-Riley, M.T.T., Merzenich, M.M., and Leake, P.A. Changes in endogenous enzymatic reactivity to DAB induced by neuronal inactivity. Brain Res, 141:185-192, 1978.

Wong-Riley, M.T.T., and Welt, C. Histochemical changes in cytochrome oxidase of cortical barrels after vibrissal removal in neonatal and adult mice. Proc Natl Acad Sci USA, 77:2333-2337, 1980.

Wooten, G.F., DiStefano, P., and Collins, R.C. Regional cerebral glucose utilization during morphine withdrawal in the rat. Proc Natl Acad Sci USA, 79:3360-3364, 1982.

Wuster, M., Dirks, B., Krieglstein, J., and Herz, A. The effect of the potent opiate agonist etorphine on local energy metabolism in the isolated perfused rat brain. Neuropharmacology, 20:901-904, 1981.

ACKNOWLEDGMENTS

Studies in the authors' laboratory were supported by USPHS Grant DA 02148 from the National Institute on Drug Abuse. Drs. L. Lichtblau, V. Seybold, A. Takemori, and M. Wessendorf, at the University of Minnesota, provided helpful ideas and advice.

AUTHOR

Robert Elde, Ph.D.
Associate Professor
Department of Anatomy
University of Minnesota Medical School
321 Church Street S.E.
Minneapolis, MN 55455

299

Effects of Opiates and Neuropeptides on Immune Functions

Robert E. Faith, N. P. Plotnikoff, and A. J. Murgo

INTRODUCTION

In recent years there has been an increase in interest in the
effects of drugs and pharmaceuticals on immune function. Indeed a
number of chemicals have been identified and developed because they
possess immunomodulatory properties. This includes both immuno-
stimulants and immunosuppressants. In addition to drugs developed
specifically for their immunomodulatory properties, it has become
clear that a number of chemicals, including environmental pollu-
tants, various anesthetics and analgesics, drugs of abuse, and
hormones, including neuropeptides, can influence immune functions.
In this chapter we will discuss the effects of the opiates and
neuropeptides on immune function.

OPIATE EFFECTS

While the opiates have been abused, or used as recreational drugs
for centuries, very little is known about the possible effects of
these chemicals on immune function, direct or indirect. Most of
what is known was recently reviewed by Sheagren and Tuazon (1977).
It is difficult to investigate the effects of opiates on immune
function in the addict. However, some knowledge has been gained
from studying these individuals. It is recognized clinically that
infectious disease is often a complication of drug abuse. It must
be kept in mind that a number of factors other than direct immuno-
suppression could lead to increased incidence of infections in
opiate addicts. These include nutritional factors, living conditions and contamination of injection paraphernalia. However,
Sheagren and Tuazon (1977) state, "Most authors do agree that the
incidence of infections is increased in most common forms of drug
abuse and that immune alterations probably do exist."

The immune system is composed of nonspecific as well as specific
components. Cellular elements, macrophages and neutrophils, and
serum factors, complement and interferon, participate nonspecifi-
cally in immunity. Several studies have shown these elements of

immunity to be affected by opiates. One study has shown that neutrophil chemotaxis is suppressed by morphine (Stanley et al. 1976) while another has shown that phagocytic and bactericidal functions of neutrophils from patients taking methadone and morphine are normal (Nickerson et al. 1970). Studies in mice have shown that injections of morphine, dilaudid or methadone significantly reduce the ability of these animals to produce interferon in response to induction by either poly I:C or bacterial endotoxin (Hung et al. 1973). Finally, Wetli et al. (1974) have shown that some heroin addicts have elevated complement levels, others have depressed complement levels and the rest are not affected.

Recent studies have presented evidence that lymphocytes possess receptors which bind opiates such as morphine (Wybran et al. 1979) and naloxone (McDonough et al. 1980, Mehrishi and Mills 1983). The presence of these receptors would indicate that the opiates may be able to affect the immune system directly. Indeed there is some evidence to suggest that this is the case. It has been reported that opiate users often have hyperglobulinemia (Sheagren and Tuazon 1977). The IgM levels are most frequently increased, but increases in IgG are also seen. These increases in immunoglobulin levels are most likely a result of either repeated injections of antigenic materials along with the abused drug or the presence of chronic infections which affect many addicts. Opiates have been reported to inhibit specific antibody production in experimental animals. Mice given large doses of morphine or methadone had reduced antibody production when compared to nontreated controls (Lefkowitz and Yang 1974; Gungor et al. 1980).

There is also some evidence that opiates may directly affect T-lymphocytes. Brown et al. (1974) investigated the ability of peripheral blood lymphocytes from heroin addicts to proliferate in response to mitogenic stimulation. They found the responses of cells from heroin addicts to stimulation with phytohemagglutinin (PHA), Concanavalin A (Con A) or pokeweed mitogen (PWM) to be significantly less than the responses of cells from normal volunteers. The proliferative responses of PBL's to mitogenic stimulation tended to return to normal when the study subjects were not taking heroin. McDonough et al. (1980) have shown that opiate addicts have a significant reduction in the number of total T-lymphocytes in circulation as measured by the ability of the lymphocytes to form rosettes with sheep red blood cells (a marker for T-lymphocytes). They also showed an increase in the number of "null" lymphocytes, but there was no significant change in the B lymphocytes or total white blood cell count in opiate addicts. The T cell decrease and "null" cell increase were reversible by naloxone. Similarly, Wybran et al. (1979) have shown that in vitro treatment of peripheral blood lymphocytes from normal human volunteers with morphine significantly reduces their ability to form active rosettes with sheep red blood cells. This effect is completely reversed by naloxone.

One final set of studies must be mentioned when discussing the effects of opiates on host defense mechanisms. These are studies involving the effects of opiates on tumor growth and survival times

of mice implanted with a transplantable neuroblastoma cell line.
Zagon and McLaughlin (1981a, b, 1983) have shown the heroin,
naloxone or naltrexone inhibit tumor growth and prolong survival
times at relatively low doses, while high doses may enhance tumor
growth. These studies are somewhat difficult to interpret because
the neuroblastoma possesses receptors for the opiates, and the
drugs may be exerting their action on the tumor cells rather than
on host defense mechanisms. The opiates may exert their effects on
both the tumor cells and host defense mechanisms, or their action
on the tumor cells may not be a factor in host resistance to this
tumor. Studies with other tumor systems are required to more fully
elucidate the effects of the opiates on the ability of a host to
resist a tumor challenge.

NEUROPEPTIDE EFFECTS (ENKEPHALINS - ENDORPHINS)

Recently several studies have been performed to investigate the
effects of the opioid neuropeptides, endorphins and enkephalins on
immune function. Initially Wybran et al. (1979) produced data
indicating that human lymphocytes possess receptors for methionine-
enkephalin. At the same time Hazum et al. (1979) reported that
cultured human lymphocytes possess specific receptors for beta-
endorphin. Subsequently it has been shown that alpha-, beta- and
gamma-endorphin are capable of suppressing the in vitro antibody-
producing cell response of mouse splenic lymphocytes immunized in
vitro (Johnson et al. 1982). Suppression with beta- and gamma-
endorphin occurred at high concentrations. There have been two
studies reported in which the effects of beta-endorphin on the
proliferative response of lymphocytes to mitogen stimulation were
investigated. McCain et al. (1982) reported that beta-endorphin is
a potent suppressor of PHA-induced T-lymphocyte blastogenesis when
human peripheral blood lymphocytes are exposed early in the course
of mitogenic activation. This suppression was not blocked by
pretreatment with naloxone. In contrast, Gilman et al. (1982) have
reported that beta-endorphin significantly enhances the proliferative response of rat splenic lymphocytes to the T cell mitogens PHA
and Con A. Treatment with naloxone did not reverse the enhancing
effect of the beta-endorphin. The differences observed in these
two studies may be due to one or more of the following:
1) Different concentrations of beta-endorphin were utilized in the
two studies; 2) Rat lymphocytes may respond differently to beta-
endorphin than do human lymphocytes; or 3) Lymphocytes in spleen
contain somewhat different subpopulations than those found in
peripheral blood, which may result in a different effect observed
following treatment with beta-endorphin. Based on results obtained
with the enkephalins in our laboratory, the first possibility
listed may be the most likely. We have observed that varying
concentrations of enkephalins exert a biphasic effect on lymphocyte
function with some concentrations exerting stimulatory effects
while other concentrations are suppressive. The final reported
study on the effects of beta-endorphin on immune functions is that
of Mathews et al. (1983). This study reports that beta-endorphin
significantly enhances natural cytotoxicity exhibited by natural
killer (NK) cells in peripheral blood lymphocytes of normal human
volunteers. In these studies lymphocytes were isolated from the

peripheral blood of normal volunteers and incubated with beta-
endorphin. This treatment resulted in enhanced NK cell activity as
measured in a cytotoxicity assay. This enhancement appears to
result from an increase in the numbers of NK cells and increased
cytotoxic efficiency of the NK cells. This enhancement of NK
activity was reversible with naloxone treatment.

TABLE 1. Effect of enkephalins on thymus
and spleen weights in mice[a]

Enkephalin dosage (mg/kg)	Thymus wt. (mg±SE)	Spleen wt. (mg±SE)
Methionine-enkephalin		
0	68.6±3.6	101.8±3.1
10	78.1±2.9 (p=0.05)[b]	68.3±2.2 (p<0.001)[b]
30	79.1±4.5 (p<0.1)[b]	69.8±1.7 (p<0.001)[b]
Leucine-enkephalin		
0	56.1±0.9	115.2±6.1
10	49.3±2.8 (p<0.05)[b]	98.0±4.0 (p<0.05)[b]
30	63.0±1.7 (p<0.005)[b]	71.3±1.9 (p<0.001)[b]

a. Mice were injected daily for 1 week with varying dilutions of methionine-enkephalin or leucine-enkephalin.
b. Statistical difference from control; N.S. = no significant difference (p>0.1).

The effects of the enkephalins on immune functions have been
studied more extensively than beta-endorphin. It is becoming quite
clear that the enkephalins have the ability to modulate a number of
immune functions. Studies in our laboratory have shown that daily
injection of mice for 1 week with either methionine- or leucine-
enkephalin results in significant changes in lymphoid organs
(table 1). This treatment resulted in significant increases in
thymus size and significant decreases in spleen size. Further

303

studies are required to completely explain the mechanism(s) of these lymphoid organ weight changes.

The finding that lymphocytes possess receptors for enkephalins (Wybran et al. 1979) prompted us to investigate the potential effects of the enkephalins on various immune functions. Wybran et al. (1979) reported that lymphocytes not only possess receptors for enkephalins but also were influenced by enkephalins. Their studies showed that peripheral blood lymphocytes from normal human volunteers were enhanced in their ability to form rosettes with sheep red blood cells (SRBC) following treatment with methionine-enkephalin. This enhancement could be inhibited by naloxone. Studies in our laboratory confirmed these findings and were expanded to include a population of immunosuppressed individuals (Miller et al. 1983). Peripheral blood lymphocytes from a group of lymphoma patients were used to investigate the effects of methionine- and leucine-enkephalin on the ability of lymphocytes from immunosuppressed individuals to form rosettes with SRBCs. It was found that both enkephalins significantly enhance the ability of these cells to form active T cell rosettes (table 2). Methionine-enkephalin was active over a wide range of concentrations (10^{-2} to 10^{-14} mg/ml) while leucine-enkephalin was only active at one low concentration (10^{-14} mg/ml).

TABLE 2. Effect of methionine- and leucine-enkephalin on the percentages of active T-cell rosettes formed by peripheral blood lymphocytes from lymphoma patients

Enkephalin concentration (mg/ml)	Methionine-enkephalin	Leucine-enkephalin
10^{-2}	27.6±5.3	32.0±4.1
10^{-6}	46.6±4.2*	41.1±5.6
10^{-10}	46.8±3.0*	40.3±5.7
10^{-14}	48.5±5.6*	52.7±2.8*

* = significant difference from untreated samples, p<0.05.

Clin. Immun. Immunopath. 26, 446-51, Copyright (1983). Academic Press

In order to gain some insight into the possible effect of enkephalin treatment on host defense mechanisms the following study was undertaken (Plotnikoff and Miller 1983). BDF$_1$ mice were inoculated intraperitoneally with either 10^2 or 10^4 L1210 tumor cells. Following tumor challenge the animals were injected daily with saline vehicle, methionine-enkephalin or leucine-enkephalin. The animals were observed daily following tumor challenge and deaths recorded

on the day of occurrence. Table 3 illustrates results obtained in
mice challenged with 10^4 tumor cells and treated with 30 mg/kg
daily of either enkephalin. Methionine-enkephalin provide ' significant protection from tumor challenge. Similar results were obtained in mice challenged with 10^2 tumor cells and treated with
10 mg/kg daily leucine-enkephalin.

TABLE 3. Effect of enkephalins on
survival of mice challenged
with L1210 tumor cells

Day of study	Treatment group[a]		
	Non-treated	Methionine-enkephalin	Leucine-enkephalin
13	$7/25^c$	5/30	3/30
14[b]	10/25	7/30	5/30
15	16/25	8/30	12/30
16	20/25	12/30	17/30
17	21/25	15/30	22/30
18	21/25	18/30	22/30
19	21/25	18/30	26/30
20	22/25	19/30	26/30
21	22/25	19/30*	26/30

a. BDF_1 mice were inoculated with 10^4 L1210 tumor cells ip.
     Follcwing tumor challenge the animals were injected daily
     with saline vehicle, 30 mg/kg methionine-enkephalin or
     30 mg/kg leucine-enkephalin. Deaths were recorded on the
     day of occurrence.
b.   The approximate median time to death is underlined for
     each group.
c.   The data is reported as the number of dead over the total
*   number of animals in the group.
     Indicates a significant difference ($p<0.05$) between
     treated and nontreated animals.

Int. J. Immunopharm., 5, 5, 437-441, 1983. Copyright (1983).
Pergamon Press Ltd.

The effect of enkephalins on in vitro lymphocyte proliferative
responses has been studied in our laboratory and in the laboratory
of Gilman et al. In our laboratory, using mouse splenic lymphocytes and varying dilutions of either methionine-enkephalin or

leucine-enkephalin, the response to varying dilutions of PHA was
investigated. Both enkephalins were found to significantly enhance
the blastogenic response of lymphocytes to PHA (Plotnikoff and
Miller 1983). Results obtained with PHA at a dilution of 1:100 are
illustrated in table 4. Similar results were obtained with other
dilutions of PHA. Methionine-enkephalin tended to enhance the
response over a broader range of dilutions than did leucine-enkephalin, while the leucine-enkephalin was active at lower concentrations than the methionine-enkephalin. These results are in
contrast to those obtained by Gilman et al. (1982) who reported no
stimulation of the blastogenic response of rat splenic lymphocytes
to stimulation with Con A following treatment of the lymphocytes
with enkephalin.

TABLE 4. Effect of enkephalins
on lymphocyte blastogenesis[a]

Enkephalin concentration (mg/ml)	Methionine-enkephalin	Leucine-enkephalin
0	1458 ± 90[b]	1458 ± 90
1	4393 ± 664[*]	1114 ± 310
10^{-1}	5258 ± 990[*]	1516 ± 207
10^{-2}	3144 ± 500[*]	1650 ± 180
10^{-4}	2123 ± 228[*]	1918 ± 293
10^{-6}	2357 ± 155[*]	2425 ± 323[*]
10^{-8}	1884 ± 188[*]	2759 ± 387[*]
10^{-10}	1538 ± 170	2065 ± 360[*]

a. Murine splenic lymphocytes were treated in vitro
    with various concentrations of either methionine- or
    leucine-enkephalin and then assayed for lymphocyte
    transformation in response to PHA stimulation.
b. Stimulation was measured by incorporation of ^{3}H-
    thymidine into acid insoluble material. The data is
    presented as mean cpm± SE.
*   Indicates significant enhancement of transformation
    in enkephalin treated cells as compared to non-
    treated cells ($p<0.05$).

Int. J. Immunopharm. 5, 5, 437-441, 1983. Copyright
(1983). Pergamon Press Ltd.

Johnson et al. (1982) have studied the effect of the enkephalins on
the in vitro antibody response. Murine splenic lymphocytes were

cultured in the presence of sheep red blood cells and varying dilutions of either methionine- or leucine-enkephalin. After 5 days of culture the number of specific antibody-forming cells was enumerated in each culture. Both enkephalins were found to cause suppression of the antibody response.

Recently studies have been undertaken in our laboratory to investigate the effects of the enkephalins on natural killer cell activity. Initially isolated peripheral blood lymphocytes from normal human volunteers were utilized in these studies. These cells were incubated for 1 hour with varying concentrations of either methionine- or leucine-enkephalin. Following incubation the cells were washed and then used in NK cell assays. Table 5 illustrates data obtained in these studies. Both enkephalins have the ability to significantly enhance natural killer activity over a range of concentrations. Leucine-enkephalin appears to be more active in this enhancement than is methionine-enkephalin. We are presently performing similar studies with peripheral blood lymphocytes from a variety of cancer patients. Our results to date indicated the enkephalins are capable of enhancing NK activity in cancer patients as well as normal volunteers.

TABLE 5. Effect of enkephalins on natural killer cell activity[a]

Enkephalin concentration[b] (mg/ml)	Mean difference of enkephalin-treated cells vs. nontreated cells	
	Methionine-enkephalin	Leucine-enkephalin
10^{-4}	1.41 ± 3.19(NS)[c]	10.00 ± 4.75($p<0.05$)
10^{-6}	6.41 ± 3.41($p<0.05$)	11.29 ± 6.06($p<0.05$)
10^{-8}	5.35 ± 3.74($p<0.05$)	12.44 ± 5.99($p<0.05$)
10^{-10}	6.56 ± 4.53($p<0.05$)	11.20 ± 6.16($p<0.05$)
10^{-14}	2.55 ± 3.19(NS)	8.72 ± 6.26($p<0.05$)

a. NK assays were performed at an effector to target cell ratio of 11:1.
b. Effector cells were incubated in the presence of the indicated concentration of enkephalin for 1 hour, washed 3 times and used in NK assays.
c. Significance of difference from control value. NS indicates not significant.

CONCLUSIONS

While there are still many questions to be answered, it is now clear that opiates and the natural opioid neuropeptides can influence immune function. We feel that part of the normal function of the enkephalins and endorphins is to participate in immune regulatory pathways. Many more studies are required to fully define the role that these neuropeptides play in immune regulations. Studies with lymphocytes from normal human volunteers as well as cancer patients suggest that methionine-enkephalin is more active than leucine-enkephalin in enhancing active T-cell rosettes (Miller et al. 1983). In addition, the two enkephalins exhibit potency differences in mouse splenic lymphocyte blastogenesis induced by PHA. Leucine-enkephalin was active at low concentrations and inactive at higher levels (Plotnikoff and Miller 1983).

These apparent differences in activity or potency of the enkephalins may indeed represent major differences in affinities for cellular receptors. Thus, Vaught and Takemori (1979) reported that leucine-enkephalin, but not methionine-enkephalin, potentiated effects of morphine. Different subpopulations of receptors for morphine, enkephalins and endorphins have now been established (Bloom 1983). These various receptors are only partially antagonized by naloxone. The difference in receptors for morphine, which has been reported to be immunosuppressive, and the enkephalins supports the concept that natural enkephalins may have separate and/or complementary functions in the immune system.

We are proposing that the enkephalins play a role in a central nervous system-endocrine-immune interrelationship in which dysfunctions in the immune system may be related to chronic stress and be accompanied by perturbations in enkephalin levels in the adrenals, the primary source of enkephalins in peripheral circulation (Viveros et al. 1980; Hanbauer et al. 1982; Dumont et al. 1983). Large amounts of enkephalins, catecholamines and steroids are secreted simultaneously from the adrenals during stress (Amin et al. 1980). It is well known that the central nervous system and behavior can influence immune function (Stein et al. 1976; Ader 1981; Brooks et al. 1982; Renoux et al. 1983). Recently behavioral states have been shown to influence cerebral spinal fluid levels of endorphins (Pickar et al. 1981), and exercise has been shown to increase plasma levels of endorphins (Carr et al. 1981; Farrell et al. 1982). Exercise has also been shown to enhance human NK activity (Targan et al. 1981). Due to these facts and the effects of enkephalins referred to above, we feel that the enkephalins, influenced by a number of factors, may play a central role in natural immunomodulation.

REFERENCES

Ader, R., ed. Psychoneuroimmunology. New York: Academic Press, 1981.
Amin, S., Brown, Z.W., and Amit, Z. The role of endorphins in stress: Evidence and speculation. Neurosci Biobehav Rev 4:77-86, 1980.
Bloom, F.E. The endorphins: A growing family of pharmacologically pertinent peptides. Ann Rev Pharmacol Toxicol 23:151-170, 1983.
Brooks, W.H., Cross, R.J., Roszman, T.L., and Markesbery, W.R. Neuroimmunomodulation: Neural anatomical basis for impairment and facilitation. Ann Neurol 12(1):56-61, 1982.

Brown, S.M., Stimmel, B., Taub, R.N., Kochwa, S., and Rosenfield, R.E. Immunologic dysfunction in heroin addicts. Arch Intern Med 134(6):1001-1006, 1974.

Carr, D.B., Bullen, B.A., Skrinar, G.S., Arnold, M.A., Rosenblatt, M., Beitins, I.Z., Martin, J.B., and McArthur, J.W. Physical conditioning facilitates the exercise-induced secretion of beta-endorphin and beta-lipotropin in women. N Engl J Med 305(10):560-563, 1981.

Dumont, M., Day, R., and Lemaire, S. Distinct distribution of immunoreactive dynorphin and leucine enkephalin in various populations of isolated adrenal cromaffin cells. Life Sci 32(3):287-294, 1983.

Farrell, P.A., Gates, W.K., Maksud, M.G., and Morgan, W.P. Increases in plasma β-endorphin/β-lipotropin immunoreactivity after treadmill running in humans. J Appl Physiol 52(5):1245-1249, 1982.

Gilman, S.C., Schwartz, J.M., Milner, R.J., Bloom, F.E., and Feldman, J.D. β-endorphin enhances lymphocyte proliferative responses. Proc Natl Acad Sci 79(13):4226-4230, 1982.

Gungor, M., Genc, E., Sagduyu, H., Eroglu, L., and Koyuncuoglu, H. Effect of chronic administration of morphine on primary immune response in mice. Experientia 36(11):1309-1310, 1980.

Hanbauer, I., Kelly, G.D., Saiani, L., and Yang, H.Y.T. [met^5]-enkephalin-like peptides of the adrenal medulla: Release by nerve stimulation and functional implications. Peptides 3: 469-473, 1982.

Hazum, E., Chang, K.J., and Cuatrecasas, P. Specific nonopiate receptors for beta-endorphin. Science 205(4410):1033-1035, 1979.

Hung, C.Y., Lefkowitz, S.S., and Geber, W.F. Interferon inhibition by narcotic analgesics. Proc Soc exp Biol Med 142:106-111, 1973.

Johnson, H.M., Smith, E.M., Torres, B.A., and Blalock, J.E. Regulation of the in vitro antibody response by neuroendocrine hormones. Proc Natl Acad Sci 79(13):4171-4174, 1982.

Lefkowitz, S.S., and Yang, C. Effects of highly abused drugs on antibody production (abstract). J Reticuloendothel Soc 16:25, 1974.

Mathews, P.M., Froelich, C.J., Sibbitt, W.L., Jr., and Bankhurst, A.D. Enhancement of natural cytotoxicity by β-endorphin. J Immunol 130(4):1658-1662, 1983.

McCain, H.W., Lamster, I.B., Bozzone, J.M., and Gabic, J.T. β-endorphin modulates human immune activity via non-opiate receptor mechanisms. Life Sci 31(15):1619-1624, 1982.

McDonough, R.J., Madden, J.J., Falek, A., Shafer, D.A., Pline, M., Gordon, D., Bokos, P., Kuehnle, J.C., and Mendelson, J. Alteration of T and null lymphocyte frequencies in the peripheral blood of human opiate addicts: In vivo evidence for opiate receptor sites on T lymphocytes. J Immunol 125(6):2539-2543, 1980.

Mehrishi, J.N., and Mills, I.H. Opiate receptors on lymphocytes and platelets in man. Clin Immunol Immunopathol 27(2):240-249, 1983.

Miller, G.C., Murgo, A.J., and Plotnikoff, N.P. Enkephalins - enhancement of active T-cell rosettes from lymphoma patients. Clin Immunol Immunopathol 26(3):446-451, 1983.

Nickerson, D.S., Williams, R.C., Boxmeyer, M., and Quie, P.G.
Increased opsonic capacity of serum in chronic heroin addiction.
Ann Intern Med 72:671-677, 1970.

Pickar, D., Naber, D., Post, R.M., van Kammen, D.P., Bellenger, J.,
Kalin, N., and Bunney, W.E., Jr. Measurement of endorphins in
CFS. Relationship to psychiatric diagnosis. Mod Probl Pharmaco-
psychiatry 17:246-262, 1981.

Plotnikoff, N.P., and Miller, G.C. Enkephalins as immunomodulators.
Int J Immunopharm, 5, 5, 437-441, 1983.

Renoux, G., Biziere, K., Renoux, M., and Guillaumin, J.M. The
production of T-cell-inducing factors in mice is controlled by
the brain neocortex. Scand J Immunol 17:45-50, 1983.

Sheagren, J.N., and Tuazon, C.U. Immunological aspects. In:
Pradhan, S.N., Dutta, S.N., eds. Drug Abuse. Clinical and Basic
Aspects. St. Louis: C.V. Mosby Co., 1977. pp. 321-331.

Stanley, T.H., Hill, G.E., Portas, M.R., Hogan, N.A., and Hill,
H.R. Neutrophil chemotaxis during and after general anesthesia
and operation. Anest Anal 55(5):668-672, 1976.

Stein, M., Schiavi, R.C., Camerino, M. Influence of brain and
behavior on the immune system. Science 191(4226):435-440, 1976.

Targan, S., Britvan, L., and Dorey, F. Activation of human NKCC by
moderate exercise: increased frequency of NK cells with enhanced
capability of effector-target lytic interactions. Clin Exp
Immunol 45(2):352-360, 1981.

Vaught, J.L., and Takemori, A.E. A further characterization of the
differential effects of leucine enkephalin, methionine enkephalin
and their analogs on morphine-induced analgesia. J Pharmacol Exp
Therapeut 211(2):280-283, 1979.

Viveros, O.H., Diliberto, E.J., Jr., Hazum, E., and Chang, K.J.
Enkephalins as possible adrenomedullary hormones: Storage,
secretion, and regulation of synthesis. In: Costa, E., and
Trabucchi, M., eds. Neural Peptides and Neuronal Communication.
New York, Raven Press, 1980. pp. 191-204.

Wetli, C.V., Noto, T.A., and Fernandez, C.A. Immunologic abnormalities in heroin addiction. South Med J 67:193-197, 1974.

Wybran, J., Appleboom, T., Famaey, J.P., and Govaerts, A. Suggestive evidence for receptors for morphine and methionine-enkephalin
on normal blood T lymphocytes. J Immunol 123(3): 1068-1070,
1979.

Zagon, I.S., and McLaughlin, P.J. Heroin prolongs survival time
and retards tumor growth in mice with neuroblastoma. Brain Res
Bull 7(1):25-32, 1981a.

Zagon, I.S., and McLaughlin, P.J. Naloxone prolongs the survival
time of mice treated with neuroblastoma. Life Sci 28(10):1095-
1102, 1981b.

Zagon, I.S., and McLaughlin, P.J. Naltrexone modulates tumor
response in mice with neuroblastoma. Science 221(4611):671-673,
1983.

AUTHORS

Robert E. Faith, D.V.M., Ph.D.
Director, Biomedical Research Center
Oral Roberts University
7777 South Lewis
Tulsa, Oklahoma 74171

Nicholas P. Plotnikoff, Ph.D.
Department of Pharmacology
School of Medicine
Oral Roberts University
7777 South Lewis
Tulsa, Oklahoma 74171

Anthony J. Murgo, M.D.
Section of Hematology/Oncology
Department of Medicine
University of West Virginia
Morgantown, West Virginia 26506

Changes in CNS Sensitivity to Cannabinoids with Repeated Treatment: Tolerance and Auxoesthesia

R. Karler, L.D. Calder, and S.A. Turkanis

INTRODUCTION

Repeated or chronic treatment with drugs can result in pharmacodynamic changes, which classically manifest themselves in decreases in drug sensitivity or tolerance. There are, however, reports that, in some instances, repeated treatment results not in tolerance but in the quantitatively opposite effect, that is, an increase in drug sensitivity or auxoesthesia*. Although this seemingly paradoxical response to repeated treatment was first described over fifty years ago for cocaine (Tatum and Seevers 1929), the phenomenon was not investigated until it was recently rediscovered (Post and Kopanda 1975). Now it is of particular significance to drug-abuse research because, in addition to cocaine, other drugs in repeated doses have been found to cause auxoesthesia; these include amphetamine (Segal and Mandell 1974), PCP (Smith et al. 1981), alcohol (Pinel and Van Oot 1976) and morphine (Shuster et al. 1975). This kind of change in pharmacodynamics presents an entirely new dimension to our understanding of the chronic effects of these drugs. With respect to the cannabinoids, the reported effects of repeated treatment range from tolerance to auxoesthesia (Fried 1977). Although what determines the direction of the change in drug responsiveness has not been elucidated, it

---

*Any descriptive consideration of a change in an effect which is quantitatively the opposite of tolerance suffers at the outset from the lack of a word to refer to the phenomenon. "Reverse tolerance" has been used, but it is at once inadequate and misleading. Other words that are sometimes used include sensitization, hypersensitivity and supersensitivity. None of these is appropriate because each already has a restricted meaning in pharmacology: Sensitization and hypersensitivity classically refer to allergic phenomena; while supersensitivity is the enhanced responsiveness of an effector system following denervation. In the absence of an appropriate existing word, we offer "auxoesthesia," which is both pristine and novel, as well as etymologically apposite. We are indebted to Dr. B.Z. Karler for coining the term.

is clear that any interpretation of the available data is compli-
cated by species differences, dosage and treatment differences,
and, possibly most important, differences in drug effects, which
include functional as well as behavioral effects. The data described below were derived from experiments designed to minimize
some of these variables, specifically by using only one species
treated daily with a constant dose of drug. Under these conditions, several different effects on CNS excitability were measured
simultaneously in order to compare the quantitative character of
changes in drug responsiveness with repeated treatment.

REPEATED CANNABINOID TREATMENT AND CHANGES IN PHARMACODYNAMICS IN
CONVULSIVE THRESHOLD TESTS

In figures 1, 2 and 3 are data obtained from mice that were
treated daily for 22 days with an anticonvulsant dose 50
determined in a maximal electroshock test (Karler et al. 1974).

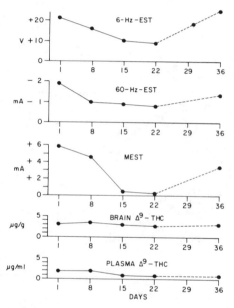

FIGURE 1. *Repeated THC treatment: ESTs and brain- and plasma-drug
concentrations. In each test 60 mice given 100 mg/kg THC (i.p.),
another 60, vehicle; median effective currents or voltage determined at peak drug effect time.* ● = *differences in EST between
drug and vehicle groups.* —— = *period of daily treatments.*
--- = *period of withdrawal. Brain and plasma values come from
6—8 mice (Karler et al. 1982).* © 1982, *Springer-Verlag.*

The activities of the drugs were assessed in three different electroconvulsive threshold tests at weekly intervals. In this study,
the effects of delta-9-tetrahydrocannabinol (THC) were compared
with those of cannabidiol (CBD), another major constituent of

313

marijuana. Both drugs have previously been extensively investigated for their acute anticonvulsant properties (Karler et al. 1974; Turkanis et al. 1974). Phenytoin (PHT) was included as a standard anticonvulsant drug in these tests. The results from the THC study are shown in figure 1. As can be seen, THC acutely (day 1) raises both the 6-Hz (6-Hz-EST) and maximal electroshock thresholds (MEST); but the identical dose decreases the threshold for convulsions in the 60-Hz-electroshock threshold (60-Hz-EST) test. With repeated treatment, however, tolerance developed to all three effects. Similar results were obtained for another proconvulsant effect not shown in figure 1; that is, THC acutely can lower the minimal seizure threshold to pentylenetetrazol (PTZ) and, here again, tolerance develops to that effect. In summary, in two seizure tests in which THC is anticonvulsant and in two tests in which it is proconvulsant, tolerance develops. That the tolerance is cellular in nature rather than metabolic is evidenced by the brain concentrations of THC which remained unchanged at the test times throughout the experiment.

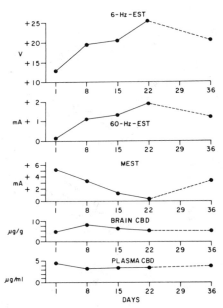

FIGURE 2. *Repeated CBD treatment (120 mg/kg): ESTs and brain- and plasma-drug concentrations. On day 1 only 6-Hz-EST and MEST vehicle-control values were significantly different from CBD-treated groups. See figure 1 for details.* © *1982, Springer-Verlag.*

The data shown in figure 2 are the results of an experimental design identical to that used to generate the data in figure 1, except that CBD rather than THC was administered daily. There are some striking differences in the results. First, acutely (on day 1), CBD has no apparent activity on the 60-Hz-EST, although, like THC, it raises the thresholds on both the 6-Hz-EST and the MEST.

314

In the 6-Hz-EST, however, daily treatment resulted in a progressive increase rather than the decrease in activity found in the THC study. In contrast, tolerance developed on the MEST as it did for THC. Although there was no CBD effect initially on the 60-Hz-EST, after one week, activity was evident, and thereafter appeared to increase progressively. Again, as in the case of THC, the changes in the activity of CBD were independent of any changes in brain-drug concentration, which remained relatively constant at the various test times.

The data from the CBD experiment clearly illustrate that the cannabinoids have the potential of producing auxoesthesia, as well as tolerance, with repeated treatment. The development of tolerance in one of the tests of CNS excitability demonstrates that under identical conditions quantitatively opposite changes in drug sensitivity can occur simultaneously. These data emphasize the necessity of identifying the specific effect when repeated treatment results in a pharmacodynamic change. A priori, there is no reason to assume, for example, that, if tolerance develops to one effect, tolerance will generalize to other effects (except in the case of a metabolic type of tolerance); therefore, to state simply that tolerance develops to a drug may be an inappropriate description of the consequences of repeated treatment on some effects.

The CBD results also raise a point in relation to the general characteristics of effects to which increased vs. decreased responsiveness develops with repeated treatment. Tolerance has generally been associated with depressant effects, such as the depressant effects of the opiates, the barbiturates and alcohol. A simplistic explanation of tolerance to a CNS depressant effect is that the nervous system compensates for the effect, thereby diminishing drug potency. The withdrawal hyperexcitation associated with CNS depressant drugs can be construed to support the concept that these agents elicit compensatory excitatory responses. On the other hand, auxoesthesia has generally been observed with excitatory effects; for example, the production of seizures by subconvulsant doses of convulsant drugs such as PTZ (Mason and Cooper 1972), and the increase in motor stimulant activity of morphine, cocaine and amphetamine (Shuster et al. 1975; Shuster et al. 1977; Segal and Mandell 1974). Because many drugs, like the cannabinoids, produce both depressant and excitatory effects, the influence of repeated treatment on a specific effect may depend upon whether the effect is excitatory or depressant. With respect to the cannabinoids, Fried (1977) surveyed the literature and concluded that tolerance developed to THC's depressant effects and an increase in sensitivity developed to its excitatory effects. The threshold data described above for THC, however, do not fit this pattern, because tolerance developed to both anticonvulsant and proconvulsant effects. Furthermore, the hypothesis is not supported by the CBD data which illustrate that increases in drug sensitivity can develop to anticonvulsant or depressant effects. The notion that chronic treatment results in opposite quantitative responses to depressant and excitatory effects does not appear to be valid, at least not for the cannabinoids.

315

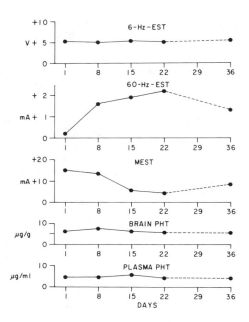

FIGURE 3. Repeated PHT treatment (7 mg/kg): ESTs and brain- and plasma-drug concentrations. On day 1 only 6-Hz-EST and MEST vehicle-control values were significantly different from PHT-treated groups. See figure 1 for details. © 1982, Springer-Verlag.

The data shown in figure 3 represent the results obtained for PHT under conditions identical to those in the experiments of figures 1 and 2. The PHT results differ from those of THC and CBD in that there is no change in the drug's activity in 6-Hz-EST. Like CBD, there is an increase in activity in the 60-Hz-EST and, like THC and CBD, tolerance developed in the MEST test. As in the THC and CBD experiments, the PHT results were independent of any change in brain-drug concentration.

The PHT data illustrate that all three possibilities resulting from repeated treatment can occur simultaneously; that is, tolerance, no change in activity and auxoesthesia. Here again, the results emphasize the hazard of generalizing from one chronic effect of a drug to other chronic effects. In addition, the enhanced anticonvulsant efficacy of PHT in one test reinforces the CBD observation that an increase in drug activity can occur in response to a depressant effect, or that such reactions are not necessarily the domain of excitatory phenomena.

The PHT data also raise the question: How common is the development of auxoesthesia with chronic drug treatment? Although PHT has been investigated extensively for about fifty years, the failure of others to observe this phenomenon earlier is

316

noteworthy. This failure probably relates to the almost complete absence of chronic studies with PHT, even though clinically the drug is used chronically. Studies of the influence of chronic treatment on the pharmacodynamics of many drugs are lacking, and the PHT data suggest that enhanced drug responsiveness with repeated treatment may be a more widespread phenomenon than hitherto recognized.

INTERACTION OF THC ON KINDLING REACTIONS

We have approached the study of auxoesthesia with the use of kindling as a potential model for this type of reaction. The term kindling was first introduced by Goddard et al. (1969), who observed that repeated electrical stimulation of the brain with a subconvulsant stimulus could ultimately elicit convulsions. In other words, the sensitivity of the nervous system to the stimulus increased with repeated application of the stimulus. Subsequently, chemical kindling to convulsions was demonstrated with the daily administration of subconvulsant doses of such drugs as PTZ (Mason and Cooper 1972). Conceivably, the development of increased responsivity to a drug or stimulus could be affected by drug interactions. Starting with this hypothesis, we tested the influence of THC treatment on electrical and chemical kindling to convulsions.

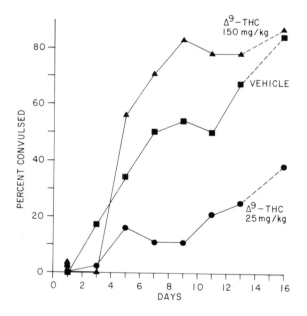

FIGURE 4. THC effects on electrical kindling to minimal convulsions. 3 Groups of 25 mice were given THC or vehicle (i.p.) every other day for 13 days; at peak brain concentration (2 hr), corneal electroshock-kindling stimulus (2 sec, 3.5 mA, 60 Hz) was given. After day 13, drug withdrawn; on day 16, electroshock only.

317

The results in figure 4 represent the interaction of THC with electrical kindling. Here we see that high doses enhance the development of convulsions, whereas low doses retard the phenomenon. The persistence of the drug-caused enhancement of kindling after cannabinoid withdrawal suggests that the interaction is a true effect on the kindling process as opposed to a readily reversible effect on the convulsive activity of the electrical stimulus. The complexity of the THC interaction with electrical stimulation is illustrated by the opposite low- and high-dose effects of the drug on the development of seizures.

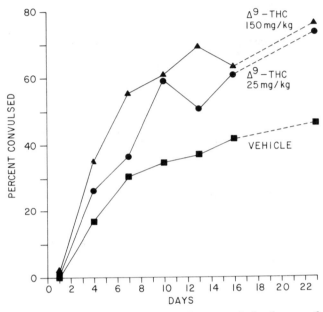

FIGURE 5. *THC effects on PTZ kindling to minimal convulsions. 3 Groups of 25 mice were given THC or vehicle (i.p.) every 3rd day for 16 days; at peak brain concentration (2 hr), PTZ kindling stimulus (40 mg/kg, s.c.) was given. After day 16, drug withdrawn; on day 23, kindling stimulus only.*

The ability of THC to enhance kindling to chemical stimuli is shown in figures 5 and 6. Figure 5 shows that THC augments the development of convulsions to PTZ and, like the results from the electrical experiment, the enhancement persisted after cannabinoid withdrawal. Figure 6 depicts the influence of THC on kindling by picrotoxin. In this instance, the interaction appears to be fundamentally different from that observed in the electrical and PTZ studies because, after cannabinoid withdrawal, there was no persistence of the convulsions associated with the THC treatment. The rapidly reversible nature of the interaction argues against a true effect on kindling, which is known to be be a long-lived phenomenon (Racine 1978; Sangdee et al. 1982).

The diversity of results from the study of THC's interactions with the various kindling stimuli illustrates that the drug-caused increase in sensitivity to convulsions appears to be a relatively selective, rather than a generalized, effect. This conclusion is based on the failure of THC to promote kindling to picrotoxin.

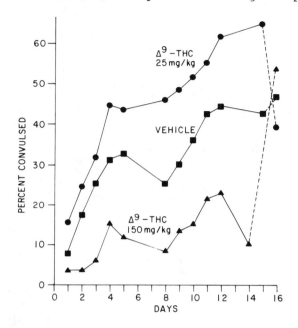

FIGURE 6. THC effects on picrotoxin kindling to minimal convulsions. 3 Groups of 25 mice were given THC or vehicle (i.p.) once daily, 5 days/week for 2 weeks; at peak brain concentration (2 hr), picrotoxin-kindling stimulus (1 mg/kg, s.c.) was given. After day 14, drug withdrawn; on day 16, kindling stimulus only.

Supporting evidence for the selectivity in the drug interaction was observed in other experiments in which we demonstrated that subconvulsant doses of PTZ do not affect the development of convulsions to an electrical stimulus (unpublished data). This failure of PTZ was surprising because it is a convulsant drug, which suggests that the mechanism of PTZ kindling is different from that of electrical kindling. This conclusion is further strengthened by our observation that animals electrically kindled to minimal convulsions do not show cross-sensitivity to PTZ-induced minimal convulsions (unpublished data).

If kindling represents a valid model for the study of auxoesthetic reactions in general, then the present data suggest that THC may augment the development of the phenomenon to some drugs but not to others. The ability of THC to enhance these reactions represents a toxic potential of the drug that has not yet been investigated.

CONCLUSIONS

Classically, repeated exposure to drugs has been viewed pharmaco-dynamically in terms of only two alternatives, either tolerance or no change in sensitivity. The data presented above, however, serve to reinforce the evidence that suggests that the consequences of repeated drug exposure may also include auxoesthesia or an increase in sensitivity. The frequency of the occurrence of auxoesthesia in pharmacology is not known. To date many such reported phenomena have involved drugs of abuse, such as amphetamine (Segal and Mandell 1974), cocaine (Shuster et al. 1977), morphine (Shuster et al. 1975), PCP (Smith et al. 1981) and alcohol (Pinel and Van Oot 1976). In general, the observed effect is an increase in locomotor activity with repeated drug exposure; the extent to which other effects are involved is also unknown. In addition, the significance of auxoesthesia to the pharmacology of drugs of abuse is not clear, but some ideas have been proposed (Post et al. 1976). Our ignorance, in part, reflects the paucity of information available on the phenomenon; nevertheless, because auxoesthesia has been described for a number of drugs of abuse, it should be considered in our attempts to understand the pharmacology of these substances.

There are many questions about auxoesthesia that should be addressed. To wit: What is the relationship of this response to dose and to the frequency and duration of exposure? How persistent and how generalized are these adaptations of the CNS? Can concomitant drug exposure influence the development of auxoesthesia? Is there a relationship between the development of tolerance and auxoesthesia? These are but a few of the questions that need to be answered in order to appreciate the significance of this phenomenon.

The data here presented on the cannabinoids represent only a beginning of the description of the characteristics of auxoesthesia as related to these drugs. Specifically, within the context of the limited number of drugs and effects observed, both tolerance and auxoesthesia can develop and these can exist simultaneously. The data indicate that to describe properly the influence of chronic treatment on the pharmacodynamics of the cannabinoids, both the specific drug and the effect must be identified. The changes, for example, do not generalize either to all cannabinoids or to all effects. Finally, THC's enhancement of kindling reactions raises the possibility that the use of marijuana may adversely interact with some environmental or pathological or pharmacological factors to result in the very long-lasting changes in CNS excitability characteristic of kindling (Racine 1978; Sangdee et al. 1982). To illustrate, the development of some types of human epilepsy, especially the posttraumatic type, appear to be kindling-like, which raises the possibility that marijuana use in such individuals may increase their liability for epilepsy. The THC potential to interact with other drugs is supported by the observation that the cannabinoid enhances PTZ kindling; in addition, others have reported that THC can also augment the motor-stimulant activity of amphetamine (Garriott et al. 1967) and of morphine (Ayhan et al. 1979). Such drug interactions deserve further investigation, especially among the drugs of abuse because many of them have been reported to produce auxoesthesia and many of them are used concomitantly.

REFERENCES

Ayhan, I.H., Kaymakcalan, S., and Tulunay, F.C. Interaction between delta-9-tetrahydrocannabinol and morphine and the motor activity of mice. Psychopharmacol, 63:169-172, 1979.

Fried, P.A. Behavioral and electroencephalographic correlates of the chronic use of marijuana--A review. Behav Biol, 21:163-196, 1977.

Garriott, J.C., King, L.J., Forney, R.B., and Hughes, F.W. Effects of some tetrahydrocannabinols on hexobarbital sleeping time and amphetamine induced hyperactivitiy in mice. Life Sci, 6:2119-2128, 1967.

Goddard, G.V., McIntyre, D.C., and Leech, C.K. A permanent change in brain function resulting from daily electrical stimulation. Exp Neurol, 25:295-330, 1969.

Karler, R., Cely, W., and Turkanis, S.A. Anticonvulsant properties of delta-9-tetrahydrocannabinol and other cannabinoids. Life Sci, 15:931-947, 1974.

Karler, R., Borys, H.K., and Turkanis, S.A. Influence of 22-day treatment on the anticonvulsant properties of cannabinoids. Naunyn-Schmiedebergs Arch Pharmacol, 320:105-109, 1982.

Mason, C.R., and Cooper, R.M. A permanent change in convulsive threshold in normal and brain-damaged rats with repeated small doses of pentylenetetrazol. Epilepsia, 13:663-674, 1972.

Pinel, J.P.J., and Van Oot, P.H. Generality of the kindling phenomenon: Some clinical implications. In: Wada, J.A., ed. Kindling. New York: Raven Press, 1976. pp. 151-171

Post, R.M., and Kopanda, R.T. Cocaine, kindling, and reverse tolerance. Lancet, 1:409-410, 1975.

Post, R.M., Kopanda, R.T., and Black, K.E. Progressive effects of cocaine on behavior and central amine metabolism in rhesus monkeys: Relationship to kindling and psychosis. Biol Psychiatry, 11:403-419, 1976.

Racine, R. Kindling: The first decade. Neurosurgery, 3:234-252, 1978.

Sangdee, P., Turkanis, S.A., and Karler, R. Kindling-like effect induced by repeated corneal electroshock in mice. Epilepsia, 23:471-479, 1982.

Segal, D.S., and Mandell, A.J. Long-term administration of d-amphetamine: Progressive augmentation of motor activity and stereotype. Pharmacol Biochem Behav, 2:249-255, 1974.

Shuster, L., Webster, G.W., and Yu, G. Increased running response to morphine in morphine-pretreated mice. J Pharmacol Exp Ther, 192:64-72, 1975.

Shuster, L., Yu, G., and Bates, A. Sensitization to cocaine stimulation in mice. Psychopharmacology, 52:185-190, 1977.

Smith, R.C., Leelavathi, D.E., Hsu, L., Ho, B.T., Tansey, W., Taylor, D., and Biggs, C. Acute versus chronic administration of phencyclidine: Effects on behavior and brain biochemistry. In: Domino, E.F., ed. PCP (Phencyclidine) Historical and Current Perspective. Ann Arbor: NPP Books, 1981. pp. 243-291.

Tatum, A.L., and Seevers, M.H. Experimental cocaine addiction. J Pharmacol Exp Ther, 36:401-410, 1929.

Turkanis, S.A., Cely, W., Olsen, D.M., and Karler, R. Anticonvulsant properties of cannabidiol. Res Commun Chem Pathol Pharmacol, 8:231-246, 1974.

ACKNOWLEDGMENT

This research was supported by research grant DA-00346 from the National Institute on Drug Abuse. Dr. Monique C. Braude, NIDA Division of Preclinical Research, served as Project Officer.

AUTHORS

Ralph Karler, Ph.D.
Larry D. Calder, B.S.
Stuart A. Turkanis, Ph.D.
Department of Pharmacology
University of Utah School of Medicine
Salt Lake City, UT 84132

Catecholamine-Independent Behavioral and Neurochemical Effects of Cocaine in Rats

Karen Gale

Classically, the mechanism of action of cocaine has been attributed to the augmentation of catecholamine neurotransmission. Many of the acute and chronic effects of cocaine administration on the CNS, and consequently on behavior, have been ascribed to such an enhancement of norepinephrine- and/or dopamine-mediated function. However, data has recently begun to accumulate indicating that cocaine may influence certain behaviors, both acutely and chronically, by mechanisms that do not involve stimulation of either dopaminergic or adrenergic receptors. The present report will describe some actions of cocaine on behavior and neurochemistry in rats that cannot be blocked or attenuated by catecholaminergic receptor antagonists: (1) behavioral sensitization produced by repeated administration of cocaine, (2) changes in GABA-related neurochemical parameters in the striatum of rats treated chronically with cocaine, and (3) cocaine-induced conditioned taste aversions.

Behavioral Sensitization Following Chronic Cocaine Treatment

Repeated administration of cocaine in rats consistently has been found to result in "sensitization" to the motor stimulant actions of this drug (Downs and Eddy 1932; Tatum and Seevers 1929; Post and Rose 1976; Stripling and Ellinwood 1976; Post et al. 1981). Activation of dopaminergic transmission is an essential feature of the stereotyped hyperactivity induced by cocaine, since drugs that block dopamine receptors can prevent the appearance of these behaviors in both naive as well as in "sensitized" animals. The experiments to be described here were designed to determine firstly, whether the blockade of dopamine receptors could prevent the sensitization to cocaine, and secondly, whether animals sensitized to cocaine would also show sensitization to a directly-acting dopamine receptor agonist.

In our studies, cocaine was administered subcutaneously to 250 gram rats; each rat received 0.1 ml of a 400 mg/ml solution.

This route of administration results in a slow rate of absorption due to the vasoconstrictive action of cocaine. By 30 min after injection, the cocaine-treated rats showed hyperactivity and sympathomimetic activation; this increased in intensity to a peak (stereotyped head movements and some gnawing) by 90 min. The stereotypies were maintained for 8-10 hr after a single injection. Injections were given daily for 10 days. After the last injection, rats were tested for behavioral responses to cocaine or apomorphine.

The chronic treatment groups were as follows:
- (1) cocaine
- (2) cocaine + droperidol (given simultaneously)
- (3) droperidol
- (4) saline

Droperidol was selected as the dopamine antagonist for this study because its short half-life made it possible to match the duration of action with the duration of the cocaine stimulation. The treatment regimen involved giving droperidol (1 mg/kg i.p.) twice a day, 3 hr apart. This resulted in noticeable catalepsy--even in those animals receiving cocaine concurrently; the catalepsy lasted for approximately 3 hr after each droperidol injection. In rats receiving cocaine and droperidol simultaneously, no stereotypy or hyperactivity of any kind was observed.

Three days following the last drug treatment, the rats were tested for their behavioral responses to cocaine (20 mg/kg i.p.) or apomorphine (.25 mg/kg s.c.). The scale used to rate the stereotyped behavior is shown in the legend to table 1.

Table 1 shows the behavioral scores of the animals after the challenge dose of cocaine, as a function of time following injection. A marked difference between "controls" (rats that received chronic injections of saline) and the "chronic cocaine" group is evident: all rats in the "chronic cocaine" group showed restricted stereotypies with gnawing during the first 30 min. Controls engaged in locomotor activity with some rearing and sniffing. This difference reflects the phenomenon of "sensitization" to the motor stimulant effects of the drug. Although not shown in table 1, we found that animals showing sensitization to cocaine also exhibited enhanced hyperactivity in response to d-amphetamine.

The rats which had been receiving chronic droperidol + cocaine simultaneously were similar to those receiving cocaine alone. The behavior of these rats was clearly distinguishable from both "control" and "chronic droperidol" groups.

Thus, despite the fact that concurrent treatment with droperidol prevented the behavioral manifestations of cocaine administration, this treatment did not prevent the development of "sensitization" to a subsequent cocaine challenge. This indicates that the acute psychomotor stimulant actions of cocaine and the changes in drug sensitivity caused by its chronic administration are separable phenomena.

TABLE 1

Stereotyped behavior induced by cocaine (20 mg/kg i.p.) in rats treated chronically with cocaine and/or droperidol

Chronic Treatment	Time After Cocaine (min)		
	10	20	30
control	2.0	2.0†	2.0
droperidol	2.0	3.0†	2.5
cocaine	4.6	5.5†	3.2
cocaine + droperidol	3.6	4.0	5.0†

Values represent behavioral ratings based on the following scoring scale: 0 = little or no activity-- occasional grooming; 1 = intermittent rearing and exploratory activity; 2 = continuous activity involving locomotion, rearing and sniffing; 3 = repetitive sniffing of cage walls or floors; 4 = repetitive head movements and restricted sniffing of small areas of the cage; 5 = continuous sniffing with discontinuous gnawing or licking; 6 = gnawing with occasional sniffing; 7 = continuous gnawing; 8 = self-directed gnawing.

Each value represents the mean of 4 rats. The range of scores for any given determination was not greater than 1 unit on either side of the mean; at peak effect, the largest difference between any 2 rats was 1 scoring unit. † Denotes peak effect.

The behavioral scores of the chronic treatment groups in response to apomorphine are shown in table 2. The control rats showed marked stereotypies in response to apomorphine. In contrast, the rats which had been chronically exposed to cocaine showed only mild stereotyped responses which were of short duration. Rats in the 'chronic droperidol' group were similar to controls in their response to the apomorphine challenge, except that many of them exhibited restricted gnawing behavior during the peak effect. The groups of rats that had been chronically treated with the combination of cocaine and droperidol were similar to controls in their response to apomorphine.

Thus, it appears that exposure to chronic cocaine causes a reduction in the subsequent responsivr ness to the behavioral stimulant actions of apomorphine. We have since replicated this study using additional test doses of apomorphine (.17-.4 mg/kg) and found that the dose-response relationship was shifted to the right in animals which had received chronic cocaine. This apparent tolerance to apomorphine was prevented by concurrent droperidol treatment, suggesting that it may be mediated by stimulation of dopamine receptors.

TABLE 2

Stereotyped behavior (scored as described in table 1) induced by apomorphine (0.25 mg/kg s.c.) in rats treated chronically with cocaine and/or droperidol.

Chronic Treatment	Time After Apomorphine (min)		
	10	20	30
control	2.0	4.4†	1.2
droperidol	2.5	5.5†	1.8
cocaine	2.5†	2.0	0.0
cocaine + droperidol	3.8	4.0†	0.5

The range of scores within each group at each time point was within 1 scoring unit. † Denotes peak effect.

The two aspects of this study, taken together, raise some interesting points. First, the same treatment--namely, chronic cocaine--which caused "sensitization" to cocaine, caused "desensitization" or tolerance to apomorphine. Second, chronic treatment with a dopamine receptor antagonist which is also, incidentally, an alpha-adrenergic receptor antagonist, blocked the development of tolerance to apomorphine but not the development of sensitization to cocaine. This suggests that at least two different phenomena are taking place in response to repeated, prolonged exposure to cocaine: (1) chronic stimulation of dopamine transmission, leading to an eventual decrease in the sensitivity of the dopamine receptors (or changes in other neural links in series with dopamine-receptive cells), and (2) alterations in parameters independent of dopamine and alpha-adrenergic receptors, which augment the sensitivity of the system to cocaine. In addition, it is noteworthy that the presence of the chronic behavioral stimulation is not required for the development of sensitization to cocaine.

Changes in GABA Synthesis and GABA Receptors in Striatum Following Chronic Cocaine Treatment

Measurements of GABA-related neurochemical parameters were made in the striatum of rats treated chronically with cocaine and/or droperidol. The striatum was examined because of its known involvement in the generation of dopamine-related stereotyped behavior; GABAergic parameters were examined because of the importance of GABAergic interneurons in striatum and the fact that GABA synthesis in this region has been previously shown to change in response to chronic interference with dopamine transmission (Gale and Casu 1981).

Table 3 shows the activity of glutamic acid decarboxylase (GAD), the enzyme responsible for GABA synthesis, in rats that had been chronically treated in the exact manner as described for the behavioral studies. A significant increase in GAD activity in striatum was seen in rats in the 'chronic cocaine' group; this effect was still present in rats that had received concurrent treatment with droperidol. The increase in GAD activity was still observed 10 days after cessation of chronic treatment. Studies are now in progress to determine the time course of recovery. It should be noted that the behavioral 'sensitization' to cocaine that we have described is still present at 10 days after stopping chronic treatment.

TABLE 3

Glutamic acid decarboxylase activity (GAD) in rat striatum after chronic cocaine administration

Chronic Treatment	(n)	GAD Activity umol/mg prot/hr	% Control
control	(12)	.35 + .02	
cocaine	(10)	.50 + .03*	143%
cocaine + droperidol	(8)	.48 + .03*	137%
droperidol	(6)	.31 + .03	
10 days after chronic cocaine	(8)	.43 + .04*	123%

*Significantly different from control p < .05

GAD activity was measured in tissue homogenates, in the presence of saturating concentrations of substrate (glutamate) and cofactor (pyridoxal phosphate), based on the method of Sims and Pitts (1970). See text for details of experimental design.

Table 4 shows the effect of the chronic cocaine treatment on the rate of striatal GABA accumulation in vivo following irreversible inhibition of GABA degradation. This gives us an indication of GABA turnover. The GABA-transaminase inhibitor, gamma-vinyl-GABA (GVG) was injected directly into the striatum and the accumulation of GABA was measured at 3 hr. The net GABA accumulation in striata of rats that had been chronically exposed to cocaine was significantly greater than that of controls. No change in steady-state levels of GABA was found. This suggests that chronic exposure to cocaine results in an enhanced turnover rate of GABA in striatum, an observation consistent with our finding of increased GAD activity in striatal homogenates.

The effect of chronic cocaine exposure on GABA binding in striatum is shown in table 5. It can be seen that a significant decrease in GABA binding in striatum was associated with chronic cocaine treatment. This effect was not prevented by concurrent treatment with droperidol. As in the case of GAD, the change in GABA binding was still present at 10 days following cessation of cocaine treatment.

327

TABLE 4

Effect of chronic cocaine administration on accumulation of GABA in vivo in striatum.

Chronic Treatment	GABA (nmol/mg prot)			
	Basal	3 hr After GVG	Net Increase	% Control
control	24.0 + 0.4	77.2 + 2.8	53	
cocaine	24.5 + 0.5	97.4 + 3.8*	73	138%

*Significantly different from control p < .05

GABA accumulation was measured 3 hr after the microinjection of gamma-vinyl-GABA (GVG, 20 ug) into striatum. Basal values are those obtained from tissue not treated with GVG. Each value is the mean + S.E. of 5 rats.

TABLE 5

Specific $[^3H]$-GABA binding in rat striatum after chronic cocaine administration

Chronic Treatment	(n)	$[^3H]$-GABA Binding fmol/mg prot	% Control
control	(12)	424 + 30	
cocaine	(10)	301 + 25*	71%
cocaine + droperidol	(8)	288 + 29*	68%
droperidol	(6)	373 + 35	
10 days after chronic cocaine	(8)	350 + 32*	83%

*Significantly different from control p < .05

Binding was done in the presence of 80-120 ug membrane protein, 30 nM $[^3H]$GABA, at 0°C in a Na^+-free medium; binding in the presence of 10 mM nonradioactive GABA was subtracted from total binding to calculate specific binding. Membranes were prepared by freeze-thawing, Triton-X 100 incubation (.01% at 37°C for 60 min) and extensive washing.

To determine whether the changes in GABA binding and GAD activity represented a general response of GABAergic synapses to prolonged cocaine treatment, cerebellum and cerebral cortex of the same rats were examined for these parameters. No significant changes in GAD or GABA binding were found in neocortex or cerebellum. This suggests that the changes in GABAergic parameters observed in the striatum of rats exposed chronically to cocaine represent adjustments which may be specifically related to the neural circuitry of this nucleus. In view of these results, it is unlikely that cocaine exerts a direct effect on GABAergic transmission.

Cocaine-Induced Conditioned Taste Aversion

We have also obtained evidence for acute actions of cocaine that are insensitive to dopaminergic and/or adrenergic blockade using a conditioned taste aversion paradigm. Since the reinforcing properties of cocaine have been demonstrated to depend upon central dopaminergic and possibly noradrenergic transmission (Gill et al. 1978; Wilson and Schuster 1972), we were interested in determining whether aversive properties of cocaine would be mediated by the same neurotransmitter systems. In these experiments, rats were trained to drink water for one 20 min session each day. On the first day of drug exposure, the rats received saccharin instead of water, and 20 min following the drinking session drugs were administered.

Cocaine was administered subcutaneously as it had been for the chronic studies previously described. In addition to cocaine, separate groups of rats received one of the following dopamine and/or adrenergic antagonists: haloperidol (1 mg/kg), chlorpromazine (20 mg/kg), pimozide (1 mg/kg), or propranolol (5 mg/kg). An additional group that received both chlorpromazine and propranolol in addition to cocaine was also examined. In this way, we were able to completely block all hyperactivity, stereotypy and/or sympathomimetic stimulation due to cocaine for the entire duration (approximately 8 hr) of the cocaine effect.

The antagonist drugs, under our experimental conditions, did not by themselves cause conditioned taste aversion. Cocaine administration caused a marked taste aversion, which was evident on the first post-drug saccharin exposure (saccharin test 1) initiated 4 or 5 days after the first saccharin exposure. The rats that had received cocaine following the pre-drug saccharin exposure showed a 50-60% decrease in saccharin intake on the first saccharin test (table 6). No change in saccharin consumption was seen in controls and in rats receiving the dopamine and noradrenergic antagonists without cocaine. None of the antagonists, or antagonist combinations, when administered concurrently with cocaine, were able to prevent or attenuate the taste aversion produced by exposure to cocaine. It should be noted that the dose of cocaine used to produce the taste aversions was equivalent to only twice the minimum dose necessary for causing a significant (but submaximal) decrease in saccharin consumption. Thus, it should have been sensitive to alteration by antagonists if the antagonists acted on a system involved in mediating the aversion produced by cocaine.

TABLE 6

Cocaine-induced conditioned taste aversions: Effect of dopaminergic and adrenergic antagonists

| | Saccharin Consumption : % Control | |
	1†	2†
control	100%	100%
cocaine	50%	20%
chlorpromazine	105%	98%
propranolol	90%	93%
propranolol + cocaine	53%	21%
chlorpromazine + propranolol	92%	85%
chlorpromazine + propranolc¹ + cocaine	45%	10%
haloperidol	110%	105%
pimozide	90%	95%
pimozide + cocaine	59%	25%

† 1 = first (2 = second) saccharin test session.

Each group contained 4 or 5 rats, matched for initial (pre-drug) saccharin consumption. Standard errors of the mean saccharin consumption for each exposure were less than 20% of the mean value. Control saccharin consumption = 25 ml on test session 1 and 23 ml on test session 2. All tests involved access to a single bottle of saccharin only.

To determine whether the cocaine-induced taste aversions were related to the local anesthetic action of cocaine, we tested a group of animals with equivalent doses of lidocaine in combination with epinephrine (the epinephrine was included to simulate the local vasoconstrictive action of the cocaine injections). This treatment resulted in no measurable change in subsequent saccharin consumption, indicating that local anesthetic actions per se are not responsible for the taste aversions produced by cocaine.

Thus, it appears that the conditioned taste aversion that develops with cocaine is mediated by a system other than one containing catecholamines. While blockade of catecholaminergic transmission eliminated all behavioral signs of motor and autonomic stimulation induced by cocaine, the aversive characteristics of the exposure to cocaine were not altered. Since the reinforcing properties of cocaine can be eliminated by blockade of central dopaminergic transmission, it appears that the reinforcing and aversive properties are mediated by distinctly different neurotransmitter systems. We have yet to identify the system responsible for the aversive characteristics of cocaine.

Discussion

We have seen several instances in which cocaine-induced effects, either chronic or acute, are obtained despite blockade of noradrenergic and dopaminergic transmission. Evidently, there are one or more noncatecholaminergic neurotransmitter systems with which cocaine can interact directly in order to induce these effects. At present, we do not know whether the relevant system or systems even involve known neurotransmitters; it is possible that the neuromodulator mediating some of these actions has yet to be described. In this context, the findings of Sershen, Reith and Lajtha (1980) are of interest. These authors have described a binding site for [^{3}H]cocaine in brain tissue which appears to be related to central stimulatory actions of cocaine (as opposed to local anesthetic actions). The binding of cocaine to this site was relatively insensitive to displacement by classical neurotransmitters such as dopamine, norepinephrine, acetylcholine, serotonin and GABA or receptor antagonists for these neurotransmitters (Reith et al. 1980a). These same authors have found that a low molecular weight peptide extracted from brain homogenates is capable of inhibiting the saturable binding of cocaine to crude mouse brain membranes (Reith et al. 1980b). Thus, it is possible that cocaine may interact with receptors for a yet-to-be-identified neuroactive peptide. It is interesting that while no loss of these cocaine binding sites occurred following lesions of dopamine neurons, at least a portion of these binding sites appeared to be associated with terminals of serotonergic neurons (Reith et al. 1983). Thus, even if cocaine may exert some of its actions via uncharacterized receptors, it is likely that one or more classical transmitter substances may indirectly mediate these effects. It will therefore be worthwhile examining the ability of agonists and antagonists of serotonin and other noncatecholaminergic neurotransmitters to prevent the development of cocaine-induced sensitization, conditioned taste aversions, and/or changes in striatal GABA utilization. In addition, by examining different cocaine analogs for their ability to elicit catecholamine-independent actions, we may be able to determine: (1) whether the different catecholamine-independent actions are correlated with each other (in terms of relative potencies of cocaine analogs), and (2) whether any of the cocaine-induced effects that are catecholamine-independent are related to the cocaine binding site described by Reith et al. (1980).

By pursuing this line of investigation, we may find that the classical actions of cocaine as an uptake inhibitor for catecholamines represent only a small part of the mechanism by which this drug can have an impact on central nervous system function, in the context of both short-term and long-term exposure to the drug.

331

References

Downs, A.W., and Eddy, N.B. The effect of repeated doses of cocaine on the rat. J Pharmacol Exp Ther, 46:199-200, 1932.

Gale, K., and Casu, M. Dynamic utilization of GABA in substantia nigra: Regulation by dopamine and GABA in the striatum, and its clinical and behavioral implications. Mol Cell Biochem, 39:369-405, 1981.

Gill, C.A., Holz, W.C., Zirkle, C.L., and Hill, H. Pharmacological modification of cocaine and apomorphine self-administration in the squirrel monkey. Proc 10th Cong of Collegium Int Neuropsychopharm, 2:1477-1484, 1978.

Post, R.M., Lockfeld, A., Squillace, K.M., and Contel, N.R. Drug-environment interaction: Context dependency of cocaine-induced behavioral sensitization. Life Sci, 28:755-760, 1981.

Post, R.M., and Rose, H. Increasing effects of repetitive cocaine administration in the rat. Nature, 260:731-732, 1976.

Reith, M.E.A., Sershen, H., Allen, D.L., and Lajtha, A. A portion of [^{3}H]cocaine binding in brain is associated with serotonergic neurons. Molec Pharmacol, 23:600-606, 1983.

Reith, M.E.A., Sershen, H., and Lajtha, A. Saturable [^{3}H]-cocaine binding in central nervous system of mouse. Life Sci, 27:1055-1062, 1980.

Reith, M.E.A., Sershen, H., and Lajtha, A. Endogenous peptide(s) inhibiting [^{3}H]cocaine binding in mouse brain. Neurochem Res, 5:1291-1299, 1980.

Sershen, H., Reith, M.E.A., and Lajtha, A. The pharmacological relevance of the cocaine binding site in mouse brain. Neuropharmacology, 19:1145-1148, 1980.

Sims, K.L., and Pitts, Jr., F.N. Brain glutamate decarboxylase: Changes in the developing rat brain. J Neurochem, 17:1607-1612, 1970.

Stripling, J.S., and Ellinwood, Jr., E.H. Sensitization to cocaine following chronic administration in the rat. In Ellinwood, E.H., and Kilbey, M.M., eds. Cocaine and Other Stimulants. New York: Plenum Press, 1976 pp. 327-351.

Tatum, A.L., and Seevers, M.H. Experimental cocaine addiction. J Pharmacol Exp Ther, 36:401-410, 1929.

Wilson, M.C., and Schuster, C.R. The effects of chlorpromazine on psychomotor stimulant self-administration in the rhesus monkey. Psychopharmacologia, 26:115-126, 1972.

Author

KAREN GALE, Ph.D.
Department of Pharmacology
Georgetown University
Schools of Medicine and Dentistry
3900 Reservoir Road, N.W.
Washington, DC 20007

Barbiturate Tolerance and Physical Dependence: Contribution of Pharmacological Factors

Michiko Okamoto

INTRODUCTION

Sedative-hypnotics and anti-anxiety drugs comprise a large group of chemically different compounds that are classified pharmacologically as CNS depressants. These compounds manifest a spectrum of effects ranging from calming and sedative activity through profound CNS depression, manifested as anesthesia, coma and respiratory paralysis, and finally death. For the most part, the acute effects exhibited by individual compounds are nonspecific, and any selectivity, in terms of the clinical indications for which an individual compound is used, is conferred by (1) the dose and schedule of administration, (2) the slope of the dose-response curve along the continuum of CNS depression, and (3) the pharmacokinetic profile of the compound. Therefore, a clear understanding of these pharmacologic properties is essential to the appropriate selection of a sedative-hypnotic or anti-anxiety drug for therapeutic use.

Since the introduction of sodium barbital into clinical medicine in 1903, considerable effort has been devoted to identifying and understanding the risks associated with both acute and chronic administration of sedative-hypnotics. Although all of these drugs have similar acute effects, there is no question that abuse among this class of drugs differs, and so do the risks. For example, the large number of deaths each year from overdose of self-administered barbiturates attests to the narrow margin of safety of these drugs. On the other hand, the more widely available benzodiazepines rarely cause death from overdose unless they are used in combination with other sedative-hypnotics.

Despite these differences, all sedative-hypnotics, including non-barbiturates, can produce tolerance, psychological and physical dependence, and a barbiturate-like withdrawal syndrome with the risk of convulsions when they are taken in sufficient amounts. Thus we chose barbiturates as the prototype sedative-hypnotic to study the underlying pharmacodynamic and pharmacokinetic factors which govern the production of tolerance and physical dependence.

333

Clinical studies indicate that the pattern of sedative-hypnotic use that culminates in withdrawal hyperexcitation is a prolonged period of continuous drug intoxication. This suggests that the functional depression of the CNS is an important factor in the development of physical dependence. Accordingly, in designing an animal model of sedative-hypnotic dependence, techniques for measurements of drug response (CNS depression), in addition to measurement of dose and frequency of drug administration throughout chronic treatment, enable the evaluation of this factor.

Quantitative measurement of response is also essential to the characterization of the tolerance to sedative-hypnotics which invariably develops during their chronic administration. According to Kalant et al. (1971), this tolerance can be dispositional (i.e., primarily due to an increased rate of elimination) or functional (i.e., decreased sensitivity of the CNS to depression) or both. The dissection of "total" tolerance into these components and the separate characterization of their development and mechanisms can be achieved by concurrent measurements of daily drug effect (CNS depression) and drug load (dose and blood or brain concentration) during chronic administration.

RESULTS

Using these techniques and pentobarbital and barbital as prototype barbiturates, we characterized the development of functional and dispositional tolerance during chronic barbiturate treatment in our animal model (Okamoto and Boisse 1981). Cats were treated with Na pentobarbital twice daily or Na barbital once every 3 days for 5 weeks. Each dose was adjusted to produce a preset peak level of CNS depression; in this case, a light surgical anesthesia (Boisse and Okamoto 1978a). The kinetics of barbiturate elimination were determined once a week to monitor the dispositional component of tolerance (Boisse and Okamoto 1978b).

The average dose required to produce the peak effect of surgical anesthesia increased during chronic treatment for both pento-barbital and barbital, showing the development of "total" tolerance to both drugs (figure 1). At the beginning of treatment, the dose of Na pentobarbital increased more rapidly than the dose of Na barbital. Elimination kinetics showed that the half-life of pentobarbital decreased rapidly during this initial rapid increase in the dose of Na pentobarbital, a demonstration of the quick onset of the development of dispositional tolerance to Na pentobarbital. The decrease in the pentobarbital half-life was presumably due to induction of the hepatic microsomal drug-metabolizing enzymes which biotransform pentobarbital (Remmer 1969). In contrast, the half-life of barbital did not change during the Na barbital treatment; thus, there was no dispositional component of tolerance to barbital, a drug which is known to be eliminated unchanged primarily through the kidney.

The development of the functional component of tolerance was shown by the steady increase in the blood concentration of pentobarbital

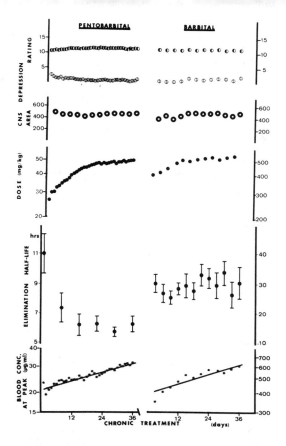

FIGURE 1. Chronic pentobarbital and barbital treatments and characteristics of tolerance in each. Ordinates: (a) average CNS depression ratings: peak after each morning dose ($\bullet$), residual depression just prior to subsequent dose ($\oplus$); (b) average total CNS depression based on areas under time-action curves summed at 3-day intervals; (c) average administered dose; (d) elimination half-life; a decrease indicates dispositional tolerance; (e) average blood concentration at the time of peak drug response; an increase indicates functional tolerance. Abscissa: time during chronic treatment (Okamoto and Boisse 1981. Copyright 1981, Elsevier Publications).

or barbital which was required to achieve the preset level of CNS depression. Cellular tolerance increased slowly and steadily as the treatment duration increased (figure 1, Boisse and Okamoto, 1978b). Most interestingly, when animals were treated with these "chronically equivalent" doses (Boisse and Okamoto 1978a) of pentobarbital and barbital (that is, doses which produce the same peak and residual CNS depression shown in figure 1, functional tolerance developed in a parallel fashion to pentobarbital and barbital.

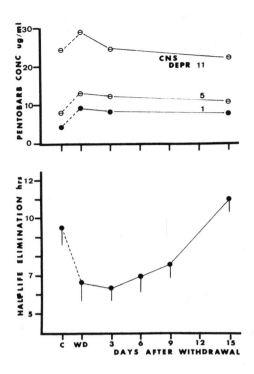

FIGURE 2. Recovery from cellular (functional) tolerance and dispositional tolerance after chronic Na pentobarbital treatment. Ordinates: (A) pentobarbital concentration (ug/ml blood) that produced CNS depression ratings of 11 (surgical anesthesia), 5 (ataxia), and 1 (loss of fine motor coordination). (B) pentobarbital elimination half-life from blood. Vertical bars indicate ± S.E. (N=6). Abscissae: "C" stands for control, prior to chronic Na pentobarbital treatment, "WD" stands for day 1 of withdrawal or just after the last dose of chronic Na pentobarbital, and numbers indicate days after the last chronic Na pentobarbital dose (Okamoto et al. unpublished observations).

The "reverse" of the development of functional and dispositional tolerance, i.e., the return to normal after abrupt termination of chronic drug administration, was also studied. To investigate this, Na pentobarbital chronic administration was abruptly terminated, and the pentobarbital elimination kinetics and CNS sensitivity to a challenging dose of Na pentobarbital were evaluated every 3 days until recovery was complete. The 3-day interval was chosen because preliminary experiments had shown that animals treated chronically with Na pentobarbital once every 2 days did not develop functional or dispositional tolerance (Okamoto et al. unpublished observations); thus, the testing procedure was not expected to affect the processes being studied.

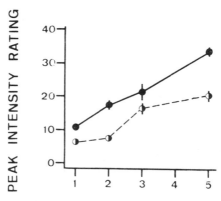

FIGURE 3. Peak withdrawal intensity rating after various durations of chronic "high" (●) or "low" (◑) dose barbiturate treatment. Ordinate: peak withdrawal intensity rating, mean + S.E. Abscissa: duration of chronic treatment in weeks. Number of observations per point: 10 to 67 for high dose barbiturate, 8 to 19 for low dose barbiturate (Okamoto et al. 1981. Copyright 1981, American Society for Pharmacology and Experimental Therapeutics).

Recovery from the two types of tolerance occurs after the abrupt termination of Na pentobarbital (figure 2). These results show that the kinetics of recovery were almost the mirror image of the induction of tolerance. Dispositional tolerance was reversed within 2 weeks. In contrast, recovery from functional tolerance was slow and not complete at the end of the 2-week observation period.

The relationship between chronic dosing levels and the degree of functional tolerance and physical dependence that develops is also an important issue to be investigated. Accordingly, we compared the development of tolerance and dependence in groups of animals treated chronically either with a "high" or "low" dose of barbiturate (Okamoto et al. 1978). The "high" dose group received Na pentobarbital twice daily sufficient to produce light surgical anesthesia (this corresponds to a CNS Depression Rating of 10-11 on our scale). The "low" dose group received Na barbital sufficient to produce gross ataxia (this corresponds to a CNS Depression Rating of 5-6). Both groups were treated for 1 to 5 weeks and groups of animals were abruptly withdrawn after treatment for various durations to evaluate the time-course of development of dependence. The severity of physical dependence was measured by an overall withdrawal intensity rating system developed in our laboratory (Okamoto et al. 1981), and the development of functional tolerance was measured as described above.

The "low" dose produced less physical dependence than the "high" dose after equal durations of treatment (figure 3). However, physical dependence increased in a parallel fashion in both treatment groups and was still increasing in the "low" dose group after 5 weeks. Indeed, when the "low" dose treatment was further increased to 100 days, it produced approximately the same severity

337

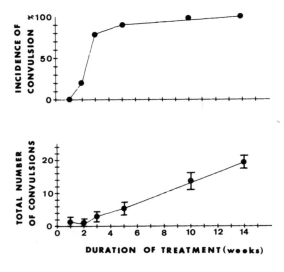

FIGURE 4. Incidence of convulsions and total number of convulsions per animal after various durations of chronic "low" dose barbital or pentobarbital treatment. Abscissa: duration of chronic treatment in weeks. Ordinates: (A) percent incidence of cats with grand mal type convulsions during withdrawal. (B) average total number of grand mal-type convulsions per animal during withdrawal. Vertical bars represent + S.E. Number of observations per point: 10 to 15 animals (Okamoto and Hinman 1984, Copyright 1984, Pergamon Press, Ltd.).

of physical dependence as had the 5 weeks of "high" dose treatment (figure 4). These results indicate that physical dependence develops more slowly with "low" dose barbiturate treatment, but that the same level of dependence eventually develops if the treatment is continued at doses sufficient to achieve a preset level of CNS depression (Okamoto and Hinman 1984).

Another important factor to consider during chronic sedative hypnotic treatment is the frequency of administration. This was clearly demonstrated by Goldstein (1972) for the production of ethanol physical dependence. The relationship between dosing frequency and elimination determines the drug concentration at any time. The maintenance of certain drug concentrations may be a major factor in the development of functional tolerance and physical dependence. Small individual differences in the half-life of drug elimination affected the development of physical dependence to Na pentobarbital when the drug was given on a fixed schedule (figure 5). A group of animals was treated with "high" dose Na pentobarbital twice a day for 5 weeks. The elimination half-life of pentobarbital was determined for each animal on the last day of treatment. The number of grand mal-type convulsions was tabulated for each animal upon abrupt termimation of the drug as a measure of withdrawal severity. The range of the half-life of pentobarbital in these animals was 3-13 hours, and the longer the half-life, the more severe was the physical dependence (Okamoto and Hinman 1983).

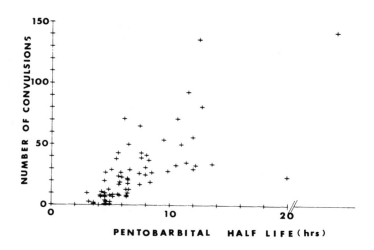

FIGURE 5. Relationship between pentobarbital half-life and total number of convulsions displayed during pentobarbital withdrawal. Abscissa: pentobarbital half-life in hours. Ordinate: total number of convulsions displayed by each animal during the withdrawal (Okamoto and Hinman, 1983. Copyright 1983, American Society for Pharmacology and Experimental Therapeutics).

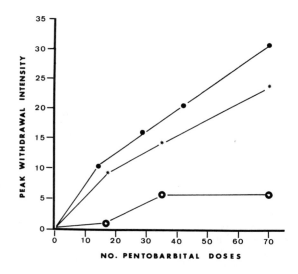

FIGURE 6. Relationship between the peak withdrawal intensity and total number of "high" Na pentobarbital doses. Abscissa: total number of Na pentobarbital doses. Ordinate: average peak with-drawal intensity. (●)dosed every 12 hours; (*)dosed every 24 hours, (◐)dosed every 48 hours (Okamoto et al. unpublished preliminary observations).

Reducing the frequency of chronic barbiturate administration reduces the risk of development of physical dependence. That is, the longer the interval between doses, the less severe was the withdrawal (figure 6). It is apparent that dosing once every 2 days produced a negligible level of physical dependence. In other experiments, as the dosing interval exceeded 36 hours, the drug concentration just prior to succeeding doses was below the limits of detection (<500 ng/ml blood; Okamoto et al., unpublished communications). These findings underscore the importance of adjusting dosing frequency so as not to maintain sufficient drug levels within biological systems that would risk producing physical dependence.

Other studies have demonstrated how critical the kinetics of elimination of sedative-hypnotics are in understanding the underlying state of physical dependence. Since physical dependence can only be measured by the intensity of the withdrawal syndrome, it is difficult to dissect the phenomena of physical dependence from withdrawal so as to study either independently. To start with, it has been accepted that long-acting barbiturates such as barbital or phenobarbital are less liable to produce physical dependence than the short-acting barbiturate drugs such as pentobarbital or secobarbital (cf. Jaffe 1980). Also, in clinical subjects and in animals, the onset of withdrawal was slower and its intensity less severe in barbital dependency than in pentobarbital dependency (Boisse and Okamoto 1978c). For example, the average elimination half-lives of barbital and pentobarbital in these animals were 30 and 5 hours, respectively. To determine whether the slow rate of barbital elimination was responsible for the slower onset of withdrawal, we experimentally "slowed" the elimination of pentobarbital by readministering proportionally smaller doses of pentobarbital intravenously at hourly intervals according to a computer calculation based on first-order elimination kinetics (Boisse and Okamoto 1978d).

The added drug effectively altered the apparent rate of pentobarbital elimination from a half-life of 5 hours to 27 hours (table 1). This procedure also slowed the onset of withdrawal and dramatically reduced its severity, as indicated by the withdrawal intensity rating and the incidence of grand mal convulsions (Boisse and Okamoto 1978d). Additional evidence that the elimination of the drug is critical for the expression of withdrawal signs was obtained by experimentally increasing the rate of barbital elimination to mimic that of pentobarbital. The rate of barbital elimination was increased by peritoneal dialysis after the last dose of chronic barbital. This procedure decreased the apparent half-life of barbital elimination from 30 hours to 7 hours (table 1). As a result, the barbital withdrawal signs appeared much sooner and were markedly intensified (Boisse and Okamoto 1978d).

These results support Hollister's hypothesis (1980) that the severity of the withdrawal reaction is related to the rate of disappearance of sedative drugs from plasma. He predicted that the sedative-hypnotics with half-lives in the range of 12-24 hours (e.g., pentobarbital, secobarbital, and glutethimide) will produce the most severe withdrawal syndrome in patients.

TABLE 1

Severity of Barbital and Pentobarbital Withdrawal
at Slow and Fast Elimination Rates

Procedure	$T\frac{1}{2}$	N	Incidences of Convulsions	Total Intensity Scores Grand total	Ratio (altered/control)
	hr				
Barbital control	29.6 ($\pm$2.6)[a]	16	6.3 (2.1 $\pm$ 2.1)	1517.2	1
Peritoneal dialysis	7.14 ($\pm$0.39)	10	100.0 (10.8 $\pm$ 2.6)	3315.0	0.986
Pentobarbital control	5.37 ($\pm$0.48)	63	100.0 (15.4 $\pm$ 1.4)	3363.1	1
First-order dose reduction	27.3 ($\pm$1.8)	7	42.9 (1.0 $\pm$ 0.4)	1239.3	0.816

[a]Values given as means with S.E. in parentheses.

TABLE 1. Reconstructed from Table 3 in Boisse and Okamoto 1978d.
Copyright 1978, American Society for Pharmacology and Experimental
Therapeutics).

In contrast, drugs which have short half-lives have little
potential for producing tolerance and physical dependence because
their residual CNS concentrations at the time of successive doses
are small. There is insufficient drug to produce and maintain
functional tolerance and physical dependence. In the other
direction, drugs which have long half-lives are less likely to
result in severe withdrawal signs and symptoms despite the fact
that they produce severe physical dependence. That is, the CNS can
gradually readapt, when the drug in no longer administered, due to
the slow elimination of the drug from the CNS.

Although the behavioral aspects of sedative-hypnotic withdrawal
have been well documented, the pathophysiology of physical
dependence in terms of underlying neuronal mechanisms has not yet
been well elucidated. Barbiturate withdrawal in humans consists of
a variety of overt signs (Isbell et al. 1950); Fraser et al. 1958;
Wulff 1959) accompanied by characteristic EEG abnormalities
recorded through surface electrodes (Isbell et al., 1950; Wikler et
al. 1955; Wulff 1959). These abnormalities consist of high
amplitude slow waves, paroxysmal discharges, and spike-and-dome
activity. Interestingly, paroxysmal discharges were more prominent
during withdrawal from moderate doses of barbiturate than in
withdrawal from high doses (Wikler et al. 1955). Seizure activity
usually originated in subcortical rather than in cortical areas
(Essig 1962, 1967); Sharpless and Jaffee 1967; c.f. Kalant et al.,
1971). Although barbiturates and other sedative-hypnotics depress
all CNS activity as a function of dose, it is possible that chronic
use of these drugs affects various CNS loci differently in relation
to the chronic dose administered. Therefore further information
regarding the most sensitive site(s) and characteristics of

341

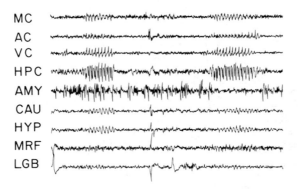

FIGURE 7. EEG recordings during moderate-intensity barbiturate withdrawal, 40 hours after last dose. Recordings are from hippocampus (HPC) with spike-and-wave activity, amygdala (AMY) with paroxysmal discharge, motor cortex (MC), auditory cortex (AC), visual cortex (VC), caudate (CAU), hypothalamus (HYP), mid-brain reticular formation (MRF), and lateral geniculate (LGB) (Hinman and Okamoto 1984. Copyright 1984, Academic Press).

abnormal brain activity during withdrawal, especially in subcortical loci, is essential to understanding the mechanisms of barbiturate tolerance and physical dependence.

To pursue this information, we have recorded electroencephalograms from cortical and subcortical brain regions during moderate-intensity barbiturate withdrawal (Hinman and Okamoto 1984). The EEG pattern showed 4-6 Hz rhythmic bursts in the hippocampus and visual cortex during withdrawal (figure 7). The bursts in the hippocampus were a spike-and-wave type. In animals which had spontaneous seizures, 4-6 Hz bursts occurred also in the motor cortex; this motor cortex abnormality did not occur in animals which did not have spontaneous generalized seizures. Prolonged high frequency, high voltage discharges and spikes were also recorded frequently from the amygdala and the LGB during withdrawal (figure 8). Animals displayed bizarre behaviors suggestive of hallucinations during these periods of prolonged discharges, especially during prolonged bursts from the hippocampus and the visual cortex (Hinman and Okamoto 1984).

In order to explore more fundamental neuronal mechanisms of the development of tolerance and physical dependence and the neuronal mechanisms responsible for the expression of CNS hyperexcitation during withdrawal, electrophysiological studies of well-characterized spinal cord reflexes were performed in our physically barbiturate-dependent animals. After 5 weeks of treatment with our standard chronic "high" dose pentobarbital regimen (Rosenberg and Okamoto 1974; Okamoto et al. 1975), animals were prepared for spinal cord reflex function studies 48 hours after the last dose. Several alterations in spinal cord reflex function during

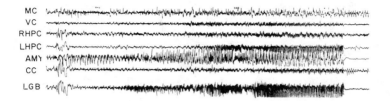

FIGURE 8. EEG recording during a spontaneous partial seizure
during moderate-intensity barbiturate withdrawal. The animal
remained standing during the seizure. Recordings are from various
loci: motor cortex (MC), visual cortex (VC), hippocampus, right
side (RHPC), hippocampus, left side (LHPC), amygdala (AMY), nucleus
centralis centralis (CC), and lateral geniculate (LGB). (Hinman
and Okamoto 1984. Copyright 1984, Academic Press).

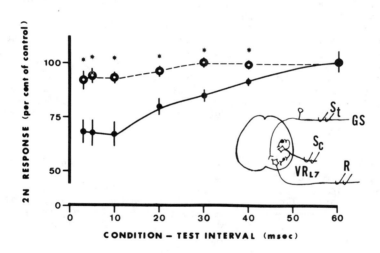

FIGURE 9. Recurrent inhibition of the reflex discharge (2N
response). Measured in 12 control (o) and 14 withdrawing animals
(o) 48 hours after the last dose of chronic pentobarbital treatment. Vertical bars indicate $\pm$ S.E.; asterisks indicate P .05 by
t-test. Inset: A schematic drawing of electrode locations: GS
(gastrocnemius-soleus muscle nerve), S_t (stimulating electrode,
test impulse), VR_{L7} (ventral root L-7), S_c (stimulating
electrode on one-sixth to one-third of L-7 ventral root to deliver
conditioning impulse), R (recording electrode). (Rosenberg and
Okamoto 1978. Copyright 1978, American Society for Pharmacology
and Experimental Therapeutics).

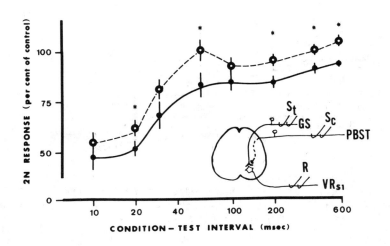

FIGURE 10. Presynaptic inhibition of the 2N response. Measured in 14 control (o) and 14 withdrawing animals (o) 48 hours after the last dose of chronic pentobarbital. Vertical bars indicate + S.E.; asterisks indicate P < .05 by t-test. Inset: Schematic drawing of experimental electrode locations: GS (gastrocnemius-soleus muscle nerve), S_t (stimulating electrode, test impulse), PSBT (posterior biceps and semitendinosus muscle nerve), S_c (stimulating electrode to deliver conditioning impulse), (VR_{S1} (ventral root S-1), R (recording electrode) (Rosenberg and Okamoto 1978. Copyright 1978, American Society for Pharmacology and Experimental Therapeutics).

barbiturate withdrawal were demonstrated (Rosenberg and Okamoto 1976). These included (1) increased polysynaptic but not monosynaptic (2N) reflex discharges; (2) decreased synaptic refractoriness, allowing more efficient transmission of repetitive impulses; (3) increased sensitivity to lower frequency tetanic stimulation in the production of post-tetanic potentiation (PTP); and (4) augmented spontaneous discharge. All of these results indicate generalized augmentation of neuronal activity during withdrawal.

Since the overall excitability of the CNS depends to a large extent on a delicate balance between excitatory and inhibitory functions, the hyper-excitability displayed in withdrawing animals may be a consequence not only of increased activity in excitatory pathways but also of decreased activity in inhibitory pathways. Further electrophysiological studies of inhibitory function at the spinal reflex level (Rosenberg and Okamoto 1978) indicate that recurrent inhibition disappeared almost totally during barbiturate withdrawal (figure 9). Presynaptic inhibition also decreased dramatically (figure 10). Loss of inhibition during withdrawal may be causally related to the enhancement of inhibition by the presence of the barbiturate, as has been demonstrated in the hippocampus (Nicoll et al. 1975), the olfactory bulb (Nicoll 1972), and possibly in the (Hurlbrink and Boyd 1969). The neurochemical basis of this drug enhancement of inhibition and reduced inhibition during withdrawal is of great interest. Barbiturates appear to selectively facilitate GABA-mediated responses (Ransom and Barker 1976; cf. Ho 1981) and to increase presynaptic inhibition in the spinal cord, which is thought to be GABA mediated (Eccles et al. 1963; Schmidt 1963; Bell and Anderson 1972; Davidoff 1972). Accordingly it was possible that our findings of decreased presynaptic inhibition during withdrawal might be related to altered GABA levels or kinetics, although this would not explain our findings of the loss of recurrent inhibition, since GABA is not thought to be involved in the recurrent inhibitory pathway. Glycine is the proposed transmitter for both the Renshaw cell and also for neurons which mediate Ia inhibition (Werman et al. 1968; Curtis 1969). However, our findings do not specifically implicate glycinergic mechanisms either. Although recurrent inhibition, involving the Renshaw cell, was nearly abolished during withdrawal, direct inhibition involving the Ia inhibitory interneuron was not changed.

The results of these studies support the hypothesis of a nonspecific adaptation of the nervous system during chronic barbiturate treatment, i.e., adaptation not specific to a particular neurochemical system. A major part of this adaptation is a decreased activity in certain inhibitory pathways. This view, if correct, means that the adaptation is a response to chronic depression of the nervous system rather than a specific response to the particular drug. Further studies should be forthcoming to elucidate the underlying mechanisms which contribute to a development of cellular tolerance and physical dependence.

REFERENCES

Bell, J.A., and Anderson, E.G. The influence of semicarbazide-induced depletion of γ-aminobutyric acid on presynaptic inhibition. Brain Res, 43:161-169, 1972.
Boisse, N.R., and Okamoto, M. Physical dependence to barbital compared to pentobarbital. I. "Chronically equivalent" dosing method. J Pharmacol Exp Ther, 204:497-506, 1978a.
Boisse, N.R., and Okamoto, M. Physical dependence to barbital compared to pentobarbital. II. Tolerance characteristics. J Pharmacol Exp Ther, 204:507-513, 1978b.
Boisse, N.R., and Okamoto, M. Physical dependence to barbital compared to pentobarbital. III. Withdrawal characteristics. J Pharmacol Exp Ther, 204:514-525, 1978c.
Boisse, N.R., and Okamoto, M. Physical dependence to barbital compared to pentobarbital. IV. Influence of elimination kinetics. J Pharmacol Exp Ther, 204:526-540, 1978d.
Curtis, D.R. The pharmacology of spinal postsynaptic inhibition. Progr Brain Res, 31:171-189, 1969.
Davidoff, R.A. Gamma-aminobutyric acid antagonism and presynaptic inhibition in the frog spinal cord. Science (Washington), 175:331-333, 1972.

Eccles, J.C., Schmidt, R., and Willis, W.D. Pharmacological studies
  on presynaptic inhibition. J Physiol (London), 168:500-530,
  1963.
Essig, C.F. Convulsive and sham rage behaviors in decorticate dogs
  during barbiturate withdrawal. Arch Neurol Psychiat (Clin),
  7:471-475, 1962.
Fraser, H.F., Wikler, A., Essig, C.F., and Isbell, H. Degree of
  physical dependence induced by secobarbital or pentobarbital.
  JAMA, 166:126-129, 1958.
Goldstein, D.B. Relationship of alcohol dose to intensity of
  withdrawal signs in mice. J Pharmacol Exp Ther, 180:203-215,
  1972.
Hinman, D.J., and Okamoto, M. EEG patterns recorded from cortical
  and subcortical areas during moderate-intensity barbiturate
  withdrawal. Experimental Neurology, 83:555-567, 1984.
Ho, I.K. Mechanisms of action of barbiturates. Ann Rev Pharmacol
  Toxicol, 21:83-111, 1981.
Hollister, L.E. Dependence on benzodiazepines. In: Szara, E.I.,
  and Ludford, J.P., eds. Benzodiazepines: A Review of Research
  Results. National Institute on Drug Abuse Research Monograph 33.
  DHEW Pub. No. (ADM) 81-1052. Washington, D.C.: Supt. of Docs.,
  U.S. Govt. Print. Off. 1981. pp. 70-82.
Hurlbrink, E.E., and Boyd, E.S. Some effects of pentobarbital and
  strychnine on transmission through the ventrobasal complex of the
  cat thalamus. J Pharmacol Exp Ther, 170:181-189, 1969.
Isbell, H., Altschul, S., Kornetsky, C.H., Eiseman, A.J., Flanary,
  H.G., and Fraser, H.F. Chronic barbiturate intoxication. An
  experimental study. Arch Neurol Psychiat (Clin), 64:1-28, 1950.
Jaffe, J.H. Drug addiction and drug abuse. In: Goodman, L.S.,
  and Gilman, A., eds. The Pharmacological Basis of
  Therapeutics. New York: MacMillan, 1980. pp. 535-584.
Kalant, H., LeBlanc, A.E., and Gibbins, R.J. Tolerance to and
  dependence on some non-opiate psychotropic drugs. Pharmacol Rev,
  23:135-191, 1971.
Nicoll, R.A. The effects of anesthetics on synaptic excitation and
  inhibition in the olfactory bulb. J Physiol (London),
  223:803-814, 1972.
Nicoll, R.A. Eccles, J.C., Oshima, T.C., and Rubia, F.
  Prolongation of hippocampal inhibitory postsynaptic potentials by
  barbiturates. Nature (London), 258:625-627, 1975.
Okamoto, M., and Boisse, N.R. Sedative-hypnotic tolerance and
  physical dependence. TIPS, 2:9-13, 1981.
Okamoto, M., and Hinman, D.J. Effects of individual variations in
  drug elimination kinetics for production of pentobarbital
  physical dependence. J Pharmacol Exp Ther, 226:52-56, 1983.
Okamoto, M., and Hinman, D.J. Physical dependence produced by long
  duration, low dose chronic barbital treatment. Subst Alcohol
  Actions/Misuse, 1984. (in press).
Okamoto, M., Boisse, N.R., Rosenberg, H.C., and Rosen, R.
  Characteristics of functional tolerance during barbiturate
  physical dependency production. J Pharmacol Exp Ther,
  207:906-915, 1978.

Okamoto, M., Hinman, D.J., and Aaronson, L.M. Comparison of ethanol and barbiturate physical dependence. J Pharmacol Exp Ther, 218:701, 1981.

Okamoto, M., Rosenberg, H.C., and Boisse, N.R. Tolerance characteristics produced during the maximally tolerable chronic pentobarbital dosing in the cat. J Pharmacol Exp Ther, 192:555-569, 1975.

Ransom, B.R., and Barker, J.L. Pentobarbital selectively enhances GABA-mediated post-synaptic inhibition in tissue cultured mouse spinal neurons. Brain Res, 114:530-535, 1976.

Remmer, H. Tolerance to barbiturates by increased breakdown. In: Steinberg, H., ed. Scientific Basis of Drug Dependence. New York: Grune and Stratton, 1969. pp. 111-128.

Rosenberg, H.C., and Okamoto, M. A method for producing maximal pentobarbital dependence in cats: Dependence characteristics. In: Singh, J.M., and Lal, H., eds. Drug Addiction: Neurobiology and Influences on Behavior. Miami: Symposia Specialist, 1974. Vol. 3, pp. 89-103.

Rosenberg, H.C., and Okamoto, M. Electrophysiology of barbiturate withdrawal in the spinal cord. J Pharmacol Exp Ther, 199:189-197, 1976.

Rosenberg, H.C., and Okamoto, M. Loss of inhibition in the spinal cord during barbiturate withdrawal. J Pharmacol Exp Ther, 205:563-568, 1978.

Schmidt, R.F. Pharmacological studies on the primary afferent depolarization of the toad spinal cord. Pfugers Arch Gesmate Physiol Menschen Tuse, 277:325-346, 1963.

Sharpless, S.K., and Jaffe, J.H. The electrical excitability of isolated cortex during barbiturate withdrawal. J Pharmacol Exp Ther, 151:321-329, 1967.

Werman, R., Davidoff, R.A., and Aprisan, M.H. Inhibitory action of glycine on spinal neurons in the cat. J Neurophysiol, 31:81-95, 1968.

Wikler, A., Fraser, H.F., Isbell, H., and Pescore, F.T., EEGs during cycles of addiction to barbiturates in man. EEG Clin Neurophysiol, 7:1-13, 1955.

Wulff, M.H. The barbiturate withdrawal syndrome; a clinical and electro-encephalographic study. EEG Clin Neurophysiol Suppl, 14:1-173, 1959.

ACKNOWLEDGEMENT

This study has been supported by research grant DA 00591 from the National Institute on Drug Abuse. Drs. Norman R. Boisse, Donald J. Hinman, and Howard C. Rosenberg contributed to various phases of this study.

AUTHOR

Michiko Okamoto, Ph.D.
Department of Pharmacology
Cornell University Medical College
1300 York Avenue
New York, NY 10021

Behavioral and Biochemical Studies in Rats After Chronic Exposure to Nicotine

Leo G. Abood, Susan Grassi, Maria Costanzo, and Jeffrey Junig

INTRODUCTION

Since nicotine is the major constituent in cigarette smoke responsible for the reinforcing effect of smoking, studies on the behavioral and pharmacologic tolerance of nicotine are of considerable interest to the health consequences of smoking. As discussed by Russell (1979) in a NIDA monograph, there are diverse pharmacologic, as well as psychologic, factors involved in the assessment of smoking as a dependence process; but attempts to develop appropriate animal models towards this end have not been very successful. Although tolerance is a requirement for a dependence producing drug, tolerance occurs with a wide variety of psychotropic drugs not producing dependence and can involve behavioral mechanisms as well as alterations in drug disposition and pharmacodynamic responsiveness (Jaffe 1980).

A review of the literature on the effect of chronic administration of agonists or antagonists on various neurotransmitter receptors reveals findings which are often conflicting and difficult to interpret. Chronic administration of amphetamine (a dopamine agonist) has been reported to decrease both agonist and antagonist binding (Muller and Seeman 1979; Howlett and Nahorski 1979), while others failed to observe any effect on striatal binding of ^{3}H-haloperidol (a dopaminergic receptor antagonist).

It was recently reported that chronic treatment of rats with diisopropylfluorophosphate (DFP) (a cholinesterase inhibitor) decreased ^{3}H-acetylcholine binding to cerebral cortex by 23%; whereas chronic exposure to nicotine increased the amount of binding by 25% (Schwartz and Kellar 1983). No change was observed on the affinity of ^{3}H-acetylcholine with either agent.

In another study involving continuous infusion of various doses of nicotine to DBA female mice for 10 days, significant increases in ^{3}H-nicotine binding, as well as α-^{125}I-bungarotoxin binding, occurred in the midbrain and hippocampus with no change in the K_d values (Marks et al. 1983). Although nicotine infusion had no effect on baseline rotarod performance to acute injections of nicotine, the nicotine-induced bradycardia was diminished. They also observed a significant tolerance to the acute effects of nicotine on rotarod performance and body temperature.

Tolerance after Chronic Administration of Nicotine

In order to determine whether behavioral tolerance develops after chronic administration of nicotine to rats, nicotine was chronically administered either intraperitoneally of by infusion into the lateral ventricles (table 1).

TABLE 1

Effect of Various Dosage Regimens and Routes of Administration on Prostration Following Nicotine Administration into Fourth Ventricles of Rats.

Dosage Schedule Syndrome	Incidence of Prostration
5 nmoles nicotine twice daily into fourth ventricles for 4 days	All rats responded day 1; 60% responded day 2; 30% responded day 4; 90% responded fully after 3 days without nicotine.
Alzet minipump (50 nmoles/hr) into lateral ventricle for 10 days	Normal response to 5 nmoles of nicotine into fourth ventricle on last day of infusion.
Acute injection of 12 μmole/kg of ip twice daily for 14 days.	Most rats responded to 5nmoles of nicotine into fourth ventricles 12 hr after last injection. Response was slightly less than in controls.

When 5 nmoles of (-)-nicotine (neutralized with HCl and in a volume of 1 μl) was administered twice daily for 4 consecutive days into the fourth ventricle, all rats exhibited prostration on day 1, 60% on day 2, and only 30% on day 4. At least 90% of the rats responded to 5 nmoles of nicotine when administered into the fourth ventricle on day 7 (3 days after the 4 daily doses of nicotine). After nicotine was infused continuously into the lateral ventricle for 10 days at a rate of 50 nmoles/hr, the rats exhibited full prostration when 5 nmoles nicotine was administered into the fourth ventricle on the last day of infusion. In a third protocol, after rats were injected intraperitoneally with 12 μmoles/kg of nicotine twice daily for 14 days, they exhibited prostration when given 5 nmoles of nicotine into the fourth ventricle 12 hr after the last injection of nicotine.

A number of conclusions can be inferred from these studies. The administration of nicotine into the fourth ventricle for 4 days appears to produce some tolerance in the prostration syndrome; however, the tolerance vanishes 3 days after the last dose. When nicotine is infused continuously into the brain for 14 days, no tolerance develops to the administration of nicotine directly into the fourth ventricle. Finally, the chronic administration of nicotine systemically for 14 days resulted in only slight tolerance to nicotine given into the fourth ventricle. It would appear that behavioral tolerance to nicotine, as assessed by the prostration syndrome, is transient and diminishes with chronic administration. The findings are in agreement with those of Stollerman et al. (1974) that following chronic exposure to nicotine, the development of tolerance initially increased and then decreased as the dose of nicotine was increased.

Effect of Chronic Nicotine Treatment on ^{3}H-Nicotine Binding in Rat Brain

After administering 12 μmole/Kg of nicotine ip twice daily to a total of 10 rats, the K_d and B_{max} for (-)-^{3}H-nicotine binding were determined 15 hr after the last injection on membrane preparations of whole brain employing Scatchard analyses. A control group of rats maintained under similar environmental conditions received saline. A third group of 5 rats, which received a continuous infusion of nicotine into the lateral ventricle from an Alzet minipump at the rate of 50 nmole/hr for a period of 10 days, was analyzed similarly 15 hr after infusion ceased. The binding studies revealed no significant differences between the control and nicotine-exposed groups in either the high or low K_d or B_{max} values (table 2).

TABLE 2

Effect of Chronic Nicotine Treatment on B_{max} and K_d of ^{3}H-(-)-Nicotine Binding to Rat Brain Membranes

Conditions	B_{max} moles/mg x 10^{14}		K_d x 10^{10}	
	High	Low	High	Low
Normal	0.5 $\pm$ 0.1	2.9 $\pm$ 0.4	1.0 $\pm$ 0.3	3.5 $\pm$ 0.2
Chronic (twice daily)	0.4 $\pm$ 0.1	2.7 $\pm$ 0.2	0.8 $\pm$ 0.2	3.3 $\pm$ 0.3
Chronic (infusion)	0.4 $\pm$ 0.1	2.8 $\pm$ 0.3	1.1 $\pm$ 0.2	3.5 $\pm$ 0.3

Values are expressed as mean $\pm$ sd with n=3-4 rat brains. Data were derived from Scatchard plots.

These findings, which fail to demonstrate any alteration in the nicotine receptor in rat brain following chronic exposure to nicotine, are consistent with the behavioral studies demonstrating only a slight decrease in the sensitivity of the nicotine-induced prostration. Although they would appear to be at variance with the study of Marks et al. (1983) reporting up-regulation of nicotine binding, their studies were performed on DBA mice which developed a significant behavioral and pharmacologic tolerance after nicotine infusion. It is also conceivable that regional brain areas may reveal differences not observable in whole rat brain.

Binding of Nicotine Analogues and Other Agents to Rat Hepatocytes Using Either (-)- or (+)-^{3}H-Nicotine

In the course of investigating the metabolism of nicotine by isolated rat hepatocytes, it was observed that the hepatocytes exhibited a specific affinity for nicotine and its analogues and that the affinity appeared to be greater for the (+)- than the (-)-enantiomer (table 3).

TABLE 3

Binding of Nicotine Analogues and Other Agents to Rat Hepatocytes Using Either (-)- or (+)-^{3}H-Nicotine.

| Agent | IC$_{50}$ M | |
	(-)-^{3}H-nicotine	(+)-^{3}H-nicotine
(-)-nicotine	1×10^{-6}	5×10^{-7}
(+)-nicotine	3×10^{-7}	3×10^{-8}
nornicotine	3×10^{-5}	1×10^{-5}
N'-nicotonium	1×10^{-3}	1×10^{-3}
(-)-cotinine	5×10^{-4}	3×10^{-4}
N'-ethyl nornicotine	3×10^{-6}	1×10^{-6}
N-methyl nicotine	1×10^{-3}	1×10^{-3}
N'-ethyl nornicotine	5×10^{-6}	2×10^{-6}
N'-propyl nornicotine	8×10^{-6}	2×10^{-6}
N'-butyl nornicotine	2×10^{-5}	8×10^{-6}
mecamylamine	2×10^{-5}	1×10^{-5}
haloperidol	2×10^{-4}	1×10^{-4}
chlorpromazine	3×10^{-4}	1×10^{-4}
imipramine	1×10^{-4}	8×10^{-5}
carbamylcholine	1×10^{-3}	1×10^{-3}
hexamethonium	1×10^{-3}	1×10^{-3}

At a final concentration of 1×10^{-9}M (-)- or (+)-^{3}H-nicotine, the IC$_{50}$ values were found to be 1×10^{-6} and 3×10^{-7}M in the presence of a 100-fold excess of the unlabeled (-)- and (+)-nicotine respectively;

whereas, with $(+)-^3$H-nicotine the values were 5×10^{-7} and 3×10^{-8}M in the presence of a 100-fold excess of the unlabeled enantiomers. With increasing chain length of alkyl substituents on the pyrrolidine N of nicotine, there was a corresponding decrease in the affinity, using either $(-)-$ or $(+)-^3$H-nicotine. As discussed elsewhere (Abood et al., 1983), there was an excellent correlation between the binding affinity of this homologous series of nicotine analogues and their ability to produce prostration when administered ivc. Quaternization of either the pyrrolidine or pyridine N of nicotine greatly reduced the affinity for hepatocytes; while nicotinic cholinergic agents such as carbamylcholine and hexamethonium exhibited no affinity.

It can be concluded from these studies that specific nicotine binding exists in isolated hepatocytes. The binding is reversible and nonstereoselective; and since it is not saturable at concentrations of $(-)-$ or $(+)-$nicotine lower than 10^{-4}M, the binding may be related to a transport system involved in the metabolism-disposition of nicotine. When the hepatocytes are even slightly damaged, they lose their ability to bind or take up nicotine. It is noteworthy that the relationship of binding affinity of the various nicotine analogues in hepatocytes agrees with the relative psychotropic potency of the analogues.

Effect of Chronic Nicotine Treatment on the Metabolism of $(-)-$ and $(+)-^3$H-Nicotine by Isolated Hepatocytes

In an effort to determine whether chronic nicotine administration (systemic administration for 14 days) altered its metabolism by liver, hepatocytes were isolated from rat liver after collagenase perfusion and modification of the method of Baur and Heldt (1971).

The hepatocytes were incubated for various times at 37°C in Hank's buffer containing 10^{-9}M $(-)-^3$H-nicotine + 10^{-5}M unlabeled $(-)-$nicotine + 10^{-3}M nicotinamide at pH 7.5. The rate of disappearance of the nicotine present was 2.5×10^{-6} mmoles/min/mg protein for the control preparation compared to a value of 3.0×10^{-6} for the rats chronically exposed to nicotine. Since the difference was not statistically different, it would appear that chronic nicotine treatment does not alter its metabolism by liver. The results are in agreement with those of Marks et al. (1983) who failed to observe any effect of chronic nicotine infusion on the rate of nicotine disappearance from the blood of DBA mice in vivo.

Effect of Chronic Nicotine Administration on Lever Press Avoidance of Aversive Shock

A number of groups have reported on the antinociceptive actions of nicotine in rodents (Tripathi et al. 1982; Sahley and Berntson 1979). Dewey et al. (1970) have reported that the analgetic action of nicotine on a molar basis was comparable to that of morphine. A number of mechanisms have been proposed for the antinociceptive action of nicotine including a nicotinic cholinergic one (Sahley and

Berntson 1979; Tripathi et al. 1982), an opioid one in mice but not rats (Tripathi et al. 1982), and one involving α-adrenergic receptors (Tripathi et al. 1982). It is apparent from such studies that the action of nicotine on antinociception is a complex one. There also remains the issue as to whether nicotine is analgetic or is simply elevating the animal's threshold to an aversive stimulus (Abood et al. 1981). In an effort to further investigate this action of nicotine, another paradigm was employed for measuring the response to an aversive stimulus.

In a previous study (Abood et al. 1981), it was reported that nicotine administered intraventricularly to rats significantly elevated the threshold to an aversive shock, employing a shock-avoidance paradigm in which the animals were delivered 16 random shocks over a 5-min period beginning with an initial near-subthreshold shock (0.4 mA) and extending to a maximal shock of 1.4 mA. (Abood et al. 1981; D'Amato and Fazzaro 1966; for experimental details.) A comparison of the effects of acute and chronic nicotine administration on the frequency of lever pressing for shock avoidance is presented in table 4. After rats had established a frequency

TABLE 4

Effect of Acute and Chronic Nicotine Administration on Discriminative Lever-Pressing for Shock Avoidance

		Mean Frequency	% Decrease
Acute Study	Before nicotine	40.4 ± 2.6	-
	After nicotine	19.9 ± 2.3	50
	Naloxone + nicotine	22.0 ± 3.0	45
After chronic nicotine	Before nicotine	35.5 ± 3.0	-
	After nicotine	25.5 ± 2.5	28

Results are presented as mean frequency of lever pressing before and after saline or 15 nmoles (-)-nicotine ivc. Analysis of variance employing a univariate and multivariate regression problems program yields p <0.0001. Values are expressed as mean frequency of responses with variance. Chronic rats received nicotine ip twice daily for 14 days as described in text. A dose of naloxone of 4 mg/kg ip was administered 20 min prior to nicotine ivc.

baseline of lever pressing, they were administered 15 nmoles of (-)-nicotine (5 µl) ivc and again tested. In the group not receiving nicotine chronically, a 50% decrease in the frequency of lever pressing occurred after nicotine ivc; and, in the chronically treated groups the decrease was 28%. After chronic administration of nicotine, the mean frequency of response prior to ivc nicotine was lowered while the frequency after nicotine ivc was elevated. When naloxone was administered 20 min prior to nicotine ivc, there was no effect on the frequency of response. It would appear from these studies that following chronic nicotine administration, some tolerance had developed to the ability of nicotine to elevate the threshold to shock. Furthermore, the effect of nicotine on aversiveness does not appear to be mediated by an opioid system.

CONCLUSION

A number of conclusions concerning the problem of tolerance to nicotine may be derived from the present study. Although tolerance develops in rats during the earlier stages of chronic administration, behavioral tolerance to intraventricularly administered nicotine tends to diminish with further exposure to nicotine. Some tolerance appears to develop in the ability of nicotine to attenuate aversiveness to electric shock; while the initial tolerance to nicotine-induced prostration appears to disappear. There does not appear to be any alteration in either the affinity or density of ^{3}H-nicotine binding sites in rat brain with chronic administration of nicotine, nor any increase in its rate of metabolism by liver.

REFERENCES

Abood, L.G.; Reynolds, D.T.; Booth, H.; and Bidlack, J.M. Sites and mechanisms for nicotine's action in the brain. Neurosci Biobehav, 5:479-486, 1981.

Abood, L.G.; Grassi, S.; and Costanza, M. Binding of optically pure (-)-^{3}H-nicotine to rat brain membranes. FEBS Lett, 157:147-149, 1983.

Baur, H., and Heldt, H.W. Use of Isolated Liver Cells and Kidney Tubules in Metabolic Studies. North Holland, Amsterdam, 1971, 357 pp.

D'Amato, M.R., and Fazzaro, J. Discriminated lever-pressing avoidance learning as a function of type and intensity of shock. J Comp Physiol Psychol, 61:313-315, 1966.

Dewey, W.L.; Harris, L.S.; Howes, J.F.; and Nuite, J.A. The effect of various neurohumoral modulators on the activity of morphine and the narcotic antagonists in tail-flick and phenylquinoline test. J Pharmacol Exp Ther, 175:435-442, 1970.

Howlett, D.R., and Nahorski, S.R. Acute and chronic amphetamine treatments modulate striatal dopamine receptor binding sites. Brain Res, 161:173-178, 1979.

Jaffe, J.H. Drug addiction and drug abuse. In: Gilman, A.G., Goodman, L.S., and Gilman, A., eds. Goodman and Gilman's The Pharmacological Basis of Therapeutics. 6th edition. New York: MacMillan, 1980, pp. 535-584.

Marks, M.J.; Burch, J.B.; and Collins, A.C. Effects of chronic nicotine infusion on tolerance development and nicotinic receptors. J Pharmacol Exp Ther, 226:817-825, 1983.

Muller, P., and Seeman, P. Pre-synaptic subsensitivity as possible basis for sensitization by long term mimetics. Europ J Pharmacol, 55:149-157, 1979.

Russell, M.A.H. Tobacco dependence: Is nicotine rewarding or aversive? In: Krasnegor, N.A., ed. Cigarette Smoking as a Dependence Process. National Institute on Drug Abuse Research Monograph 23. DHEW Pub. No. (ADM) 79-800. Washington, D.C.: Supt. of Docs., U.S. Govt. Print. Off., 1979. pp. 158-184.

Sahley, T.L., and Berntson, G.G. Antinociceptive effects of central and systemic administration of nicotine in the rat. Psychopharmacology 65:279-283, 1979.

Schwartz, R.D., and Kellar, K.J. Nicotinic cholinergic receptor of binding sites in the brain: Regulation in vivo. Science 220:214-216, 1983.

Stollerman, J.P.; Bunker, P.; and Jarvik, M.E. Nicotine tolerance in rats: Role of dose and dose interval. Psychopharmacologia 30:329-342, 1974.

Tripathi, H.L.; Martin, B.R.; and Aceto, M.D. Nicotine-induced antinociception in rats and mice. Correlation with nicotine levels. J Pharmacol Exp Ther 221:91-96, 1982.

ACKNOWLEDGEMENTS

This research was supported by DA00464 from The National Institute on Drug Abuse and a grant from the Council for Tobacco Research.

AUTHORS

Leo G. Abood, Ph.D.
Center for Brain Research—Box 605
University of Rochester Medical Center
601 Elmwood Avenue
Rochester, New York 14642

Susan Grassi
Center for Brain Research—Box 605
University of Rochester Medical Center
601 Elmwood Avenue
Rochester, New York 14642

Maria Costanzo
Center for Brain Research—Box 605
University of Rochester Medical Center
601 Elmwood Avenue
Rochester, New York 14642

Jeffrey Junig
Center for Brain Research—Box 605
University of Rochester Medical Center
601 Elmwood Avenue
Rochester, New York 14642

Psychobiological Foundations of Behaviors Induced by Amphetamines

Philip M. Groves and David S. Segal

The abuse of psychomotor stimulants such as amphetamine and
cocaine is a problem of major proportions in contemporary life.
It has been well documented that drug abuse results in serious
untoward medical and social consequences. Research on the effects
of amphetamine has attempted to establish models of the behavioral
consequences of stimulant administration in animal subjects and to
determine the biomedical sequelae of acute and long-term abuse of
amphetamine, especially as the stimulant drug affects the structure and function of the brain. It is now well known that long-
term amphetamine administration can result in the development of
psychosis in humans. Further, when amphetamine is administered to
animal subjects it produces a characteristic pattern of behavioral
response which includes locomotor activation and the occurrence of
repetitive species-specific stereotyped behaviors. Extensive
research efforts have now established numerous sites of action of
stimulant drugs in the brain and have begun to relate the biochemical and neurophysiological effects of the drug to the characteristic behavioral profiles that have been described.

BEHAVIORAL CONSEQUENCES OF ACUTE AND CHRONIC AMPHETAMINE ADMINIS-
TRATION

When administered acutely to animal subjects, amphetamine produces
a characteristic dose- and time-related pattern of behavioral
responding. The laboratory rat has now been studied extensively
as a model for understanding the biomedical and behavioral effects
of the drug. Some of the features of the amphetamine response
following acute administration of the drug and following multiple
daily injections are illustrated in figure 1 where it can be seen
that the acute effects of the drug as well as the changes that
occur in the behavioral response with chronic administration are
both dose- and time-dependent. Repeated administration of relatively low doses (0.5 - 1.5 mg/kg), which initially produce
enhanced locomotion as the predominant response, results in a gradual increase in locomotor activity with respect to both peak
effect and duration. With moderate doses of the drug (1.5 - 2.5
mg/kg), amphetamine-induced locomotion during the early period of

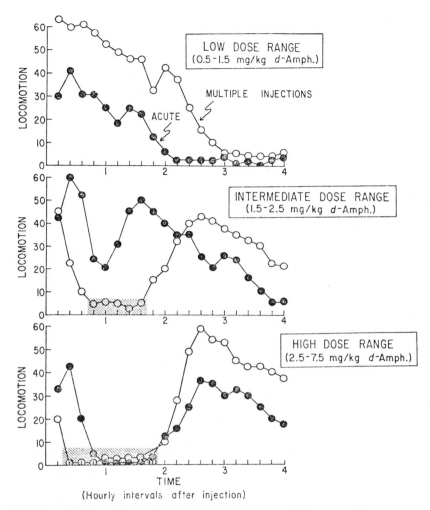

FIGURE 1. Alterations in response pattern with repeated daily
injections of a constant dose of d-amphetamine sulfate. Top: For
low doses, 5 to 10 days of administration results in a progressive
increase in locomotion as reflected in the magnitude and duration
of the response. Middle: For intermediate doses, the duration of
stereotypy episodes is increased, and by 3 to 5 days, a continuous
stereotypy phase (stippled shading) emerges. Poststereotypy
hyperactivity is also enhanced. Bottom: For the high dose range,
stereotypy (stippled shading) appears more rapidly and is intensified by the second injection, although the duration of the stereotypy phase is not correspondingly prolonged. Locomotion after the
stereotypy phase is progressively increased. Reprinted from David
S. Segal, Marc A. Schuckit, 1983, with permission. © Raven Press,
1983.

the response pattern is gradually replaced by progressively longer
episodes of focused stereotypies. Repeated injections of higher
doses (2.5 - 7.5 mg/kg), which acutely produce triphasic response
patterns consisting of an initial increase in locomotion followed
by a period of intense stereotyped behavior and a subsequent phase
of enhanced locomotion, result in a more rapid onset of the
stereotypy and a progressive augmentation in the later phase of
hyperactivity. Observation of the animal subjects confirms the
more rapid onset of stereotypy with a corresponding decrease in
locomotion.

Although repeated amphetamine administration augments various components of the acute response without apparent qualitative change,
the behavior that emerges does not simply reflect a shift to the
left in the amphetamine dose-response curve. Although the stereotypy appears more rapidly and is intensified at some doses, the
duration of the stereotypy phase is not correspondingly increased,
as it is with increasing doses administered acutely. Evidence
such as this has now accumulated and shows a complex, dose- and
time-dependent alteration which can be characterized as a sequential pattern of behavioral change resulting from multiple amphetamine injections in an extensive array of animal species. Such
evidence is clearly important in the evaluation of potential
underlying mechanisms. Further, alterations in the behavioral
response to amphetamine have now been detected in animal subjects
at least one month following a single acute injection of the drug,
suggesting an extremely powerful and potentially long-lasting
influence of amphetamine and related psychomotor stimulant drugs
on the brain.

NEURONAL MECHANISMS OF ACTION OF AMPHETAMINE

Substantial evidence accumulated over the past 2 decades suggests
that a significant site of action of amphetamine in the brain can
be identified with the catecholamine cell groups of the brainstem.
By releasing catecholamines, amphetamine is believed to act
indirectly on various targets in the brain including both postsynaptic targets of catecholamine neuron projections as well as
the presynaptic neurons themselves (Groves et al. 1975; Groves and
Rebec 1976; Groves and Tepper 1983; Segal and Schuckit 1983).
This has been demonstrated convincingly by recording the activity
of catecholamine neurons during the administration of amphetamine
to experimental animals. Among the early and best documented evidence illustrating the effect of amphetamine on catecholamine neurons was the demonstration that amphetamine administration led to
a marked inhibition of neuronal activity in two intensively studied cell groups of the brain, the dopaminergic pars compacta of
substantia nigra (Bunney et al. 1973) and the noradrenergic locus
coeruleus (Graham and Aghajanian 1971). This effect is illustrated for two representative neurons in figure 2. Intravenous
administration of amphetamine produces a decline in neuronal firing of dopaminergic neurons of the substantia nigra while a similar and even more pronounced effect also occurs for neurons in the
noradrenergic locus coeruleus.

358

This profound influence of amphetamine on the activity of catecholamine neurons was originally believed to be due to changes in
long-axoned feedback loops from sites of catecholaminergic innervation but is now thought to include the release of catecholamines
locally within these cell groups. For example, amphetamine has
now been shown to release dopamine from dopaminergic neurons of
substantia nigra both in vitro (Paden et al. 1976) and in vivo
(Cheramy et al. 1978). Anatomical evidence suggests that both
catecholaminergic presynaptic axons and dendrites are found within
the catecholaminergic cell groups (Groves et al. 1979; Groves and
Wilson 1980; Groves and Linder 1983) and would be available to
release these neurotransmitters in response to amphetamine.

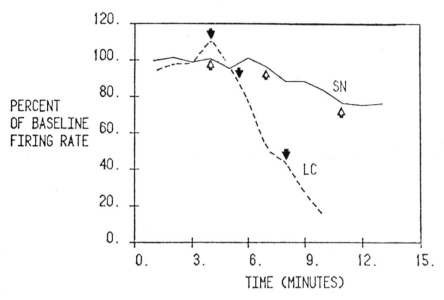

FIGURE 2. Illustration of the difference in sensitivity to
intravenously administered amphetamine between noradrenergic neurons of the nucleus locus coeruleus and dopaminergic neurons of
the substantia nigra pars compacta. The solid line indicates the
spontaneous firing rate of a representative dopamine neuron; the
dashed line is the firing rate of a noradrenergic neuron. Sequential intravenous injections of 0.25 mg/kg d-amphetamine sulfate
were given (arrows) for a cumulative dose in each case of 0.75
mg/kg. Whereas the locus coeruleus cell shows greater than 80%
inhibition to 0.75 mg/kg, the substantia nigra neuron only exhibits a 25% reduction in firing rate to this dose. Reprinted from
Philip M. Groves, James M. Tepper, 1983, with permission. © Raven
Press, 1983.

NEUROPHYSIOLOGICAL CONSEQUENCES OF PRESYNAPTIC RECEPTOR ACTIVATION

Since activation of catecholamine receptors on dopaminergic and noradrenergic neurons causes an inhibition of neuronal firing by these cells, it was of particular interest to determine if activation of presynaptic receptors presumed to exist on the terminals of these neurons would affect excitability in the same way. Groves and associates have now developed a method for measuring the excitability of catecholaminergic synaptic endings in the brain. This method is illustrated in figure 3. Electrical stimulation of the dopaminergic terminal field is effected while recording simultaneously from the region of the dopaminergic cell body. Antidromic action potentials reaching the initial segment and/or cell body of the dopaminergic neuron are recorded to determine whether the stimulus has produced an action potential. By plotting the probability of antidromic activation of the neuron against a range of stimulation currents, a excitability curve may be constructed that may be used to define the excitability of the synaptic terminal field. Now by administering various pharmacological or other treatments, variations in terminal excitability can be seen and appear to correlate with the release of catecholamines by the catecholaminergic synaptic endings. Using this paradigm for determining terminal excitability of individual dopaminergic and other monoaminergic neurons in the brain, Groves and associates have now been able to show that activation of these receptors, like those in the region of the cell body and dendrites, also seems to be accompanied by a decrease in terminal excitability, as illustrated in figure 4. As shown there, the currents necessary to activate dopaminergic cells antidromically by stimulation of their terminal fields in the neostriatum are uniformly increased by systematically administered amphetamine, and a similar effect occurs when amphetamine is infused in low concentrations and volumes directly into the vicinity of the terminals activated by the electrical stimulus. As illustrated in figure 5, antidopaminergic drugs such as the receptor-blocking agent haloperidol produce increased terminal excitability and can reverse the agonist-induced decrease in terminal excitability, the effects being represented by a uniform shift to the left in the excitability curve.

Evidence such as this suggests that the extracellular accumulation of dopamine that is produced by amphetamine causes activation of presynaptic receptors and that these, in turn, result in a change in polarization and/or conductance of the dopaminergic synaptic ending. Such an effect could, for example, represent a hyperpolarization of the synaptic ending produced by presynaptic receptor activation (Groves et al. 1981).

When similar experiments are carried out while monitoring the excitability of noradrenergic terminals in frontal cortex, a similar influence is also seen. Catecholaminergic agonists for the alpha-2-noradrenergic receptor lead to reduced terminal excitability when infused locally into the region of the terminal field, including low concentrations and volumes of d-amphetamine

360

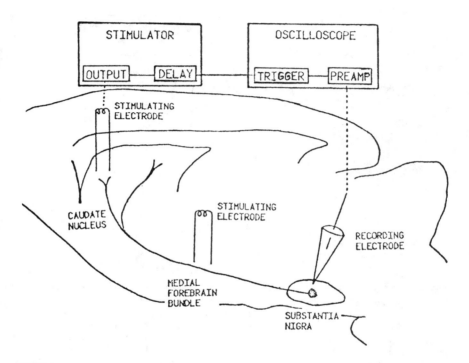

FIGURE 3. Schematic illustration of the experimental paradigm used
for measuring nigrostriatal dopaminergic terminal excitability. A
bipolar electrode is positioned within the neostriatum for
antidromic stimulation of the dopaminergic striatal afferents ori-
ginating in the ipsilateral substantia nigra pars compacta. An
extracellular recording electrode is positioned within the ipsilateral pars compacta, and the frequency of antidromic response to
neostriatal stimulating currents of varying strengths is measured.

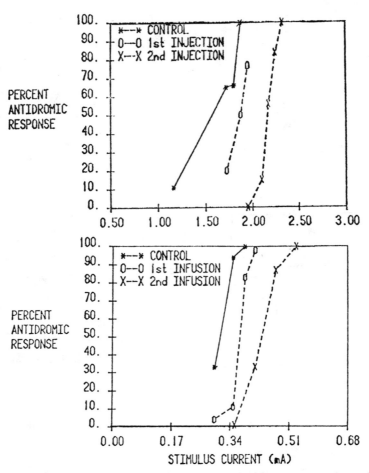

FIGURE 4. Top: Decrease in neostriatal dopamine terminal excitability following intravenous administration of d-amphetamine sulfate. Following an initial injection of 0.5 mg/kg d-amphetamine, the plot of neostriatal stimulating currents versus the proportion of antidromic responses detected by an extracellular recording in the ipsilateral substantia nigra pars compacta is shifted uniformly to the right, indicaing a decrease in terminal excitability at all current values. A second injection of 0.5 mg/kg d-amphetamine produces a further shift to the right in the excitability curve and an additional decrease in terminal excitability. Bottom: Decrease in excitability of dopaminergic terminnal in neostriatal induced by the local microinfusion of d-amphetamine directly into the stimulating site. Following an infusion of 0.31 µl of 1 µM d-amphetamine, the excitability curve is shifted to the right, indicating a decrease in terminal excitability. A second infusion of d-amphetamine (0.31 µl, 1 µM) 5 min later produces a further decrease in terminal excitability. Reprinted from Philip M. Groves, James H. Tepper, 1983, with permission. © Raven Press, 1983.

(Nakamura et al. 1981). However, systemically administered amphetamine produces a more complex influence on terminal excitability.
Low doses of the drug that do not lead to a profound inhibition of
firing produce a decrease in terminal excitability, but this
effect is reversed when the drug is administered in quantity sufficient to produce a cessation of impulse flow in the neuron
(Nakamura et al. 1981). This has been interpreted to indicate
that the release of catecholamine by the noradrenergic neuron in
response to amphetamine is partly dependent upon impulse traffic.

Evidence such as this has now demonstrated persuasively that
amphetamine, by releasing catecholamines, affects the activity and
excitability of the catecholamine neuron and, by inference, the
various postsynaptic targets of these systems throughout the
brain. While there has been a continuing effort to ascertain the
mechanisms underlying the inhibition of neuronal activity in these
cell groups following amphetamine administration, there has only
recently been a concerted attempt to determine mechanisms of
action at these manifold sites where amphetamine produces alterations in the brain. A recent review of such evidence indicates
that amphetamine administration leads to marked alterations in
neuronal firing throughout the reticular formation of the brainstem, the caudate nucleus, putamen and globus pallidus and related
striatal cell groups, the hypothalamus, cerebellum, and the cerebral cortex (see recent review by Groves and Tepper 1983). From
evidence such as this, it becomes apparent that the influence of
the drug is extremely widespread, is both dose- and time-
dependent, and cannot be easily explained by a monotonic increase
in the release of catecholamines.

A recent theoretical framework for intrastriatal neuronal circuitry has emphasized the interconnections of the common spiny neurons of neostriatum and has proposed that these form a large,
lateral inhibitory network which has been termed the Spiny I cell
matrix (Groves 1983). When this network is affected by amphetamine, we can imagine that at low doses of the drug, the processing
of information through this lateral inhibitory matrix is improved
but as the dose is increased or as repeated doses are administered, the ability of the neostriatum to respond to the patterns
of activation that arrive from substantia nigra, midline thalamus,
and cerebral cortex in time and space becomes compromised, and
stereotyped behaviors and other emergent patterns of behavioral
responding become apparent. The analysis of the environment and
the interaction with it that normally require information processing by the neostriatum become impaired and only those most primitive and securely represented patterns of behavioral responding
emerge, signalling a progressive constriction of the behavioral
repertoire. The various components of the emergent behaviors may
reflect an augmentation or diminution of component behaviors that
appeared upon acute administration of the drug, and lateral inhibitory processes intrinsic to the neostriatum may be expected to
lead to the evolution of these different degrees of apparent
behavioral sensitization and tolerance. New approaches toward
understanding the manifold mechanisms of action of amphetamine and

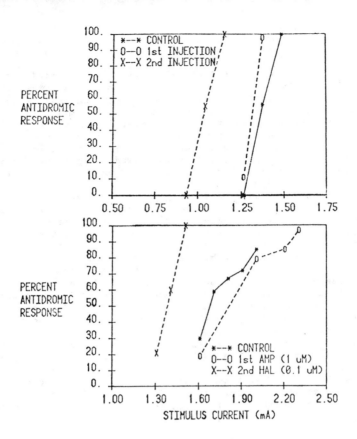

FIGURE 5. Top: Increase in neostriatal dopaminergic terminal excitability induced by intravenous injection of haloperidol lactate
(Haldol). Following an initial injection of 0.025 mg/kg haloperidol the excitability curve is shifted nearly uniformly to the
left, indicating an increase in terminal excitability inferred
from the reduced neostriatal stimulating currents necessary to
elicit varying proportions of antidromic responses in the ipsilateral substantia nigra pars compacta. A second injection of 0.025
mg/kg haloperidol produces a further increase in terminal excitability. Bottom: Reversal of the increase in dopaminergic terminal
excitability caused by a local infusion of amphetamine by a subsequent local infusion of haloperidol. In this representative example, after a control level of excitability was determined, an
infusion of d-amphetamine (0.31 μl, 1 μM) was made into the neostriatal stimulating site which resulted in a shift to the right
in the excitability curve (O--O), indicating a decrease in excitability. Approximately 5 min later, an infusion of haloperidol
(0.31 μl, 0.10 μM) was made into the same site via a second cannula. This infusion reversed the effects of the first infusion
and within 5 min the excitability curve was shifted dramatically
to the left (X--X), past the baseline, representing an overall
increase in terminal excitability. Reprinted from Philip M.
Groves, James M. Tepper, 1983. © Raven Press, 1983.

the way in which its actions are altered by long-term administration of the drug have now begun (e.g., Gale, this volume). Continued effort along these various lines of research holds considerable promise for further understanding the ways in which this and related drugs affect the brain and behavior.

REFERENCES

Bunney, B.S., Walters, J.R., Roth, R.H. and Aghajanian, G.K. Dopaminergic neurons: Effect of antipsychotic drugs and amphetamine on single cell activity. J Pharmacol Exp Ther, 185:560-571, 1973.

Cheramy, A., Nieoullon, A. and Glowinski, J. In vivo changes in dopamine release in cat caudate nucleus and substantia nigra induced by nigral application of various drugs including GABAergic agonists and antagonists. In Garattini, S., Pujol, J.F., and Samanin, R., eds. Interactions Between Putative Neurotransmitters in the Brain. New York: Raven Press, 1978. pp. 175-190.

Graham, A. and Aghajanian, G. Effects of amphetamine on single cell activity in a catecholamine nucleus, the locus coeruleus. Nature, 234: 100-102, 1971.

Groves, P.M. A theory of the functional organization of the neostriatum and the neostriatal control of voluntary movement. Brain Res Rev, 5:109-132, 1983.

Groves, P.M., Fenster, G.A., Tepper, J.M., Nakamura, S., and Young, S.J. Changes in dopaminergic terminal excitability induced by amphetamine and haloperidol. Brain Res, 221:425-431, 1981.

Groves, P.M., and Linder, J.C. Dendro-dendritic synapses in substantia nigra: Descriptions based on analysis of serial sections. Exp Brain Res, 49:209-217, 1983.

Groves, P.M., and Rebec, G.V. Biochemistry and behavior: Some central actions of amphetamine and certain antipsychotic drugs. Annu Rev Psychol, 27:91-127, 1976.

Groves, P.M., Staunton, D., Wilson, C.J., and Young, S.J. Sites of action of amphetamine intrinsic to catecholaminergic nuclei: Catecholaminergic presynaptic dendrites and axons. Prog Neuropsychopharmacol, 3:315-335, 1979.

Groves, P.M., and Tepper, J.M. Neuronal mechanisms of action of amphetamine. In: Creese, I., ed. Stimulants: Neurochemical, Behavioral, and Clinical Perspectives. New York: Raven Press, 1983. pp. 81-129.

Groves, P.M., and Wilson, C.J. Monoaminergic presynaptic axons and dendrites in rat locus coeruleus seen in reconstructions of serial sections. J Comp Neurol, 193:853-862, 1980.

Groves, P.M., Wilson, C.J., Young, S.J., and Rebec, G.V. Self-inhibition by dopaminergic neurons. Science, 190:522-529, 1975.

Nakamura, S., Tepper, J.M., Young, S.J., and Groves, P.M. Neurophysiological consequences of presynaptic receptor activation: Changes in noradrenergic terminal excitability. Brain Res, 226:155-170, 1981.

Paden, C., Wilson, C.J., and Groves, P.M. Amphetamine-induced release of dopamine from the substantia nigra in vivo. Life Sci, 19:1499-1506, 1976.

Segal, D.S., and Schuckit, M.A. Animal models of stimulant-induced psychosis. In: Creese, I., ed. Stimulants: Neurochemical, Behavioral, and Clinical Perspectives. New York: Raven Press, 1983. pp. 131-167.

ACKNOWLEDGEMENTS

This work was supported in part by USPHS Grants DA-02854 and DA-01568 from the National Institute on Drug Abuse; P.M.G. and D.S.S. are the recipients of Research Scientist Awards DA-00079 from the National Institute on Drug Abuse and MH-70183 from the National Institute of Mental Health.

AUTHORS

Philip M. Groves, Ph.D., Professor of Psychiatry, Department of Psychiatry, School of Medicine, University of California, San Diego, La Jolla, California 92093

David S. Segal, Ph.D., Professor of Psychiatry, Department of Psychiatry, School of Medicine, University of California, San Diego, La Jolla, California 92093

Index

National
Institute on
Drug
Abuse

Research

monograph series

While limited supplies last, single copies of the monographs may
be obtained free of charge from the National Clearinghouse for
Drug Abuse Information (NCDAI). Please contact NCDAI also for
information about availability of coming issues and other
publications of the National Institute on Drug Abuse relevant to
drug abuse research.

Additional copies may be purchased from the U.S. Government
Printing Office (GPO) and/or the National Technical Information
Service (NTIS) as indicated. NTIS prices are for paper copy.
Microfiche copies, at $4.50, are also available from NTIS.
Prices from either source are subject to change.

Addresses are:

NCDAI
National Clearinghouse for Drug Abuse Information
Room 10A-43
5600 Fishers Lane
Rockville, Maryland 20857

GPO   NTIS
Superintendent of Documents   National Technical Information
U.S. Government Printing Office   Service
Washington, D.C. 20402   U.S. Department of Commerce
                                           Springfield, Virginia 22161

1 FINDINGS OF DRUG ABUSE RESEARCH. Not available from NCDAI.
Vol. 1:   GPO out of stock   NTIS PB #272 867/AS $32.50
Vol. 2:   GPO out of stock   NTIS PB #272 868/AS $29.50

2 OPERATIONAL DEFINITIONS IN SOCIO-BEHAVIORAL DRUG USE RESEARCH
1975. Jack Elinson, Ph.D., and David Nurco, Ph.D., eds. Not
available from NCDAI.
GPO out of stock   NTIS PB #246 338/AS $16

3 AMINERGIC HYPOTHESES OF BEHAVIOR: REALITY OR CLICHE? Bruce J.
Bernard, Ph.D., ed. Not available from NCDAI.
GPO Stock #017-024-00486-3 $6.50   NTIS PB #246 687/AS $16

371

4 NARCOTIC ANTAGONISTS: THE SEARCH FOR LONG-ACTING PREPARATIONS.
Robert Willette, Ph.D., ed.
GPO out of stock   NTIS PB #247 096/AS $8.50

5 YOUNG MEN AND DRUGS: A NATIONWIDE SURVEY.   John A. O'Donnell,
Ph.D., et al. Not available from NCDAI.
GPO Stock #017-024-00511-8 $6.50   NTIS PB #247 446/AS $16

6 EFFECTS OF LABELING THE "DRUG ABUSER": AN INQUIRY.   Jay R.
Williams, Ph.D. Not available from NCDAI.
GPO Stock #017-024-00512-6 $4.75   NTIS PB #249 092/AS $8.50

7 CANNABINOID ASSAYS IN HUMANS.   Robert Willette, Ph.D., ed.
GPO Stock #017-024-00510-0 $6.00   NTIS PB #251 905/AS $14.50

8 Rx: 3x/WEEK LAAM - ALTERNATIVE TO METHADONE.   Jack Blaine, M.D.,
and Pierre Renault, M.D., eds.
Not available from GPO   NTIS PB #253 763/AS $14.50

9 NARCOTIC ANTAGONISTS: NALTREXONE PROGRESS REPORT.   Demetrios
Julius, M.D., and Pierre Renault, M.D., eds. Not available from
NCDAI.
GPO Stock #017-024-00521-5 $7.00   NTIS PB #255 833/AS $17.50

10 EPIDEMIOLOGY OF DRUG ABUSE: CURRENT ISSUES. Louise G. Richards,
Ph.D., and Louise B. Blevens, eds. Not available from NCDAI.
GPO Stock #017-024-00571-1 $6.50   NTIS PB #266 691/AS $22

11 DRUGS AND DRIVING.   Robert Willette, Ph.D., ed. Not available
from NCDAI.
GPO Stock #017-024-00576-2 $5.50   NTIS PB #269 602/AS $16

12 PSYCHODYNAMICS OF DRUG DEPENDENCE.   Jack D. Blaine, M.D., and
Demetrios A. Julius, M.D., eds.   Not available from NCDAI.
GPO Stock #017-024-00642-4 $5.50   NTIS PB #276 084/AS $17.50

13 COCAINE: 1977.   Robert C. Petersen, Ph.D., and Richard C.
Stillman, M.D., eds.   Reports the extent and limits of current
knowledge about cocaine, its use and misuse.
GPO Stock #017-024-00592-4 $6.00   NTIS PB #269 175/AS $19

14 MARIHUANA RESEARCH FINDINGS: 1976.   Robert C. Petersen, Ph.D.,
ed.   Technical papers on which the 6th Marihuana and Health report
to Congress was based.
GPO out of stock   NTIS PB #271 279/AS $22

15 REVIEW OF INHALANTS: EUPHORIA TO DYSFUNCTION.   Charles Wm.
Sharp, Ph.D., and Mary Lee Brehm, Ph.D., eds.   Review of inhalant
abuse, including an extensive bibliography.
GPO Stock #017-024-00650-5 $7.50   NTIS PB #275 798/AS $28

16 THE EPIDEMIOLOGY OF HEROIN AND OTHER NARCOTICS.   Joan Dunne
Rittenhouse, Ph.D., ed. Not available from NCDAI.
GPO Stock #017-024-00690-4 $6.50   NTIS PB #276 357/AS $20.50

17 RESEARCH ON SMOKING BEHAVIOR. Murray E. Jarvik, M.D., Ph.D., et al., eds. Includes epidemiology, etiology, consequences of use, and approaches to behavioral change. From a NIDA-supported UCLA conference.
GPO Stock #017-024-00694-7 $7.50   NTIS PB #276 353/AS $29.50

18 BEHAVIORAL TOLERANCE: RESEARCH AND TREATMENT IMPLICATIONS. Norman A. Krasnegor, Ph.D., ed. Theoretical and empirical studies of nonpharmacologic factors in development of drug tolerance.
GPO Stock #017-024-00699-8 $5.50   NTIS PB #276 337/AS $16

19 THE INTERNATIONAL CHALLENGE OF DRUG ABUSE. Robert C. Petersen, Ph.D., ed. Papers from the VI World Congress of Psychiatry.
GPO Stock #017-024-00822-2 $7.50   NTIS PB #293 807/AS $28

20 SELF-ADMINISTRATION OF ABUSED SUBSTANCES: METHODS FOR STUDY. Norman A. Krasnegor, Ph.D., ed. Techniques used to study basic processes underlying abuse of drugs, ethanol, food, and tobacco.
GPO Stock #017-024-00794-3 $6.50   NTIS PB #288 471/AS $22

21 PHENCYCLIDINE (PCP) ABUSE: AN APPRAISAL. Robert C. Petersen, Ph.D., and Richard C. Stillman, M.D., eds. For clinicians and researchers, assessing the problem of PCP abuse.
GPO Stock #017-024-00785-4 $7.00   NTIS PB #288 472/AS $25

22 QUASAR: QUANTITATIVE STRUCTURE ACTIVITY RELATIONSHIPS OF ANALGESICS, NARCOTIC ANTAGONISTS, AND HALLUCINOGENS. Gene Barnett, Ph.D.; Milan Trsic, Ph.D.; and Robert Willette, Ph.D.; eds. Not available from NCDAI.
GPO Stock #017-024-00786-2 $8.00   NTIS PB #292 265/AS $35.50

23 CIGARETTE SMOKING AS A DEPENDENCE PROCESS. Norman A. Krasnegor, Ph.D., ed. Discusses factors involved in the onset, maintenance, and cessation of the cigarette smoking habit. Includes an agenda for future research.
GPO Stock #017-024-00895-8 $6.00   NTIS PB #297 721/AS $19

24 SYNTHETIC ESTIMATES FOR SMALL AREAS: STATISTICAL WORKSHOP PAPERS AND DISCUSSION. Jos. Steinberg, ed. Papers from a work-shop on statistical approaches that yield needed estimates of data for States and local areas. Not available from NCDAI.
GPO Stock #017-024-00911-3 $8.00   NTIS PB #299 009/AS $23.50

25 BEHAVIORAL ANALYSIS AND TREATMENT OF SUBSTANCE ABUSE. Norman A. Krasnegor, Ph.D., ed. Papers on commonalities and implications for treatment of dependency on drugs, ethanol, food, and tobacco.
GPO Stock #017-024-00939-3 $5.00   NTIS PB #80-112428 $22

26 THE BEHAVIORAL ASPECTS OF SMOKING. Norman A. Krasnegor, Ph.D., ed. Reprint of the behavioral section of the 1979 Report of the Surgeon General on Smoking and Health; introduction by editor.
GPO out of stock   NTIS PB #80-118755 $17.50

27 PROBLEMS OF DRUG DEPENDENCE, 1979: PROCEEDINGS OF THE 41ST
ANNUAL SCIENTIFIC MEETING, THE COMMITTEE ON PROBLEMS OF DRUG DE-
PENDENCE, INC. L.S. Harris, Ph.D., ed. Not available from NCDAI.
GPO Stock #017-024-00981-4 $9.00   NTIS PB #80-175482 $37

28 NARCOTIC ANTAGONISTS: NALTREXONE PHARMACOCHEMISTRY AND
SUSTAINED-RELEASE PREPARATIONS. Robert Willette, Ph.D., and
Gene Barnett, Ph.D., eds. Papers report research on sustained-
release and long-acting devices for use with the narcotic antag-
onist naltrexone.
GPO Stock #017-024-01081-2 $7.00   NTIS PB #81-238875 $23.50

29 DRUG ABUSE DEATHS IN NINE CITIES: A SURVEY REPORT. Louis A.
Gottschalk, M.D., et al. Not available from NCDAI.
GPO Stock #017-024-00982-2 $6.50   NTIS PB #80-178882 $17.50

30 THEORIES ON DRUG ABUSE: SELECTED CONTEMPORARY PERSPECTIVES.
Dan J. Lettieri, Ph.D.; Mollie Sayers; and Helen Wallenstein
Pearson, eds. Volume presents summaries of major contemporary
theories of drug abuse by each of 43 leading theorists.
GPO Stock #017-024-00997-1 $10.00   Not available from NTIS

31 MARIJUANA RESEARCH FINDINGS: 1980. Robert C. Petersen, Ph.D.,
ed. The text of the 8th Marijuana and Health report to Congress
and the background scientific papers on which it was based.
GPO out of stock   NTIS PB #80-215171 $20.50

32 GC/MS ASSAYS FOR ABUSED DRUGS IN BODY FLUIDS. Rodger L. Foltz,
Ph.D.; Allison F. Fentiman, Jr., Ph.D.; and Ruth B. Foltz. A
collection of methods for quantitative analysis of several
important drugs of abuse by gas chromatography- mass spectrometry.
GPO Stock #017-024-01015-4 $6.00   NTIS PB #81-133746 $19

33 BENZODIAZEPINES: A REVIEW OF RESEARCH RESULTS, 1980. Stephen
I. Szara, M.D., D.Sc., and Jacqueline P. Ludford, M.S., eds.
A RAUS (Research Analysis and Utilization System) Review Report
on the abuse liability of the benzodiazepine "tranquilizers."
GPO Stock #017-024-01108-8 $5.00   NTIS PB #82-139106 $13

34 PROBLEMS OF DRUG DEPENDENCE, 1980: PROCEEDINGS OF THE 42ND
ANNUAL SCIENTIFIC MEETING, THE COMMITTEE ON PROBLEMS OF DRUG
DEPENDENCE, INC. Louis S. Harris, Ph.D., ed. Not available from
NCDAI.
GPO Stock #017-024-01061-8 $8.00   NTIS PB #81-194847 $34

35 DEMOGRAPHIC TRENDS AND DRUG ABUSE, 1980-1995. Louise G.
Richards, Ph.D., ed. Estimates of probable extent and nature of
nonmedical drug use, 1980-1995, based on age structure and other
characteristics of U.S. population.
GPO Stock #017-024-01087-1 $4.50.   NTIS PB #82-103417 $13

36 NEW APPROACHES TO TREATMENT OF CHRONIC PAIN: A REVIEW OF MULTI-
DISCIPLINARY PAIN CLINICS AND PAIN CENTERS. Lorenz K.Y. Ng, M.D.,
ed. Discussions by active practitioners in the treatment of pain.
GPO Stock #017-024-01082-1 $5.50.   NTIS PB #81-240913 $19

37 BEHAVIORAL PHARMACOLOGY OF HUMAN DRUG DEPENDENCE. Travis
Thompson, Ph.D., and Chris E. Johanson, Ph.D., eds. Presents a
growing body of data, systematically derived, on the behavioral
mechanisms involved in use and abuse of drugs.
GPO Stock #017-024-01109-6 $6.50   NTIS PB #82-136961 $25

38 DRUG ABUSE AND THE AMERICAN ADOLESCENT. Dan J. Lettieri,
Ph.D., and Jacqueline P. Ludford, M.S., eds. A RAUS Review
Report, emphasizing use of marijuana: epidemiology, socio-
demographic and personality factors, family and peer influence,
delinquency, and biomedical consequences.
GPO Stock #017-024-01107-0 $4.50   NTIS PB #82-148198 $14.50

39 YOUNG MEN AND DRUGS IN MANHATTAN: A CAUSAL ANALYSIS.
Richard R. Clayton, Ph.D., and Harwin L. Voss, Ph.D. Examines
the etiology and natural history of drug use, with special focus
on heroin. Includes a Lifetime Drug Use Index.
GPO Stock #017-024-01097-9 $5.50   NTIS PB #82-147372 $19

40 ADOLESCENT MARIJUANA ABUSERS AND THEIR FAMILIES. Herbert
Hendin, M.D., Ann Pollinger, Ph.D., Richard Ulman, Ph.D., and
Arthur Carr, Ph.D. A psychodynamic study of adolescents
involved in heavy marijuana use, to determine what inter-
action between family and adolescent gives rise to drug abuse.
GPO Stock #017-024-01098-7 $4.50   NTIS PB #82-133117 $13

41 PROBLEMS OF DRUG DEPENDENCE, 1981: PROCEEDINGS OF THE 43RD
ANNUAL SCIENTIFIC MEETING, THE COMMITTEE ON PROBLEMS OF DRUG
DEPENDENCE, INC. Louis S. Harris, Ph.D., ed. Not available from
NCDAI.
Not available from GPO   NTIS PB #82-190760 $41.50

42 THE ANALYSIS OF CANNABINOIDS IN BIOLOGICAL FLUIDS. Richard L.
Hawks, Ph.D., ed. Varied approaches to sensitive, reliable, and
accessible quantitative assays for the chemical constitutents of
marijuana, for researchers. Not available from NCDAI.
GPO Stock #017-024-01151-7 $5   NTIS PB #83-136044 $1643

43 PROBLEMS OF DRUG DEPENDENCE, 1982: PROCEEDINGS OF THE 44TH
ANNUAL SCIENTIFIC MEETING, THE COMMITTEE ON PROBLEMS OF DRUG
DEPENDENCE, INC. Louis S. Harris, Ph.D., ed. Not available from
NCDAI.
GPO Stock #017-024-01162-2 $8.50   NTIS PB #83-252-692 $40

44 MARIJUANA EFFECTS ON THE ENDOCRINE AND REPRODUCTIVE SYSTEMS.
Monique C. Braude, Ph.D., and Jacqueline P. Ludford, M.S., eds.
A RAUS Review Report of animal studies and preclinical and
clinical studies of effects of cannabinoids on human endocrine
and reproductive functions.

45 CONTEMPORARY RESEARCH IN PAIN AND ANALGESIA, 1983. Roger M.
Brown, Ph.D.; Theodore M. Pinkert, M.D., J.D.; and Jacqueline P.
Ludford, M.S., eds. A RAUS Review Report on the anatomy,
physiology, and neurochemistry of pain and its management.
GPO Stock #017-024-01191-6 $2.75   NTIS PB #84-184670 $11.50

46 BEHAVIORAL INTERVENTION TECHNIQUES IN DRUG ABUSE TREATMENT.
John Grabowski, Ph.D.; Maxine L. Stitzer, Ph.D., and Jack E.
Henningfield, Ph.D., eds. Reports on behavioral contingency
management procedures used in research/treatment environments.
GPO Stock #017-024-01192-4 $4.25   NTIS PB #84 184688 $16

47 PREVENTING ADOLESCENT DRUG ABUSE: INTERVENTION STRATEGIES.
Thomas J. Glynn, Ph.D.; Carl G. Leukefeld, D.S.W.; and
Jacqueline P. Ludford, M.S., eds. A RAUS Review Report on a
variety of approaches to prevention of adolescent drug abuse, how
they can be applied, their chances for success, and needed future
research.
Not available from GPO   NTIS PB to be assigned

48 MEASUREMENT IN THE ANALYSIS AND TREATMENT OF SMOKING
BEHAVIOR. John Grabowski, Ph.D., and Catherine S. Bell, M.S.,
eds. Based upon a meeting cosponsored by NIDA and the National
Cancer Institute to delineate necessary and sufficient measures
for analysis of smoking behavior in research and treatment
settings.
GPO Stock #017-024-01181-9 .$4.50   NTIS PB 84-145-184 $14.50

49 PROBLEMS OF DRUG DEPENDENCE, 1983: PROCEEDINGS OF THE 44TH
ANNUAL SCIENTIFIC MEETING, THE COMMITTEE ON PROBLEMS OF DRUG
DEPENDENCE, INC. Louis S. Harris, Ph.D., ed. A collection of
papers which together record a year's advances in drug abuse
research; also includes reports on tests of new compounds for
efficacy and dependence liability.

51 DRUG ABUSE TREATMENT EVALUATION: STRATEGIES, PROGRESS, AND
PROSPECTS. Frank M. Tims, Ph.D., ed. A state-of-the-art review
of drug abuse treatment evaluation, identifying research needs,
promising approaches, and emerging issues.

52 TESTING DRUGS FOR PHYSICAL DEPENDENCE POTENTIAL AND ABUSE
LIABILITY. Joseph V. Brady, Ph.D., and Scott E. Lukas, Ph.D.,
eds. Describes animal and human test procedures for assessing
dependence potential and abuse liability of opioids, stimulants,
depressants, hallucinogens, cannabinoids, and dissociative
anesthetics.

54 MECHANISMS OF TOLERANCE AND DEPENDENCE. Charles Wm. Sharp,
Ph.D., ed. Review of basic knowledge concerning the mechanism of
action of opiates and other drugs in producing tolerance and/or
dependence.

IN PRESS

50 COCAINE: PHARMACOLOGY, EFFECTS, AND TREATMENT OF ABUSE. John
Grabowski, Ph.D., ed. Content ranges from an introductory
overview through neuropharmacology, pharmacology, animal and
human behavioral pharmacology, patterns of use in the natural
environment of cocaine users, treatment, through commentary on
societal perceptions of use.